MIND: A PROPERTY OF MATTER

ALSO BY PENELOPE ROWLATT

Group Theory and Elementary Particles

Inflation

MIND: a property of matter

Penelope Rowlatt

Ionides Publishing
London

IONIDES PUBLISHING
London

ISBN 978 1 5272 1949 6

Published by Ionides Publishing 2018

Cover design by Hari Wyn Williams at *hariwilliams.co.uk*

Printed by Amazon KDP

For Charles

Preface

The purpose of this book is to explore the consequences of assuming that mind is a property of matter and that it can be causally effective, influencing the properties of matter that are suitable for study in physics.

A key result of the investigation is the proposition that, given the nature of the science of physics along with the existence of an epistemic gap, it *cannot* be the case that mental states can be explained in terms of physics. This means that the version of physicalism known as 'reductive physicalism', which requires that mental states are suitable for study in physics, can be ruled out because it is not a viable option. This follows from the fact that putting the case for mind being reducible to the science of physics requires an explicit definition of what is meant by the terms 'physics' and 'the physical sciences'; something that, to the best of my knowledge, does not exist in the philosophy literature today. However, it is a fundamental tenet of the science of physics that all the experiments relating to it that are performed by one person can be reproduced by other people, and this means that all the facts studied in physics must be perfectly communicable between people linguistically. If we then accept that we know *ab initio* (from introspection) that we cannot communicate exactly what it feels like to experience something to another person who has not had the experience in question, it follows that mental states are not suitable for study in the science of physics. Reductive physicalism cannot hold.

I therefore examine the case for an approach to the nature of mind that I have called "causally effective property dualism". This takes 'mind' to be a property of matter that is *different* from those properties that are studied in the physical sciences, with 'mental states' instantiations of that property. It also takes it that states of mind, mental states, can be causally effective, influencing the properties of matter that are suitable for study in physics through the implementation of decisions. This possibility has been neglected in the academic philosophy literature; but there are reasons why it looks to be a plausible approach: it does not fall foul of the anti-physicalist claims (the knowledge argument, the conceivability argument and the hard problem); it encompasses a role for consciousness (consciousness is necessary for the taking of complex decisions, decisions that require 'values', that is 'feelings', in order to identify the best option); and, it enables a form of free will, and therefore

i

moral responsibility, to obtain (where a 'person' can be held responsible for the consequences of his/her chosen actions).

There are then two interesting questions that need to be addressed. First, how does this property arise? Second, if we want to maintain that mental states can be causally effective, what is the mechanism through which a mental state affects the physical (non-mental) properties of matter? An obvious place to start is with the possibility that consciousness could derive from one of the phenomena associated with fundamental particles, which would have been around since soon after the Big Bang. This seems the most probable answer simply because all the other properties of matter are related in some way to the fundamental particles (although, of course, it does not necessarily follow that it is the case for this one). Speculating further, a striking feature of consciousness is the fact that it enables complex decisions to be taken, and decision theory decrees that these involve a maximising procedure (a procedure akin to a cost-benefit analysis). But physics at the macro-level operates with the "if A then B given C" type of law of nature; physics does not do cost-benefit analysis. So could it be that there is something associated with the fundamental particles that is subject to a maximising law of nature? Perhaps the weak nuclear force is involved, or perhaps the collapse of the wave function, or perhaps some quite different aspect of physics at the micro-level. If that were the case, a maximising type of law (presumably without 'consciousness' associated with it) could have played a role in some process relating to, say, the green algae from which land plants are thought to have developed, and then, later, that type of law might have been an important aspect of the survival of the first creatures that developed. Subsequently, given the existence of 'feelings', more complex creatures were able to develop, and the decisions they faced became more complex; along with this, the feelings that steered the decisions and enabled them to be taken would also become more complex, involving 'consciousness'. Given the pressures of survival, evolution would then have ensured that these creatures developed a wide portfolio of different feelings designed in such a way that creatures' behaviour enhanced the likelihood of survival, both of the individual and of the species.

If some process such as this were the case it would justify our assumption that 'mind' is a fundamental property of matter in its own right, different from the properties of matter generally studied in physics; and it would explain why we cannot describe what it feels like to experience something in terms of the physics of a person's brain state.

A sub-text to the analysis presented in this book is my attempt to understand why the neglect of this possible explanation of mind has arisen and, with this in mind, much of the book is devoted to an examination of the current thinking regarding the ontology of consciousness. I have come to think that the reason for the neglect might be related to the way modern philosophers view language. They often seem to treat words as if they have a meaning that exists independently of us and that this meaning can be discovered if we work at it, just as a physicist will assume that objects have an existence independent of us and properties that can be discovered. However, occasionally they will use a word without defining it (*e.g.*, 'physics'); they sometimes don't seem to notice when a word has more than one meaning (*e.g.*, 'physical', and therefore 'physicalism'); and they sometimes define a word in a manner that is at variance with common usage (*e.g.*, 'fact') or so that it incorporates an implicit assumption (*e.g.*, 'matter', or 'person').

I hope the book will be found to be of interest, of course, and that some of the ideas in it will prove useful. It seems unlikely that there are no errors in the book, errors of omission, errors of logic or fact, or presentation, or errors of some other kind; I have done my best and can only hope. I have a huge debt of gratitude. First, I am grateful to Paul Snowdon, who helped me through the initial stages of this work and has advised me throughout, and to Luke Fenton-Glynn who generously gave his time and energy to picking holes in my arguments and quarrelling with my use of words, thereby improving the quality of this work beyond recognition. Second, I appreciate the contributions of other members of the staff at University College London, and of the students there: the comments I received at seminars and at other times proved invaluable; also, the support of Fiona Leigh was crucial in making this work possible. Next, I would like to thank the examiners of my PhD thesis, first for identifying a gap in my coverage of the subject, and second for a multitude of wise comments on the initial version of my PhD thesis. Of course, it does not follow that any of these people agree with the ideas presented here. Finally, I am immensely grateful to my husband, Charles, and to my family and friends for their interest and support throughout.

Contents

Contents

Appendix 1   Substance dualism 201

Appendix 2   Structure of the mind 209

Appendix 3   Glossary 219

References 226

Index 246

Figures

Mind: a property of matter

1

Introduction

1 The purpose of the book

The question of the nature of 'mind' is one of a handful of fundamental questions that relate to our existence which surely everyone must wonder about from time to time.[1] An obvious issue that arises on these occasions is whether mind is something to do with matter, most probably with brains, or whether instead it is quite distinct from matter. If it is taken to be related to matter another question arises: are states of mind, 'mental states', part of the world of physics, in the sense of being related to nothing more than the properties of matter that are studied in the physical sciences, the approach known as 'reductive physicalism', or is this not the case? And if this is not the case, so mental states are instantiations of a property of matter not suitable for study in the physical sciences, there is yet another question. Could there be causal processes which are such that the mental state that we experience as the taking of a decision has a direct effect on our actions through its influence on the

---

[1] We know that we have 'mental states', states of which a creature can be conscious. The term 'mind', however, could simply be a convenient way of referring to the range of our possible mental states. Or it could pick out a property of matter that instantiates (gives rise to) mental states as in the title of this book. Notes regarding the meanings attributed to some of the key terms used in this book are listed in the Glossary attached at Appendix 3.

properties of matter studied in the physical sciences, or must such a mental state be 'epiphenomenal' (*i.e.*, have no causal effect whatsoever on events that relate to the physical sciences)? These are some the questions that are addressed in this book.

There are three main possibilities concerning the relationship of mind and matter, and they can broadly be described as: 'dual substances' (with mind *not* a property of matter), 'reductive physicalism' (in which mental states are reducible to the properties of matter studied in the science of physics) and 'nonreductive physicalism' (where mind is a property of matter that is different from the properties that are studied in the science of physics, and is not reducible to them).[2] In this book, we will not examine in any depth the possibility that mind is not related to matter; Appendix 1 contains a summary of this case, often known as 'substance dualism'.

Given the definition of 'reductive physicalism' (above), a key issue in understanding the relationship that might operate between mind and matter is the question of what is suited for study in the science we call 'physics'. It is a fundamental tenet of the physical sciences, the sciences that are reducible to physics, that all experiments in these sciences must be capable of being reproduced by others (see Chapter 2, Section 2.1). This means that a fact is suitable for study in the physical sciences only if it can be communicated, perfectly, from one person to another linguistically. It then follows that if we accept that we know, from our own experience (introspection), that it is impossible to inform someone who has not had some sensory experience (such as tasting truffles) what it is like to have that experience using language, and we want to maintain that mental states such as sensory experiences are related to matter, we have to accept that there must be other facts that relate to matter besides those facts that are suitable for study in the science of physics (see Chapter 2, Section 4.2 and Chapter 3, Section 5 for more details). If that is the case, there *must* be another property of matter besides those studied in physics: property dualism must hold.

Another issue that arises relates to the specification of non-reductive physicalism, the case in which mind is a property of matter that is *not* reducible

---

[2] A phenomenon is 'reducible' to the properties of matter studied in the science of physics if there are causal (nomological) relations that carry the implication that all the facts pertaining to that phenomenon can be identified with facts that are suitable for study in the science of physics (that is, they are 'public facts'). Any statement involving the 'is' of composition is a case in point, *e.g.*, "water is H_2O", or "lightning is electrostatic discharge".

to those properties that are suitable to be studied in physics. Consideration of non-reductive physicalism in the literature has often been confined to the case in which mental states 'supervene' on the properties of matter that are studied in physics (as in Figure 1a, below), with the implication that mind has a different ontological status from the other fundamental properties of matter and could be called a 'higher level' property. In this case it is generally considered likely that if a situation that involves a mental state obtains and has a causal effect on some property of matter suitable for study in physics, it would be the case that it is the physical (non-mental) aspects of the situation, not the mental aspects, that do the causing.

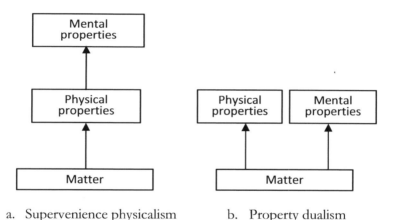

a. Supervenience physicalism   b. Property dualism

Figure 1: Non-reductive physicalism

The arrows imply that the thing at the sharp end exists because of the existence of the thing at the blunt end. The figure illustrates the difference between the case in which mental properties are taken to 'supervene' on physical (non-mental) properties and the case in which mental states are instantiations of a property of matter that has the same ontological status as the properties of matter that are suitable for study in physics.

But there is another possible form of non-reductive physicalism, see Figure 1b. In this book I make the case for the possibility that mind could be a fundamental property of matter in its own right, different from the properties of matter studied in physics but with the same ontological status as those properties. Whereas this is clearly a logically possible situation, people often seem to have difficulty accepting it as a practical possibility. So, for the sake of argument, and perhaps somewhat fancifully, let us suppose that something one might call 'proto-consciousness', the building blocks of consciousness, is associated with some aspect of one or more of the fundamental particles of the Standard Model or with quantum mechanics (see also Section 5.2 of Chapter 7). As complex creatures developed out of simple creatures in evolution, with proto-consciousness built into the structure of their brains, consciousness as we know it with its wide range of feelings might have developed from proto-consciousness because experiencing certain types of feeling enhances the probability of survival. But it seems likely that the way it feels to experience these feelings (such as fear, or hunger) would then be impossible to deduce from the physical state of the brain, even given perfect knowledge of it. If this were the case proto-consciousness, and therefore 'mind', would be a fundamental property of matter in its own right, different from the properties of matter studied in physics at the macro level.

Given this 'property dualism' approach, in Figure 1b, there seems to be no reason to assume that the property of matter that we call 'mind' is epiphenomenal: first, there is no obvious physical (non-mental) property of matter to play the causal role as is the case with supervenience physicalism, and second, all the other properties of matter can be causally effective so there seems to be no reason why this one should not be so too. Indeed, as many have observed, one might think that the mere fact that whenever you decide to raise your arm it performs exactly the gesture you intended would be enough to convince any reasonable person that there is a significant likelihood that such a decision *is* causally effective. Further, as we shall see, there are reasons to suppose that feelings, and therefore consciousness, are a key factor in practical reasoning, the cognitive process underlying the taking of such decisions (see Chapter 2, Section 4.3), and if this were the case, it *must* be that mental states are causally effective *per se*.

The purpose of this book is to explore the consequences of assuming that mind is a property of matter and that it can be causally effective, affecting the properties of matter that are suitable for study in physics. Given the argument above concerning reductive physicalism, spelt out in more detail in Chapters 3 and 4, the book puts the case for the ontological basis of consciousness being the version of non-reductive physicalism illustrated in Figure 1b, that I call 'property dualism'; and since I take it that mental states can be causally effective I call the approach 'causally effective property dualism'. Although this general approach is familiar to philosophers (see Chapter 5, Section 6.4), to the best of my knowledge there are currently no academic papers or books that spell out in any detail or depth the implications of assuming that causally effective property dualism is the correct ontological account of mind.

2 Benefits/problems of causally effective property dualism

The main benefits of causally effective property dualism are the following:

- None of the philosophers' three anti-physicalist claims (the knowledge argument, the conceivability argument and the hard problem/explanatory gap), which are all generally thought to cause serious problems for reductive physicalism, have any power against causally effective property dualism (see Chapter 3, Section 6), so there is no reason why this approach should not be accepted as a logically viable and plausible form of physicalism. It enables physicalism to be the case, even if reductive physicalism is ruled out; it also means that we don't need to postulate that something exists that it not related to matter in order to accommodate the existence of mental states.

- Effective mental causation suggests that the reason why creatures with consciousness abound in our world could be that consciousness has been selected for by the pressures of survival. I argue that the ability to experience feelings enables creatures to take decisions appropriate to their future welfare given the circumstances in which they find themselves (that it is a form of 'homeostasis', see Chapter 2, Section 4.3 and Chapter 6, Section 4), and that this gives these creatures an evolutionary advantage. If that were so, facilitating the taking of such decisions would be the 'role' played by consciousness (Chapter 6).

- If causally effective property dualism holds, this would explain why people feel as if they have freedom of the will; if mental states are causally effective there would be a sense in which a 'person' *does* have freedom of the will (Chapter 8).

However, the proposal also has the obvious implication that, if it were to hold, physics would not be 'causally complete' in the sense that: "all physical effects are fully caused by purely *physical* prior histories" (see Papineau, 2002, p 17); and this causal completeness of physics is an assumption that it seems every philosopher of mind signs up to these days, albeit, in some cases, not without question.[3] But science as we know it today is unfinished, and if there turns out to be another property of matter, and/or a localised, additional force, and/or some effect related to quantum mechanics, which obtains in the brains of creatures taking decisions, there is no reason to suppose that this would have any effect on the way the physical sciences operate at the macro level, in the situations in which they are normally studied.[4] Although the influence of effective mental causation on the future course of the world can obviously be huge, the fact that mental states are causally effective, if that turns out to be so, seems unlikely to have any significant effect on the way in which science operates outside the brains of conscious creatures. Further, it seems highly unlikely that neuroscientists would have happened on the existence of such a phenomenon, given the current stage of development of that specialty, particularly if they were not actually looking for it.

There seems to be no reason why these mental states and the causal processes relating to them should not be part of the combination of causal processes and events which, taken together, make up the discipline that we call 'science', so there would seem to be no reason why science, the combination of the physical sciences and the facts that relate to mental states along with the causal processes that involve them, should not be 'complete', in the broad sense of being the study of all the events that can be causes or effects along with all possible causal processes. Although science would then be 'complete', physics, of course, would not.

It soon becomes apparent, as one reads the words of philosophers and scientists, that many of those who consider this question of the nature of mind and also assume that there is only one substance do not share the above view that there could be something different from that which is suitable for study in

---

[3] Questions have been raised about the completeness of physics by Baker (1993, p 77), who puts the case that *something* that is presently accepted by everyone has to go, perhaps the 'completeness of physics', and by Burge (1993), see the discussion in Yoo (2016); but neither of these develops the possibility into a coherent proposal.

[4] I take it here that all the events that are studied in the "sciences" other than the physical sciences, such as biology, psychology, economics *etc.*, can be explained in terms of the causal processes of the physical sciences along with some additional causal processes that involve mental states, see Chapter 2, Section 2.2.

the physical sciences.[5] Further, the proposition that mental states are non-reductive and can be causally effective *per se* (that completeness of physics in the form: all physical effects are fully caused by purely *physical* prior histories, does not hold) is a philosophical position that receives little support nowadays from philosophers. Lewis (1988, p 90) finds it impossible to accept that phenomenal facts exist and continue to believe in reductive physicalism, so he rejects the existence of phenomenal facts and mental causation *per se* goes out with it (see Chapter 5, Section 2).[6] Papineau (2002) accepts the existence of phenomenal facts, taking it that: "Conscious states involve awareness, feelings, the subjectivity of experience" (*ibid.*, p 1), but he also signs up to the completeness of physics as above (*ibid.*, p 17; indeed, in this book I use his formulation of it). Kim (2005, p 15) rules out mental causation by assuming the same approach to the completeness of physics as Papineau. Chalmers, however, while ruling out what he calls 'materialism' in 'An Argument against Materialism' (Section1 of Chapter 4 in his 1996 book, p 123) is also one of the few modern philosophers to acknowledge the possibility of effective mental causation, but only in the form of 'over-determination' (*ibid.*, p 152 and see Chapter 5, Section 7). These are just a few of a great many who have signed up to this causal completeness of physics principle in the recent philosophy literature.

3 Structure of the book

With this as background, I start by spelling out, in Chapter 2, the assumptions I make regarding the fundamentals of science, the nature of consciousness and the things that we can know about mental states purely as the result of introspection. This chapter contains the background theory needed to establish the points I want to make about the likely ontology of mind.

Chapter 3 then looks at some issues relating to 'physicalism', the proposition that mind is a property of matter: the increasing evidence supportive of it, the arguments for and against the key assumption of the completeness of physics, and the three anti-physicalist claims – the knowledge argument, the

---

[5] Which is not to deny that there are also plenty who support some form of non-reductive physicalism.
[6] Phenomenal facts are what it is like for a creature to experience something, *e.g.*, what it feels like for person X to see red (see Chapter 2, Section 3.2).

conceivability argument and the hard question. It turns out that whereas each of these is thought to cause problems of some sort for reductive physicalism, none of them need cause any problems for a physicalism in which consciousness is a property of matter different from those studied in physics, each for quite simple and straightforward reasons.

In Chapters 4 and 5 we examine the two versions of a physicalist approach to the nature of mind, the identity thesis/reductive physicalism approach and the approach known as non-reductive physicalism, including both supervenience physicalism and the form of property dualism explored in this book, which I call "causally effective property dualism", summarising the *pros* and *cons* for each of them. This clarifies the reasons why it seems sensible to examine our causally effective property dualism assumption regarding the nature of mind in some depth.

Next, in Chapter 6, we look at the implications of the assumption that we know from our own experience, from introspection, that 'feelings' play a role in decision-taking. If the facilitation of effective decision-taking is the role of consciousness this would explain why evolution has ensured that conscious creatures have taken the world by storm in the way they have. If this is the role of consciousness it must be the case that mental causation is effective.

Chapter 7 then examines the implications of taking mental states to be causally effective; it includes some controversial speculations on the possibilities for how a causal relation between mental events and physical (non-mental) events might arise, and how it might operate.

In Chapter 8 we ponder on the question of whether, with this assumption regarding the nature of mind, we can justify the proposition that humans, and maybe other creatures, possess something that could be called 'free will', and whether, therefore, we can justify considering ourselves to be 'morally' responsible, in some sense, for our actions.

The book finishes with a summary of the findings, in Chapter 9.

2

Fundamental Assumptions

1 Introduction

This chapter lays out the fundamentals on which the analysis in the rest of the book rests. In questioning the nature of consciousness and the way in which it relates, or does not relate, to matter and the properties of matter that are studied in the physical sciences, I am raising questions that concern the foundations of science, and therefore I need to spell out various fundamental issues relating to science that clarify the rationale underlying propositions that arise later in the book. I do this in Section 2.

Section 3 then addresses the question of what is meant by the term 'consciousness', and notes some facts that have been established by scientists and others about what we are conscious of, about the different ways in which we can 'know' something, and about the role of memory stores and the possibility that one day we may be able to take a view about whether a creature is conscious by examining the structure of its brain.

In Section 4 I present three fundamental propositions about 'mind' which I suggest that we *know* to be true from subjective experience (introspection) and which are key to what comes later. Other people are presumably not signed up to these propositions, since if these were all generally accepted I would not be writing this book; therefore, they should be considered to be controversial.

9

2 Assumptions about science

I take 'science' to be the systematic study, through observation, experiment and analysis, of the structure and the behaviour of everything in the universe. I start my discussion of the fundamentals of science by addressing the question of what is suitable for study in the particular branch of science that we call 'physics' and therefore in the physical sciences (the sciences that are reducible to physics); I then address the question of whether it could be the case that there are some things that are not suitable for study in the physical sciences and, given that this is the case, the question of why they are not suitable.

In science, we assume that there are causal (nomological) processes that operate consistently "out there" and we aim to discover what they are. A distinction therefore needs to be drawn between the causal processes "out there" that we seek to discover and our current view concerning them, that is, the "laws of nature" that we propound. Importantly, some of these so-called "laws of nature" could, on further investigation, be found to be in error. The language we use needs to allow for this possibility.

Related to that, there are some statements that we *know* are true and some which, whereas we believe them to be true given our current knowledge, could need revision when further information is available. These issues are addressed in Section 2.3 of this chapter. Also, what do we mean by 'matter', particularly in the light of the developments in physics in recent decades? What is important about what we call 'matter' in the context of the assertion: "we assume that there is only one substance, and we call it matter"; indeed, what do we mean here by 'substance'? I examine these issues in Section 2.4.

Finally, in Section 2.5 of this chapter, I note that the word 'physical' has various meanings and that this has given rise to some confusion, for example relating to the meaning of 'physicalism'. The implication is that great care is needed when using the word 'physical'. I have found this to be a frequent cause of problems, so I generally note the meaning intended when I use that word.

2.1 Defining 'physics' and 'physical sciences'

It is often assumed by philosophers, either implicitly or explicitly, that *everything* is reducible to facts relating to physics, chemistry, neuroscience *etc.*, known as the physical sciences, and therefore to physics itself, since it is generally assumed that all these so-called 'physical sciences' are reducible to the science of physics. But we can only take a view on whether *all* the facts that we can know are suitable for study in these sciences, or whether there is a type of fact which is not suitable, if we have a definition of 'physics'. To address this issue, we need first to be clear about what type of fact is studied in physics; then we can address the further question of whether there may be some other type of fact that is not suitable for study in physics. If we think there could be another type of fact, not suitable for study in the physical sciences, we need to understand *why* it is not suitable.

There currently seems to be no explicit agreement amongst philosophers as to what is necessary for a property of matter to be suitable for study in the sciences that we call 'the physical sciences'. Further, since in philosophy the term 'physicalism' is often defined in terms of physics (see Section 2.5 of this chapter), without clarity about the definition of 'physics' we cannot be clear about precisely what the important word 'physicalism' can mean.

A great many philosophers have asked the question "what is physical science?", see for example Crane and Mellor, 1990 (pp 186-187).[7] Beckermann is one of the few who have tried to spell out an answer to the question, saying of 'physicalism' (1992, p 2):

"It [physicalism] was set forth as a theory of science and especially as a theory of the foundations of science. Its main claim was that 'physical language' is 'the universal language of science' and that therefore, even protocol sentences, *i.e.*, those basic sentences of science which form the starting point of all hypotheses and the evidence by which to check their validity, should be couched not in phenomenalistic, but in physical language. The main reason for this claim was that only physical language is intersubjective and therefore apt to provide a suitable basis for scientific research".

Beckermann, however, then finds it unclear how the term 'physical language' is to be understood, noting (in a footnote to the above passage) that sometimes it is understood to be "thing language" and that on other occasions it

---

[7] Amongst many others addressing this question are Papineau (2002, pp 40-44), Tye (2011, p 26), and Chalmers (1996, pp 118-119, 128-129).

includes only terms referring to physical quantities that can be ascribed to "space-time-points" (*ibid.*, p 2).

A somewhat similar response, relating the science of physics to language, was posited by Davidson (1970, p 210) when he said:

"What does it mean to say that an event is mental or physical? One natural answer is that an event is physical if it is describable in a purely physical vocabulary, mental if describable in mental terms".

So how do we know what 'physical language', 'physical vocabulary', is; how do we know what can or cannot be referred to as 'mental terms'?

A fundamental requirement of the physical sciences is that everything about experiments relating to some property of matter that are performed by one person is perfectly reproducible by other people, including both how the experiment should be performed and the experimenters' observations regarding the outcome of the experiment. It then follows that these must all consist of 'public facts', public in the sense that the experimental design and the observations that result must all be capable of being examined and noted by any number of people on an *equal* basis. This means that it is necessary that these things can be communicated between people, perfectly, using language.

Therefore, we start from the fact that an essential feature of the physical sciences is the testing of hypotheses by experimentation and the reproducibility of one person's experimental results by another person.

This requirement, which relates to interpersonal communication, enables us to take a view about which properties of matter are and which are not suitable to be studied in the physical sciences. It is only if a fact relating to some property of matter is a public fact, one that is equally accessible to everyone (the weight of a stone in certain specified conditions, for example), that it can be referred to in words with no ambiguity ("this stone weighs 5 kilograms" combined with the definition known as the International Prototype Kilogram or IPK).[8] If *all* the facts relating to a property of matter are public facts that property of matter is suitable for study in the physical sciences for the simple reason that facts of this sort are equally available to everyone.

---

[8] Of course, there are other facts that are public facts, in the sense of being equally available to everyone, besides those suitable for study in physics, such as historical facts and certain types of fact about economics, or sociology.

So we define the science of physics as follows:

The science of physics comprises the results of our investigation of the properties of matter that are such that all the facts relating to them are public facts, facts that are equally accessible to everyone and that can therefore be communicated perfectly between people using language.

Importantly, this carries the implication that if everything relating to some property of matter is 'reducible' to facts suitable for study in the science of physics it will be the case that *all* the facts relating to that property can be communicated perfectly from one person to another person linguistically.

However, it is difficult to dispute the proposition that other facts exist, in addition to these public facts (see Section 3.2 of this chapter). These are facts to which one person or creature has privileged access, such as "what it feels like for X to see red" (we can never be sure whether it feels the same for Y to see red) or "what it feels like for Z to be sad about the death of his mother". These "what it feels like"-type facts are 'phenomenal facts' (or *qualia*).[9] If some of the facts relating to a property of matter are not public facts, because they are not equally accessible to everyone, that property is not suitable for study in the physical sciences. It follows from this that "what it is like"-type information about experiences relating to our senses and to our feelings, because it can only be directly observed by the person/creature who experiences the feelings, is not suitable to be studied in what we call "the physical sciences".[10]

Importantly, the above definition of the science of physics combined with the existence of *qualia* (the existence of an epistemic gap, see Section 4.2 of this chapter) has the simple implication that there must be something else in the universe besides that which is suitable for study in "the science of physics".

---

[9] Some philosophers deny the existence of *qualia*, which seems strange given that the term refers to the only things that we can be *absolutely* sure exist, namely the experiences that make up our own feelings.

[10] Where some of the facts relating to a property can be perfectly communicated verbally between experimenters, like the results of surveys relating to how "happy" people "feel" about some experience, indicated on a scale of 1 to 10, for example, but others, like what it actually *feels* like to have the experience, cannot, the property is not suitable for study in the physical sciences.

2.2 *Causal processes, laws of nature and science*

I assume in this book that some form of universal causation holds, either "certain", as in 'determinism', or probabilistic (see Chapter 8, Section 2 for more details). That is, I take it that every event arises as the result of a causal process that may be probabilistic, and that every event may cause other events to occur, given the causal processes and the situation that pertains. Following Davidson's comment "… laws are linguistic" (1970, p 215 in 2001 reprint) I take the 'causal process' to be something that exists "out there" and I take a 'law of nature' to be our linguistic/mathematical expression of a presumed causal process (so it can be the case that a law of nature is found wanting, given new information, see below).[11] I assume that a causal process accounts for the occurrence of every event. Where these relate to events that can be described in public language, they can be captured precisely by laws of nature and these can generally be expressed in the form (in the simplest possible terms): "if event A occurs then event B will occur given circumstances C" or perhaps "if A then B_1 with probability p_1, B_2 with probability p_2 …, given C".[12] Where a mental characteristic is relevant to a causal process (for example, "pain gives rise to avoidance behaviour") it will obviously be impossible to capture individual occurrences of it precisely in language/mathematics; but that should not be taken to imply that the causal process does not exist, or that true law-like statements cannot be made regarding it (such as "hunger causes a creature to seek food" or "person X is likely to choose action A in circumstances C").

I assume that causal closure pertains; that is, I assume that *every* event is subject to a causal process and I take it that whereas the collection of all the laws of nature that can be expressed precisely in language/mathematics would constitute what we call 'the physical sciences' if the physical sciences were finished and complete, a finished and complete 'science' would require a statement of *all* the (correct) laws of nature.

I take the standard, necessitarian, approach to the 'causal processes' (the laws of nature which are actually true, so they do exist "out there"): a causal

---

[11] The reader should note that I am making an unorthodox use of terminology here. Philosophers generally take 'laws of nature' to be things 'out there' in the world that we may or may not have discovered.

[12] See Section 4.3 of this chapter for a very different specification of a causal process, a fact that I suggest just might prove important to our understanding of the ontology of consciousness.

process is a necessity relation in which the type of necessity is different from logical necessity (as discussed in O'Connor, 1995; see also Johansson, 2006); I refer to this as 'nomological necessity'. However, many of the nomological relations that we humans postulate to hold at any point in time and therefore *assume* describe causal processes, having observed regularities in the way events occur in the world, are in fact contingent because there is a possibility that some new observation (a 'black swan', that is, an observation that does not fit the current view, as in Planck's important 1900 paper) suggests that we have got it wrong and that a reassessment is needed. Also, I do not rule out the possibility that, although we might be correct in assuming that the causal processes that we seek to discover exist, it could be impossible for us ever to discover the truth about some of them (see Chapter 5, Section 7).

We often refer to the type of causal relation described above as taking the form "A causes B given C", but we don't usually spell out exactly what we mean by the word 'cause'; and I have no need to take a view on this in the context of this book.

2.3 *The truth of "statements of fact"*

We noted in Section 2.1 above that two different types of fact exist: phenomenal facts (facts about what something feels like, facts that are "privileged" in that one person has special access to them and "private" in that they cannot be communicated perfectly to another person), and public facts (facts that are equally accessible to everyone and that can therefore be communicated perfectly using language). Here, we are concerned with public facts.[13] Setting aside statements concerning historical events, there are three different situations that typically arise regarding the truth of statements about public facts. From time to time in this book we will need to note which of these seems likely to apply (for example, in the cases of the three anti-physicalist claims, see Chapter 3, Section 6). The reason why there are three such situations follows from the fact that there are two distinctions that can be made regarding our knowledge of the truth of statements of such facts.

---

[13] Some of the issues addressed in this section are addressed in Kripke's book *Naming and Necessity* (1972, and see also Chapter 4, Section 4), but I approach them here from a very different point of view. See also Johansson (2006).

Before we start, however, there are two further issues to address. First, it is important to note that there can be a problem with the word 'fact'. The word 'fact' is generally defined as: "a thing that is known or proved to be true". Indeed, in philosophy, as Mellor (1995, p 8) makes clear, 'facts' are taken to be: "actual states of affairs, corresponding to true statements". If we take it that something that is referred to as a 'fact' always corresponds to a true statement, the implication is that when I say to my friend: "you've got the facts wrong" that statement is incoherent. But it does not strike one as incoherent. In general parlance, the states of affairs that are presented to us as 'facts' all too often turn out to be false. This word, 'fact', is important to the analysis in this book, but I need to be able to use it in circumstances in which we are not certain whether a statement regarding some so-called fact is, or is not true. Therefore, I take it here that all we can be sure about regarding a 'statement of fact' is that it is a proposition the truth of which is conceivable; that is, the proposition is not incoherent, it does not obviously express a contradiction. Typical statements of fact, given this usage, are "Paris is in France", "the leaves are green" and "unicorns exist", where the first is true, the second may or may not be true, and the third is generally reckoned to be an untrue, or false, fact.

Next, it might be expected that the terms *a priori* and *a posteriori* would be used in the situations that I examine in this section. But the term *'a priori'* describes things that can be known without access to empirical evidence and the term *'a posteriori'* is used when something is known to be true (or not true) following experimentation or observation.[14] The distinctions I want to make here are different, see Figure 2 below; I want to distinguish the cases in which a person can know a proposition to be true (or false) from information that is readily available to him/her with just a bit of serious thought, so the truth of the statement can be said to be known *ab initio*, from the cases in which either experimentation or expertise and analysis are required if the person is to ascertain the truth (or falsity) of some proposition, that is, the person either has to do some serious and difficult reasoning or some experimentation, or else he/she has to take the truth (or falsity) of the statement on trust from others who have done the work.

The first distinction I want to make, then, is between a statement of fact the truth of which is transparent *ab initio* (whilst seated in an armchair), and a

---

[14] See *https://en.oxforddictionaries.com.*

16

statement of fact the truth of which is contingent (in the sense that it is not apparent to us) *ab initio*.[15]

	ab initio	after investigation
a priori	simple logic	complex logic
a posteriori	introspection	experimentation

Figure 2: *Ways of knowing the truth of a statement*
This figure illustrates two alternative classifications of the way in which the truth of a statement can be known. First, it can be known *ab initio* (whilst seated in an armchair) or following some form of investigation (complex logical analysis or experimentation). Second, it can be known *a priori* (as the result of logical analysis) or *a posteriori* (after observation, such as introspection or experimentation).

Thus, a statement of fact can be known to be true *ab initio* if it is a matter of simple logic. This will be the case if the statement derives from a statement that is true because of the definitions of the terms involved, such as "no unmarried man is married" combined with the replacement of one of its terms by a synonym, as in the case of: "no bachelor is married" (see Quine, 1951, p 23). But a statement can also be known to be true *ab initio* as the result of subjective experience (introspection), as in "I think, therefore I am" (Descartes, 1637), which has the implication that each of us knows *ab initio* that mental

---

[15] There are two circumstances in which the truth or falsity of a statement is generally considered to be 'contingent', meaning that it appears to be not necessarily true (or not necessarily false). First, this can be the case when we don't know whether the statement is true until we've made some observations, but once we have made those observations we will know, once and for all, that it is or that it is not true (I call this type of contingency the "needs investigation" type; but see Kripke, 1972, p 99). Second, a statement can be said to be contingent if the statement is true in some circumstances but not true in others so we have to check each time (I call this one the "happenstance" type).

17

states exist (see Section 4.1 of this chapter). If our distinction had been based on truths that are known *a priori*, known without empirical evidence, advanced theorems in mathematics and in logical theory, which are highly complex and cannot be known without a great deal of expertise in mathematics or logical theory, would have been included in the category, while things that can be known from subjective experience (introspection) would have been excluded. I want to base my analysis of the ontology of mind on the facts we can know to be true *ab initio*; I want to include the facts we know from introspection as some of my fundamental assumptions and I have no need to assume the truth or falsity of obscure mathematical theorems which no one has yet been able to prove. This is the reason why my first case consists of things that we can know *ab initio* (while seated in an armchair); things that can be known from simple logic and things that can easily be discovered using introspection.

A further distinction can then be made between two types of statement of fact which are contingent *ab initio* (contingent in the "needs investigation" sense, see footnote 15 on p 17), so initially it is conceivable that they are true but it is also conceivable that they are false; their truth cannot be known *ab initio*. For some of these propositions, once analysis or an observation has indicated support for it we know that it is necessarily true; for others, although investigations may be supportive of it, so we might at some point in time *believe* it to be true, we know that it remains possible that it could be falsified by future observations.

Consider the situation in which, once some analysis or experiment supports a proposition, we know that the statement is indubitably true; we know that it cannot be found in the future to be false (that is, we know that the 'black swan'/aberrant observation situation cannot arise). Identities involving the 'is' of composition such as "H_2O is water" where the meaning of 'water' is "that which gives rise in humans to the waterish *qualia*" (given that we also take it that there can be only one such substance) come into that category, as does the proposition that Hesperus is the same object as Phosphorus or the proposition that the person who invented bifocals was the same person as the first Postmaster General in the US (see Kripke, 1972, pp 28 and 98), and as do simple observations such as "the world is round".[16] Some of these come into

---

[16] Apparently, it was thought by many in past centuries that the earth was flat and that you could sail to the edge of it and then you might fall off, but now we have been out there and seen what it looks like we know that it is spherical.

the class referred to as 'laws of nature' or 'natural laws' (see Section 2.2 above) in which case the truths they convey are deemed to be 'nomologically necessary', but some are cases in which there are two names for one thing (they are simple numerical identities) so their truth can be considered to be logically necessary.[17] In any case, these propositions as well as those that are true as the result of logical analysis, are propositions that are necessarily true in our world.

The other type of contingent statement consists of those statements regarding facts which, although thought to be true as the result of some experimentation, might be found to be false on further investigation. This third category can give rise to confusion of exposition. This is the category which is not always spelt out clearly in the literature. Although we can *never* be sure that statements of this sort are true, we often treat them as being true (perhaps with a general understanding that they may not be), so the language used in relation to them can be confusing. Like some of the statements in the previous category, these may be thought of as being 'laws of nature' of some sort and, when it is taken that they are a true representation of some causal process that operates, their validity would be viewed as being 'nomologically' necessary. But we know that they could turn out to be false. For example, various laws relating to classical physics (such as Wien's energy distribution law, which Planck and others thought "must be necessarily true", see Planck, 1900, p 1) were found wanting (this one failed at high energies) and this led to the birth of quantum mechanics (on 14 December 1900, see Boya, 2004); and laws such as: "all ravens are black" are always vulnerable to being proved untrue. These 'contingent' laws are statements of fact that appear to be true given current observations or experimentation relating to the world around us, but sometimes a statement of this sort turns out to be false on further investigation (as is the case with "all swans are white").[18]

---

[17] The word 'identity' has two meanings; it can mean that two words have the same referent (numerical identity), or it can mean that two things appear to us to be so similar that we cannot tell them apart (qualitative identity). The grammar of saying that two things are 'identical' when the situation is that of numerical identity, so there are in fact two words but only one thing, may have created some confusion; see Chapter 4, Section 3.2.

[18] A proposition is said to be *necessary* if it cannot fail to be the case, and in science there are propositions that are logical necessary and propositions that are nomologically necessary. In philosophy there is a third kind of necessity, 'metaphysical necessity' with logical necessity entailing metaphysical necessity, but not *vice versa*, and metaphysical

Finally, from time to time in this book statements arise regarding the 'existence' of something (in Chapter 3, Section 6.3 concerning the hard problem, for example, and implicitly in Figure 1, in Chapter 1), such as the proposition that some constituents of what we call 'matter' give rise to (instantiate) an electric charge. Obviously, these statements are not true as a matter of logic. However, some of them are, indubitably, true. So there is a question as to how to refer to this fact about them. There seems to be no agreed form of words with which to describe this type of true statement, leaving us with a difficulty of exposition. Here, I simply refer to them as "laws of nature"; they are statements of truths of the "you can't have one without the other" variety that we have discovered from our observations of the circumstances in which certain phenomena arise, but they are not 'causal' in the usual "if A then B given C" manner often associated with laws of nature (but see Section 4.3 of this chapter). Thus, if we were to discover that certain configurations of neurons are *always* associated with consciousness (*cf.*, the particles we call electrons *always* have a negative charge) I would refer to this fact as a law of nature and state that it is nomologically true.

2.4 *The meaning of "there is only one 'substance' ..."*

An element of the background to the proposal regarding the nature of mind that is presented in this book is the assumption that there is only one 'substance', which we call 'matter'. We all understand broadly what is meant, in this context, by the words 'substance' and 'matter', which I use from time to time throughout this book (one of which occurs in its title). But both these terms raise questions.

First, the word 'substance' can take different meanings (see Robinson, 2014). It can be used to pick out something that could be said to 'stand under' or 'ground' things. Used in this sense, the term picks out the things in some philosophical system that are the "foundational or fundamental entities of reality". Other times, as here, it is used in the sense of 'substratum',

---

necessity entailing physical necessity, but not *vice versa*. The analysis in this section suggests that the type of law of nature which, when supported by experimentation is known to be true (such as "water is H_2O") could be said to be *metaphysically* necessary; while the type of law of nature that could be falsified in the future by an aberrant observation (such as "all ravens are black") would not be so classified because whereas we believe it to be the case we also know that it could fail to be the case.

to pick out that which instantiates properties. In Crane's words, then, a substance is that which is the bearer of properties:

"A substance is what *has* properties, what is the *bearer* of properties. Properties are *possessed* by a substance, they *belong* to a substance or they *inhere* in a substance" (see Crane, 2001, p 35).

When I refer to a 'substance' here I use the word in this sense, and I refer to it as "instantiating", or "giving rise to", properties.

Second, we should note that the way in which the word 'matter' used to be used in physics encapsulates a view of the universe that is now somewhat out of date: that view can be characterised as assuming that matter consists of particles much like billiard balls or marbles in that they occupy space and have mass (along with other properties). We now know that some so-called particles, photons for example, have no mass and so cannot really be said to be "made of matter" in the old-fashioned understanding of that term, and we also know that energy is as fundamental to our understanding of the universe as mass and that the two can convert, one into the other. We also know now that there is a type of matter, "dark matter", that interacts with the gravitational force, and possibly with the weak nuclear force, but is not responsive to electromagnetic forces. We need a more sophisticated statement of what we mean when we refer to there being "only one 'substance' and we call it 'matter'".[19]

The aspect of a 'substance' or of 'matter' that is important in this examination of the ontology of mind is the existence of what we call "properties of matter". This raises two questions. First, should we be replacing the proposition that there is something that could be called a 'substance', in the sense of a *substratum* that is the bearer of properties (see Armstrong, 1989, and Schneider 2013), by the proposition that there is nothing other than a simple bundle of properties, an approach known as 'bundle theory'? But there is no necessity to take a view on this issue here; what matters here is the completeness (or otherwise) of physics/science, and therefore the existence of causal processes relating to the properties we associate with this hypothetical substance we call matter, and to those properties' interactions.

---

[19] Crane and Mellor make this point in their 1990 paper (see p 186).

The second question is probably the more interesting: could the proposition that there is only one 'substance' be replaced by a different type of proposition, such as the proposition that science is causally closed?   As explained in Section 2.2 of this chapter, in this book I assume that events are involved in causal processes; that is, I assume that every event that occurs has some sort of a cause or collection of causes (that every event can be viewed as being the end-point of a forking chain of causes going back to the Big Bang, see Chapter 8, Section 4.1), and that every event may have a causal role with respect to some subsequent event. Where possible, we encapsulate these causal processes in the statements that we call 'laws of nature' or 'natural laws', which may take a probabilistic form (see Section 2.2 of this chapter and Chapter 8, Section 2). These laws of nature are part of the systematised body of knowledge about the natural world that we call 'science'. And we assume in this book that a finished science would be 'complete', in the sense that all the causes and all the effects along with all the causal processes would be included within it.

This suggests that we could replace the requirement that "there is only one 'substance' ..." with the requirement that "a finished 'science' would be complete" ('complete' in the sense noted in the previous paragraph).

The implications of this become clearer if we consider counter-examples. If supervenience physicalism (see Figure 1a) were to hold it would not be the case that physics (to which a subset of the natural laws in science would belong, see Section 2.1 above) would be complete in this sense. This is because if mental states supervene on the properties of matter studied in physics but do not have the characteristics that make it appropriate for them to be included in the science of physics (because there are facts relating to them that cannot be communicated perfectly by one person to another linguistically), there would be natural laws that specify the way the physical (non-mental) properties of matter must be for some particular mental state to arise, but these natural laws would have an effect that is outside physics. So physics would not be complete in the required sense – although, of course, the science of physics could still be 'causally complete' in the sense that: all physical effects are fully caused by purely physical (non-mental) prior histories.

Another example of a lack of completeness of this sort arises in the case of libertarianism as it is described in Chapter 8, Section 2.3, where a mental event could arise uncaused. If such libertarianism pertained, various physical (non-mental) properties could, effectively, be influenced by something that was not part of science, and this would mean that some events that affect the properties of matter studied in science would have no cause. In this case, therefore, science would not be 'complete' in either of the above senses.

Before leaving this discussion of the meanings of 'substance' and 'matter' we should note that in general conversation the word 'matter' is often implicitly taken to connote "lifeless", and therefore "non-experiential"; "that which occupies space and is distinct from mind and spirit". In this case, 'matter' would be lifeless and lack consciousness because of its *definition*. But there is no reason to suppose that matter, in the sense of that which is studied in science (*e.g.*, that which is made up of protons, electrons *etc.*), is lifeless or that it is non-experiential. Indeed, one could argue that there is every reason to suppose the opposite: casual observation suggests that matter is closely associated with both life and consciousness (see, for example, Strawson, 2008). It may be that people sometimes commit themselves to this rather restricted conventional meaning associated with the word 'matter' without being aware of what they are doing, and that that has led to some of the problems that arise in this area of philosophy, such as the well-known 'hard problem' ("how can it be that consciousness arises in the context of matter?") and the lack of belief in micro-psychism, panpsychism and emergence (see Levine, 1983A and Chalmers, 2007 and Chapter 5, Section 9).

2.5 *The meaning of 'physical' and 'physicalism'*

The term 'physical' has two distinct meanings in common parlance: it can mean "pertaining to objects such as the body, as opposed to the mind" (or "non-mental") and it can mean "pertaining to matter".[20] In modern philosophy, however, the term 'physical' almost invariably takes the meaning: "pertaining to that which is studied in the physical sciences" which I take to be the sciences that are reducible to physics as well as physics itself.[21]

This distinction between meanings is touched upon by Searle when, in his 1983 paper entitled 'Why I am not a property dualist', he complains of: "the inadequacy of the traditional terminology" saying:

---

[20] See for example *http://www.dictionary.com/browse/physical*.

[21] If physical is used in the "pertaining to matter" sense, then mind, if it is an irreducible property of matter, could still be termed a 'physical' phenomenon although in that case facts relating to mental states would be excluded from the science that we call "physics".

"The property dualist wants to say that consciousness is a mental and therefore not physical feature of the brain. I want to say consciousness is a mental and therefore biological and therefore physical feature of the brain" (*ibid.*, p 61).

Horgan (1984), also, notes the ambiguities that can arise regarding the use of the term 'physical' (see below in Chapter 3, Section 6.1). Strawson (2006, p 4) refers to the physicalism that assumes that everything is reducible to the physical sciences as 'physicsalism', while calling the physicalism that requires that everything pertains to matter, the physicalism that is in his view "fully realist" about consciousness, 'real physicalism'.

To take 'physical' as having both meanings at the same time is implicitly to take the proposition that there is a property of matter that is unsuited for study in the physical sciences to be incoherent, when in fact there may be no reason why that should be the case. Thus:

1.   If a thing is 'physical', all the facts relating to it must be suitable for study in the physical sciences.
2.   Matter is 'physical'.
3.   Therefore, everything about matter is suitable for study in the physical sciences.
4.   Therefore, the proposition that there could be a property of matter with facts relating to it that are not suitable for study in the science of physics is incoherent.

If the meaning of 'physical' is taken to be "suitable for study in the physical sciences", as in this book, then taking it *also* to be the case that "everything that pertains to matter is physical" is to make an important implicit assumption. The conclusion in 4. above, therefore, is not necessarily correct.[22]

---

[22] If dualism holds, mental states are not "suitable for study in the physical sciences" and do not "pertain to matter". If reductive physicalism holds, mental states are "suitable for study in the physical sciences" and they do "pertain to matter". If non-reductive physics holds, mental states are not "suitable for study in the physical sciences" but they do "pertain to matter". Finally, if either reductive physicalism or non-reductive physicalism hold, although 'physical' might mean 'non-mental', mental states could be described as 'physical' because they do pertain to matter.

We should also note that if the word 'physicalism' in 'non-reductive physicalism' (which refers to the possibility that mental states are *not* reducible to things that are studied in physics) is interpreted as implying that everything relating to matter is of the sort that *is* suitable for study in physics then 'non-reductive physicalism' is a self-contradictory term (see also Schneider, 2013).

In terms of our investigation into the nature of mind the fact that the word 'physical' has these different meanings matters because it causes confusion. In academic philosophy nowadays, *both* the term 'physicalism' *and* the term 'materialism' are generally taken to imply reductive physicalism. This means that arguments presented against reductive physicalism appear to be arguments against all forms of physicalism even when they do not rule out the possibility of mind being an instantiation of a property of matter that is unsuitable for study in physics, so they do not carry the implication that if something exists that cannot be explained in terms of the physical sciences that thing must be 'immaterial'.[23] But in addition, simply to assist general communication about things that are important to us, we could do with another "-ism" besides "physicalism", one that encapsulates the assumption that there is only one substance, matter, but which does not carry with it the automatic implication that the stuff called matter has no properties other than those that are studied in physics. If mind is independent of matter it remains possible that minds survive the death of the body, while if mind is a property of matter (albeit not a property suitable for study in the science of physics) this seems unlikely.

It could be helpful to distinguish different meanings for the terms 'physicalism' and 'materialism'. The meaning of the term 'physicalism' would remain unchanged, implying that every aspect of everything that exists is of the type that can be incorporated into the science of physics, and that the causes of the occurrence of every event are the type of causes that are studied in the science of physics (see Jackson 1982, p 127, and Kim 2005, pp 149-150, for

---

[23] Philosophers often seem to treat words as if they have a meaning that exists independent of us, which can be discovered if we work at it, just as a physicist will assume that objects have an existence independent of us. And yet, they often use a word without defining it (*e.g.*, 'physics'); they sometimes don't seem to notice when a word has more than one meaning (*e.g.*, 'physical'); and, they sometimes define a word in a manner that is at variance with common usage (*e.g.*, 'fact'). This could be the reason why the approach to the ontology of mind that I promote in this book has been so neglected by philosophers.

example; this is also the starting point for the discussion of the question "What is physicalism?" in Crane and Mellor 1990, see p 185). The term 'materialism' could then apply to the metaphysical or ontological proposition that: "there is only one substance and we call it matter". It would therefore be a form of monism and would require that the substance referred to has certain properties that distinguish it from the form of monism known as 'idealism', in which reality is viewed as being fundamentally mental. 'Materialism', with this definition, would allow for the possibility of property dualism, the situation in which mind, albeit a property of matter, is different in some fundamental way from the properties of matter that are studied in physics.

If mental states are, in fact, instantiations of a property of matter that is not reducible to the properties studied in the science of physics, the idea that is examined in this book, then materialism (as defined above) would be a true description of the world, but physicalism (as defined above) would not.

3 Facts about consciousness

In this section I summarise some of the things known about consciousness that are relevant to the material in the rest of this book. I start by defining consciousness; then I note the different sorts of things of which we can be conscious and then the different types of things which we can 'know'. A summary of the relation between consciousness and memory and a formalised hypothetical structure of the mind, showing the relations between different types of consciousness, different types of memory store and attention is available in Appendix 2. The section finishes by noting that one day we might be able to form a view concerning which creatures besides ourselves are conscious based on observations relating to the structure of their brains and the types of memory they have, but this is likely to be considered controversial.

3.1 Defining consciousness

In this book I take mental states to be states, probably states of the brain, that *can* be conscious, so it seems sensible to take a look at what is meant by the term 'conscious' before proceeding further.[24] What do we mean when we use the term 'consciousness', or when we assert that a creature "is conscious" or appears to be "conscious of" something?[25] People have often remarked that it can be difficult to define consciousness, since most of the initial thoughts people have as they make the attempt turn out to be near-synonyms for consciousness (awareness, wakefulness, cognizance, and so on). I therefore start by examining what a definition is required to achieve.

Suppe (2000, p 76) says that "[i]n the most fundamental scientific sense, to define is to delimit", and suggests that a formal definition of a term Y, might assert that a thing is a Y if it is a thing of type X and has the property Z, thereby enabling us to decide, definitively, whether some thing is, or is not, a Y. The definition of being conscious that I use in this book takes that broad form, but it needs to be slightly adapted to cater for the fact that, at any rate given the current state of science, we cannot be certain whether another creature is capable of consciousness (as in "the problem of other minds"). It is derived from the definition proposed by Nagel, in 1974. He said: "an organism has conscious mental states if and only if there is something it is like to *be* that organism – something it is like *for* the organism" (1974, p 436, his italics). Of course, Nagel's definition is concerned with organisms; but it is easily generalised to cover robots as well.

Taking both of the above points on board the result can be expressed, in Suppe's type of formulation, as:

> we consider a thing to have conscious mental states if we take the view that it has the property of there being something it is like to *be* that thing – something it is like *for* the thing.

---

[24] Psychologists tell us that most of what goes on in our minds is not conscious, it is hidden from our view, with many of our routine decisions taken on automatic pilot. Kahneman says (2011, p 52): "The notion that we have limited access to the workings of our minds is difficult to accept because, naturally, it is alien to our experience, but it is true: you know far less about yourself than you feel you do." I take a mental state to be something of which a person/creature *could* be conscious, if it was attending to it, but at any point in time may not be.

[25] To suggest that a creature "is conscious" or may be "conscious of" something seems to be a meaningful suggestion. Because that is so, we have coined a noun, "consciousness", but it is unclear to what, exactly, it refers.

We can check this definition for plausibility by looking at examples. Given this definition of being conscious most of us would probably reckon that a table, a plant, a stone or a tree is not conscious. A person in a deep sleep or a person in a coma might be viewed as not conscious, although judged to be capable of being conscious in other circumstances. A wakeful person would be judged to be conscious by everyone (barring only solipsists, if such exist).[26] We might be less certain when it comes to other animals or robots. Is a dog capable of being conscious, or a horse, a mouse or an ant, or a robot? Importantly, it seems to be impossible for us to be 100 percent certain about the answers to some of these questions (see Section 4.2 of this chapter), although that situation might change if neuroscience, as it becomes more highly developed, were able to identify, convincingly, the neuroscientific counterparts of being conscious (see Section 3.4 of this chapter).

3.2 *What we are conscious of*

Mental states, states that can be conscious, consist of what are generally known as 'feelings' and 'thoughts'. In this section we identify three different types of mental state, commonly known to psychologists as: phenomenal consciousness, access consciousness and (somewhat confusingly) reflexive consciousness.

First, there is the type of mental state known as 'phenomenal consciousness'. This is the term used for the wide variety of sensory experience and emotions of which we can be aware, picking out the "what it feels like" element of the things of which we can be conscious; it also picks out the what it feels like element of things that are "viewed with the mind's eye" after being recalled from the long-term memory. 'Phenomenal facts' is the term we use for the facts regarding what something *feels* like. Chalmers, in his 1995 paper 'Facing up to the Problem of Consciousness', cites a number of examples of phenomenal experiences in his list of things we might be conscious of:

"the felt quality of redness, the experience of dark and light, the quality of depth in a visual field ... the sound of a clarinet, the smell of mothballs

---

[26] A solipsist is one who believes in solipsism. Solipsism is the metaphysical position that other minds do not exist.

... bodily sensations, from pains to orgasms; mental images that are conjured up internally; the felt quality of emotion ..." (*ibid.*, p 201).

As mentioned above, the quality of these experiences has been given the name '*qualia*' by philosophers. In his book *An Essay Concerning Human Understanding*, published in 1690, John Locke used the taste of pineapple to argue that true knowledge can only be based on experience. He wrote:

" ... if you doubt this, see whether you can by words give anyone who has never tasted pineapple an idea of the taste of that fruit. He may approach a grasp of it by being told of its resemblance to other tastes of which he already has the ideas in his memory, imprinted there by things he has taken into his mouth; but merely raising up in him other simple ideas that will still be very different from the true taste of the pineapple."

David Hume constructed a catalogue of the types of things of which we are conscious, in 1739/40. He also described the nature of phenomenal consciousness, stressing the fact that what something feels like cannot be communicated in words, saying:

"To give a child an idea of scarlet or orange, of sweet or bitter, I present the objects, or in other words, convey to him these impressions; but proceed not so absurdly as to endeavour to produce the impressions by exciting the ideas" (1739/40, p 52);

And he also referred to a pineapple in this context, saying:

"We cannot form to ourselves a just idea of the taste of a pineapple, without having actually tasted it" (*ibid.*, p 53).

This type of consciousness consists of information about "what it feels like" to experience something. Knowing "what it feels like" to experience something is one of the ways that have been identified in which we can "know" something (see Section 3.3 of this chapter).

A person/creature has privileged access to this type of "what it feels like" fact, known as phenomenal facts; we can never be certain that the same sensory input – seeing some shade of red, for example, or the characteristic pain of a stubbed toe – feels the same for different people. Indeed, it clearly can be the case that it does differ if only in the case of synaesthesia, where a person is "wired up" in such a manner that stimulation of one sense or part of the body produces a sense impression relating to another sense or part of the body. Information about these phenomenal facts, or *qualia*, can be stored in our long-term memories and recalled, as in Chalmers' "mental images that are conjured up internally" (see above), for use in cognitive analysis. Facts relating to the current phenomenal experience of our external and internal senses (the items potentially available for phenomenal consciousness that have been chosen for attention, see Appendix 2, Section 2.2) is information that we can use in cognitive processing – in thinking, reasoning, taking decisions, *etc.* Recalled phenomenal facts often form an element of what we call a 'concept' (using the word 'concept' in the sense of "an abstract idea that picks out the fundamental characteristics that define a set of objects", see footnote 63 on p 94).

We can make a distinction between two kinds of phenomenal information: first, there is something it is like to receive information about things that are external to our bodies by our external senses such as sight, hearing, taste and so on, and to receive information about the state of our bodies through the directly body-related internal senses such as proprioception and pain receptors *etc.* Second, information about the emotions we experience, such as anger, love, sadness and so on consists of a bundle of bodily sensations received through senses, containing information about the physical aspects of emotions (such as the effects on the body of adrenalin, serotonin and the like), along with the effects we observe emotions to have on the patterns of our thoughts, our feelings and our desires.

A second type of mental activity of which we can be conscious relates to certain aspects of our thoughts. Block has suggested (1995), that although much of the information consciously used in cognitive processing is of the phenomenal type, there is another type of information of which we are conscious, and which we use in cognitive processing, alongside these phenomenal facts. He stresses that these other things of which we are conscious are available: "for use in reasoning and rationally guiding speech and action" (*ibid.*, p 227). He calls this 'access consciousness', and stipulates that a state is access conscious if: "a representation of its content is (1) … poised to be used as a premise in reasoning, (2) poised for [rational] control of action, and (3) poised for rational control of speech" (*ibid.*, p 231, his brackets). Here,

I take this second type of information of which we can be conscious to consist of information that is equally available to everyone, so it can, in principle, be communicated perfectly from one person to another using language. As mentioned above, because information of this sort is available equally to everyone, I call it 'public information' or 'public facts'. Consciousness of public facts, facts that can be expressed in language, may not be precisely what Block had in mind for what he called "access consciousness". But in this book a lot rests on the question of whether information can or cannot be perfectly communicated linguistically, given our definition of physics and therefore of physicalism (Sections 2.1 and 2.5 of this chapter), so I hope I can be forgiven for adapting Block's classification to take account of this distinction between different types of fact.

So, as well as being conscious of knowing what it feels like to experience something, we can be conscious of knowing that the statement of some supposed fact about the external world may be true (the conscious experience of knowing a public fact has been named 'cognitive phenomenology'). Such a statement might be that "Paris is in France" or that "elephants cannot jump" or that "this stone weighs 5 kilograms". These facts differ from the phenomenal facts described above in that they are statements relating to 'public' facts, facts that are equally available to everyone and that can therefore be readily communicated from one person to another linguistically. Like the phenomenal facts, these public facts also can be fed into and retrieved from our long-term memories and, in addition to the memories of the types of thing on Chalmers' list of phenomenally conscious experiences, memories of these facts are also available 'for use' in cognitive analysis. And, again like the phenomenal facts, they can be an element in a concept. Where phenomenal consciousness corresponds to "knowing what it feels like to experience something", access consciousness (defined in this manner) can be described as "knowing that something is the case".

In addition to these two different types of fact of which we are conscious, there is another, third, type of mental activity of which we are aware, and it is cognitive processing, that is, thinking (imagining, reasoning, taking decisions, *etc.*) along with the implementation of decisions (the triggering of speech, muscular activity and so on); this third type of mental activity makes use of both the types of fact identified above. This third type of conscious mental activity is less well represented in the philosophical and psychological literature than phenomenal consciousness and Block's access consciousness (but see Peacocke, 2007 and Prinz, 2007). Chalmers refers to it in his 1995 paper (p 201) citing: "… the experience of a stream of conscious thought …" as an example of 'experience'. Block (2001) has called consciousness of cognition by the slightly confusing name 'reflexive consciousness'.

3.3 Varieties of 'knowing'

The types of things we can 'know' is relevant to what we can be conscious of (see, for example, Chapter 3, Section 6.1). It is often said that there are several different ways of 'knowing': Ryle (1949, Chapter 2) famously argued that "knowing that" is different from "knowing how". But some philosophers have raised questions regarding Ryle's proposal, suggesting that the "knowing how" variety of knowing could be just a collection of "knowing that's" (see Stanley and Williamson, 2001 and Snowdon, 2003). "Knowing things", as in being acquainted with specific items, or tokens, is another way in which the verb "to know" is used.[27] Many people maintain that "knowing what it feels like" is different again, but this can be controversial; some philosophers deny the existence of phenomenal facts, the "knowing what it feels like" type of knowledge, saying that all that is learned when a new experience takes place is an ability, something of the "knowing how" variety (see Lewis 1988 and Chapter 5, Section 2.4).

These issues matter because they arise in the context of Jackson's knowledge argument (see Chapter 3, Section 6.1) and Lewis' case against the existence of phenomenal information (see Chapter 5, Section 2), both of which raise important questions about the ontology of consciousness. It is certainly true that the words "knowing how" can be used both in a "knowing what it feels like" situation (knowing how to identify the smell of bacon) and in a "knowing that" situation (knowing how to get to British Museum); the linguistic constructions are not unique to just one variety of knowing.

It seems likely, however, that the different types of knowing identified above take place in very different parts of the brain; for example:

---

[27] Snowdon (2003, p 1) notes the use in English of 'know' as in "acquaintance", 'know' followed by a specific noun. He says: "we talk of knowing a poem, or a place, or a person".

- The phrase "knowing what it feels like" picks out something about an experience related to one's senses, internal and/or external. The parts of the brain related to what a person is experiencing when he/she receives sensory information are presumably well-connected to those areas that are responsible for receiving the information, the areas related to the internal or external sense that is involved in the experience. This would be the Occipital lobe for sight, the Temporal lobe for smell and sound and the Parietal lobe for visuospatial processing.

- The phrase "knowing that" is typically used to describe knowledge of the type described as 'public facts', information that can be communicated perfectly from one person to another using words (see Sections 2.1 and 3.2 of this chapter). This type of knowing is likely to be connected to the verbal areas of the brain (generally contained in the left-hand side of the cerebral cortex and in the structures known as Wernicke's area and Broca's area).

- There is a type of "knowing how" that involves the cerebellum (at the back of the brain, below the cerebrum) and relates to doing things like riding a bicycle or playing the piano on automatic pilot (see Appendix 2, Section 2.4 and the case of HM). For example, I may know all the "knowing that" type of facts that I need to know in order to play Beethoven's Moonlight Sonata, but I cannot "know how" to play it to anything like an acceptable standard without weeks or years of practice, causing multitudes of new neural connections to develop within my cerebellum so my fingers can operate without me being directly conscious of telling them what to do.[28]

It should be noted that the phrase "knowing how" can also be used in the context of the other types of knowing described above. So, if I "know how" to get myself from London to Paris all I need is a bunch of "knowing that"-type facts (apart from routine "knowing how"-type facts relating to the use of

---

[28] Recent research by neuroscientists into the learning of "the Knowledge" (how to get around London) by London cabbies demonstrates that this has an effect on the neural connections. The cabbies' hippocampus, the bit of the brain in which the new connections supporting such an activity are developed, was found to be significantly larger, on average, than those of the rest of the population (see Woollett and Maguire, 2011.

my body); but "knowing how" when used of the ability to play the sonata or ride a bicycle has a very different meaning. Knowing what it's like to taste truffle because I have already had the experience certainly results in my "knowing how" to imagine the taste of truffle, but only because I then "know what it feels like" to experience it.

All this suggests that we do, indeed, have different ways of "knowing", and that these take place in different parts of the brain. But more importantly, it also suggests that the brain activity involved may be a better indicator of which variety operates in any particular circumstances than the linguistic constructs people use to describe "knowing".

3.4 Identifying conscious creatures

Many have noted that there seems to be a close relationship between memory and consciousness (see Appendix 2). Charles Richet says (1886): "Without memory no conscious sensation, without memory no consciousness", and: "to suffer for only a hundredth of a second is not to suffer at all; and for my part I would readily agree to undergo a pain, however acute and intense it might be, provided it should last only a hundredth of a second, and leave after it neither reverberation nor recall" (Richet, 1884, p 32). Nicholas Humphrey refers to the "Self" as being "phenomenally thick and substantial" and says: "a temporally-thick Self is something to build a rich subjective life on" (2006, p 131), perhaps making the same point. Without some form of short-term memory for sensory information (a 'sensory memory store'), it seems, a creature could not be 'aware' of the information it receives through its senses. Many experiments support this intuition; they demonstrate that interrupting the formation of the record of a signal in a sensory memory store can disrupt phenomenal consciousness (see footnote 106 on p 204). It seems that if a creature had no short-term sensory memory stores, although its eyes and ears (if it had such) would receive information relating to the surroundings and send this information in a message to the brain, each bit of information would be gone an instant after it arrived, so no record would be available for the creature to access and connect to the information received subsequently.

This suggests that some form of memory store associated with the receipt of sensory information is *necessary* for the experience of *qualia*, and therefore, for phenomenal consciousness; by the same token, it seems that some sort of memory store associated with information that can be expressed in words is necessary for a person to have thoughts that involve words. Given this, a question arises as to whether, if we knew how to identify the existence of such memory stores in some particular type of creature's brain, and we discovered that it had none of the relevant memory stores, we would conclude that there could not be "something it is like" to be that type of creature.[29] Indeed, could we take it further and propose the obverse of this; that is, if we found that a creature did have memory stores of this sort, should we conclude that that creature does have some form of consciousness? Could we argue that a foetus acquires 'personhood' at the point at which it acquires effective memory stores of this type, so it becomes the case that there is something it is like to be that foetus?

The definition of consciousness that I have used for this book (which derives from that of Nagel, 1974, see Section 3.1 of this chapter) is highly subjective in nature, in that it deliberately leaves room for dispute about which creatures are and which are not conscious. The ideas presented in this section suggest that it might be possible for science, at some point in the future, to give us a more satisfactory, more objective (although likely to be controversial) indication of which creatures, or things, are capable of consciousness.

4 Propositions relating to mental states

In developing the approach to the theory of mind presented in this book I found that I needed to accept three fundamental propositions. The approach for which I make the case in this book (see Chapter 7, Section 4) is implied by these propositions along with my definition of the science of physics. In this section I present these propositions as fundamental propositions relating to mental states and, whilst they are clearly not true as the result of logic, I suggest that their validity can be ascertained through introspection (see Section 2.3 of this chapter).[30] But it seems that most people are not signed up to all three of

---

[29] If the only way of being conscious was to have this sort of a sensory memory store, this would rule out the possibility that there could be a computer that is conscious.

[30] Of course, what we think we introspect is what we are aware of introspecting (*cf.*, what we think we see is what we are aware of seeing) but it must be possible to misinterpret the significance of what we introspect just as what we think we see may not correspond to the reality out there of what we are looking at (see Dennett, 1991, Chapter 3), so care is needed.

these propositions, so in Chapters 4 and 5 and in Appendix 1 I examine the cases for and against other proposals regarding the ontology of consciousness.

4.1 Conscious mental states exist

The first proposition I suggest that we know, *ab initio*, to be true is:

>   *Proposition 1: We think, therefore we know mental states exist.*

This proposition is a variant on Descartes' profound insight (1641), usually presented as "cogito, ergo sum" or "I think, therefore I am".[31]

If we can think, we know that we have experiences of the type that can be referred to using statements such as "this is what it is like to see red" or "this is what it is like to feel hungry" or "this is what it is like to know that the pond has fish in it", so we know that mental states exist. An implication of this is that we know that phenomenal facts, facts of the type "*this* is what it is like to experience X", exist (see Chapter 5, Section 2 for Lewis' argument against the existence of phenomenal facts). See also Chapter 3, Section 5.

4.2 There is an epistemic gap

Our second *ab initio* proposition is:

>   *Proposition 2: We cannot communicate to another person, in language, exactly what it is like to experience something.*

So long as we don't sign up to solipsism we accept that there are phenomenal facts relating to other people's/creatures' experiences. So the question here is whether it could be possible for phenomenal facts (facts to which one person or creature has privileged access and which may depend on aspects of that person/creature, such as the nature of their taste buds or the wiring in their brain) to be converted in some way into public facts (facts that are equally

---

[31] Descartes first wrote this phrase "I think, therefore I am" in French ("je pense, donc je suis") in his Discourse on the Method (1637).

available to everyone and so can be communicated perfectly using language). If that is not possible there is said to be an 'epistemic gap'.[32]

But we know that we cannot do that. If someone were to try to tell you what it is like to taste truffle when you haven't previously tasted it, you know that they will not succeed. It seems that it is impossible to explain phenomenal experience in terms of the concepts relating to the physical sciences. The argument in support of the existence of an epistemic gap is spelt out in more detail in Chapter 3, Section 5.

The proposition that there is an epistemic gap, when combined with our definition of physics and the meaning of 'reducible' (see footnote 2 on p 2), carries the implication that reductive physicalism cannot hold. For if mind were reducible to facts that are suitable for study in the science of physics and someone were to use the right words to describe to you what some experience felt like you would then know, exactly, what it felt like; there would be no epistemic gap. Therefore, if the existence of an epistemic gap is accepted and mental states are taken to be instantiations of a property of matter it follows, given our definition of the science of 'physics', that there *must* be another property of matter besides those that are studied in the science of physics.

4.3 Feelings are necessary for the taking of certain types of decision

The third proposition that I propose we know, *ab initio,* is:

> Proposition 3: *When taking a decision between possible actions we pick the one we expect to lead to the most desirable outcome.*

At first sight this may look obvious, even tautologous; but the word 'desirable' involves feelings, and feelings involve consciousness. When faced with certain

---

[32] The 'epistemic gap' is sometimes confused with the 'explanatory gap'. 'Epistemic gap' refers to the fact that there is a class of facts, phenomenal facts relating to other people or creatures, that we can never know. 'Explanatory gap' refers to the fact that any attempt to explain the relation between phenomenal facts and physical (non-mental) facts seems, in Levine's words: "to leave something crucial unexplained" (see Levine, 1983B, p 357 and Section 5 of Chapter 4). However, given our definition of physics, the existence of an epistemic gap implies that there is an explanatory gap and *vice versa.*

types of decision regarding actions, decisions that involve consequences that cannot be directly compared, this says that the chooser examines the way he/she *feels* about the likely consequences of choosing each of the alternative options available in order to identify the action that is likely to result in the most desirable outcome, all things considered. [33] This process is described by philosophers as 'practical reasoning' and the feelings involved in practical reasoning, which often involve events that affect other people and have consequences which are risky in different ways and that take place at widely varying points in the future, are related to what is often called the person's 'values' (the dispositions people have to experience certain types of feelings in particular circumstances).[34] What a person needs in order to take decisions of this sort effectively is a mechanism that can enable the "desirability" of different bundles of non-comparable properties to be gauged one against another.[35]

For the complex decisions that involve practical reasoning a type of process that is altogether different from the causal processes described in Section 2.2 of this chapter is required. In this situation, what is needed is a process that can, in the simplest possible terms, be described by:

$$\text{choose } A_i \text{ to maximise (or satisfice) } F_i(p_i^1, E_i^1, p_i^2, E_i^2, \ldots, p_i^m, E_i^m)$$

where the set of available options, given the situation that pertains, is $\{A_1, A_2, \ldots, A_n\}$, the set of events perceived as likely to follow the choice of the option A_i is $\{E_i^1, E_i^2, \ldots, E_i^m\}$, the p_i^j are the perceived probabilities of occurrence of the E_i^j, and $F_i(..)$ is an indicator of the desirability of the perceived bundle of events following the choice of option A_i, given their perceived probabilities. The E_i^j *cannot* be directly compared because they are not commensurable; perhaps one is the remote possibility of something very

---

[33] The fact that certain rather trivial timing decisions have been shown by Libet and others (see Libet *et al.*, 1982, for example) to have been taken before the person concerned is aware of having taken them does not necessarily have the implication that every decision is taken in that way (see Chapter 3, Section 4.2).

[34] As Watson says (1975, p 346): "The *valuation system* of an agent is that set of considerations which, when combined with his factual beliefs (and probability estimates), yields judgements of the form: the thing for me to do in these circumstances, all things considered, is *a*".

[35] There is empirical support for the theory outlined in this section, see Chapter 6, Section 3.

beneficial for survival or procreation and another the certainty of something totally different which has some small positive value to the chooser (a pleasant taste, say). [36] The F_i are viewed as indicating the 'desirability' to the chooser of the i'th bundle and it is assumed that the F_i *can* be directly compared (psychologists refer to the feelings that are associated with the 'desirability' of the perceived outcomes and that therefore affect the person's choice as 'motivational affect', see Chapter 6, Section 3). In practice, therefore, the result of practical reasoning is often viewed by the chooser as being a "gut feeling" that one action is "probably the best one to choose". [37]

It may be significant to the ontology of consciousness that the normal format of the laws of physics at the macro level (in simplest form "if A then B given C") is not suited to finding a solution to a decision problem of this type; it requires a 'maximisation' type of process. For example, if it turns out that consciousness derives from something that one might call 'proto-consciousness', the building blocks of consciousness, and that this proto-consciousness is associated with fundamental particles (see Chapter 1, Section 1), then the fact that choices of this sort are based on a maximising principle suggests that a search for proto-consciousness might entail seeking that which enables a 'maximisation' type of causal process to take place amongst

---

[36] The desirability of some bundle, as indicated by the way one individual feels about it, may be quite different from its desirability as perceived by some other individual.

[37] This 'desirability' or the intensity of 'motivational affect' associated with an option depends on the probability distribution of the 'value' (or 'utility' or 'salience') associated with the option. It is often taken that that the desirability of the option depends only on the expected value of the utility or salience, but this is not correct. It does depend on the discounted expected value, of course, but it is also affected by the likelihood of the actual value turning out to be different from the discounted expected value and the amount by which it might deviate. Markovitz (1952, p 77) explains why we should reject: "the rule that people maximise discounted expected, or anticipated returns. ... both as a hypothesis to explain, and as a maximum to guide investment behaviour", and says that we should take the variance into account. Kahneman and Tversky (1979, p 263) present: "... a critique of expected utility theory as a descriptive model of decision making under risk, and develop an alternative model, called prospect theory"; this can be viewed as taking account, also, of the third moment of the probability distribution, the skew.

the fundamental particles (see also Chapter 7, Section 5.2 and Chapter 8, Section 8.2).[38]

Issues relating to decision-taking are discussed in more depth in Chapters 6, 7 and 8. The implication of the fact that it is a person's *feelings* that determine what action they choose to implement in a choice situation is that the ability to experience feelings is *necessary* for the taking of this sort of decision. Somehow, the information contained in the feelings must be transmitted to the physics that underlies the action; mental states *must* be capable of being causally effective, see Chapter 7, Section 5.[39]

---

[38] Speculating further, if such a thing were found at the level of the fundamental particles, we might expect to find maximising laws of nature in Biology, using this thing we have called proto-consciousness, but without carrying the implication that plants experience anything analogous to that which we experience as consciousness.

[39] However, there remains a question as to whether it would be possible for a decision such as this to be taken by the type of process studied in the physical sciences, this possibility is addressed in Chapter 7, Section 2.

3

Issues relating to physicalism

1 Introduction

In this chapter, I start by summarising very briefly in Section 2 the three possibilities for the relation between mind and matter. Then, in Section 3 I note the recent evidence in support of 'physicalism' – interpreted here in the sense 'materialism', the proposition that mind is a property of matter. The arguments given in the literature for the key issue of the causal completeness of physics are spelt out in Section 4. In Section 5, I explain the reasons for thinking that there is an epistemic gap, that is, that there is something in the world that does not reduce to physics, potentially causing problems for the causal completeness of physics. This is followed, in Section 6, by a discussion of the three anti-physicalist claims, the knowledge argument, the conceivability argument and the hard problem, taking into account the possibility that causally effective property dualism holds.

2 Possibilities for the relation between mind and matter

As we saw in Chapter 1, there are three possibilities concerning the relationship of mind and matter, and they can broadly be described as: dual substances, reductive physicalism and non-reductive physicalism.

In the dual substance approach, it is assumed that there is some "essence of mind", perhaps "consciousness", which is not related to matter; so mind would be outside science in the sense that it would be unrelated to the laws of nature that would constitute the body of knowledge in a "finished science" (see Chapter 2, Section 2.2). This can be viewed as being the case in which there is another 'substance' besides that which we know as 'matter'. The dual substance approach cannot be ruled out as a matter of logic, and it cannot be ruled out on empirical grounds, at least given the current state of knowledge; it could be said that it seems a bit ontologically extravagant, violating the principles of parsimony (*e.g.* Ockham's Razor), but that is hardly enough reason to discard it. In this book, which is about the possibility that mind is a property of matter, it is summarised briefly in Appendix 1 and is not discussed elsewhere – apart from getting a brief mention in the context of free will (see Chapter 8, Section 2.3).

If it were to turn out that there is only one substance, matter, consisting of stuff that we often refer to as being "physical", then this thing we call 'consciousness' must be in some way related to this so-called "physical" stuff. A question then arises as to whether mental states can be wholly explained in terms of the properties of matter we study in the physical sciences (this is discussed in Chapter 4), or whether there could be another property of matter associated with the existence of minds (this is discussed in Chapter 5).

In reductive physicalism (Chapter 4) it is taken that mental states are reducible to the properties of matter that are studied in the physical sciences (clearly this position requires clarity regarding what is suitable for study in the physical sciences and what is not, see Chapter 2, Section 2.1). However, as we have seen, given that reproducibility by others of the results of some person's experiments regarding some property of matter is necessary for that property of matter to qualify for inclusion in the physical sciences, if we accept that we cannot communicate in language exactly what it is like to experience something (Chapter 2, Section 4.2), it *cannot* be the case that feelings are reducible to that which is studied in the physical sciences; there must be an epistemic gap. If that is accepted, reductive physicalism is ruled out. Other possibilities that may require there to be nothing over and above that which is studied in the physical sciences include "eliminativism", in which it is assumed that some types of mental state (or, indeed, all of them) simply don't exist, and "behaviourism" in which the only 'real' thing about mental states is taken to be the behaviour with which they are associated (see Chapter 4, Section 8).

The relation between mind and matter for which I am putting the case in this book is a form of non-reductive physicalism, the third of the three possibilities mentioned above, and the varieties of non-reductive physicalism are discussed in Chapter 5. In this case, again, there is just one substance, matter (and science is taken to be complete); however, as well as the properties of matter studied in physics this approach assumes that there exists another type of property of matter, one which we call 'mind', and which is *not* reducible to those properties that are studied in physics. Indeed, if reductive physicalism is ruled out, as is implied by the acceptance of the fact that there is an epistemic gap combined with our definition of physics, and yet there is only one substance, mental states *must* be instantiations of another property of matter, one that is not suitable for study in the science of physics. Perhaps mental states are instantiations of an emergent property of matter, one that arises as basic living creatures evolve into more complex ones (see Chapter 5, Section 9), or perhaps panpsychism is the answer, the proposition that proto-consciousness, some building block of consciousness, has pervaded the entire universe since the beginning of time, or perhaps micro-psychism (the proposition that some fundamental entities are intrinsically experiential) holds, in which case consciousness is related to the fundamental particles in some way, as are mass, electric charge, and so on. I suggest in Chapter 5, Section 9, that micro-psychism resulting in something that one might call 'emergence' looks a likely candidate.

3 Evidence in support of some form of physicalism

Increasingly neuroscience has been discovering that when a person experiences some particular mental state, a particular brain state arises too, a development that is clearly supportive of the proposition that mental states are instantiations of a property of the matter in the brain. A person (A) using an electroencephalograph (EEG) can observe on a screen the brain state of another person (B) and through these observations may be able to identify certain aspects of their mental state. For example, it is already well-established that if A observes that the "fusiform face area" of the brain (FFA) is active, then he/she knows that person B will be considering the features of someone's face, and a great many similar correlations have been established between brain areas and conscious experiences.

Recent experiments at MIT (Louie and Wilson, 2001), found that patterns of brain activity identified when rats explored a maze during the day were exactly replicated when the rats were sleeping at night, so the experimenters reckoned that they knew what the rats were dreaming about. Further, it is currently thought that complex choices are made in the basal ganglia (see Chapter 6, Section 5.1), and indeed, if the basal ganglia are damaged, as was the case for Phineas Gage (Chapter 6, Section 5.2), the person becomes incapable of taking sensible decisions.

We now know enough about the structure of the human brain to enable direct brain-to-brain communication to take place; a very simple message has been sent direct from the brain of a person in Kerala (extracting the information by electro-encephalogram, EEG) to the brain of a person in Strasburg (inducing conscious reception by robotised transcranial magnetic stimulation, TMS) with email wired to carry the information, automatically (using the Morse Code!), across the globe (see Grau *et al.*, 2014).

The proposition that there is a relationship between a person's brain activity and the mental state he or she is experiencing is thus well established now as a fact that can be observed; and although this obviously does not prove that mental states are, indeed, a property of the material in the brain, it is just what one would expect if that were the case.

4 Arguments for the causal completeness of physics

We now look at the case for the "causal completeness of physics". The "completeness of physics" is generally taken in philosophy to refer to *causal* completeness, the thesis that "all physical effects are fully caused by purely physical prior histories" (where the term 'physical' means "pertaining to the science of physics"). Its usual name is therefore somewhat deceptive, since it does not rule out the possibility that physical (non-mental) states give rise to non-physical effects (*e.g.*, effects on mental states, where mental states are deemed to be outside physics, as in non-reductive physicalism); so although, as usually presented, it does ensure that physics contains all the *causes* of physical (non-mental) events, it allows physical properties to interact causally on a one-way basis with things that are outside physics (if such things exist).

The completeness of physics therefore implies that mental states *per se* can play no causal role in the physical (non-mental) world, that is, that everything that happens would be explained by this science we call physics, if it were

44

finished. I suggest in this book, however, that there is a certain class of physical (non-mental) events, the physical consequences of complex decisions taken by sophisticated creatures (see Chapter 2, Section 4.3 and Chapter 6) that depend on *feelings* and that therefore these events can only take place if conscious mental states *can* influence physical (non-mental) events; I suggest that we know from introspection that it cannot be the case that it is the physical (non-mental) correlates of those feelings that are doing the causing. If this is correct, then if the world did not include whatever it is that enables creatures to experience conscious mental states, these creatures would have been unable to take complex decisions in the way they have and a great number of the events that have taken place in the world would never have happened.

Also, although "the completeness of physics" thus defined appears at first sight to rule out the possibility of mental causation, and it often seems to be thought that this is the case, it does not actually do so. A physical event (non-mental) could be caused by an event that has mental characteristics, as well as physical (non-mental) characteristics (see Figure 4 in Chapter 5, Section 7.2), and we humans could take the view that there are two causal processes, one with a mental cause and the other with a physical (non-mental) cause, each of which could fully explain the occurrence of the physical event (on a regular basis, not as a one-off coincidence), just so long as there is also a law of nature ensuring that if one of these causal processes operates the other one does too. This situation is often ruled out by philosophers as being something called 'over-determination', which is deemed unacceptable, see Chapter 5, Section 7; but dual causation of this sort is not obviously unacceptable. Laws of nature encapsulate our understanding of the causal processes that operate in the world, and there is no reason in logic why a causal process should not operate in this way.

4.1 The success of physics

Probably the most convincing reason for signing up to the proposition that physics is complete in the above, causal, sense is the incredible success of physics during the last couple of centuries in explaining so many things that have puzzled people during previous aeons. As bastion after bastion of unknowns and questions fall to the approach of the physical sciences it seems that this process is unstoppable; surely a day must come when physics explains everything in terms of physical properties of matter and laws of nature?

However, the scientists who have developed physics as we know it today have made no attempt to incorporate decision-taking by creatures into their discipline, as an effective causal phenomenon, although it meets all the criteria of good science: every time I decide to tap my finger on the table my finger makes the precise movement I intended. In any other branch of science, one would expect this to be taken seriously as a possible cause of the repeatable event.

Although the Standard Model, the structure the physicists have developed in recent years that classifies fundamental particles and forces, has no obvious gap that suggests that something might be missing it could be that consciousness derives from some already known aspect of the fundamental particles, and there are still many unexplained phenomena which sometimes lead physicists to postulate new particles, forces or other phenomena. For example, there could be something related to quantum mechanics that enables consciousness to influence physical (non-mental) outcomes (see Chapter 7, Section 5.2). Alternatively, if it turned out that so-called 'dark matter' exists on earth, the postulated weakly interacting massive particles (WIMPs), might play a role, interacting with "ordinary" matter through the weak nuclear force. Or consciousness could arise as the result of some aspect of fundamental particles which is familiar to physicists today. So there is still room for more developments when neuroscientists, or physicists, apply their scientific expertise to the minutiae that arise within the brain and seek to identify such an effect.

4.2 The brain decides before we are aware

Evidence that at first sight looks to be supportive of the causal completeness of physics comes from Libet's famous experiment on the timing of decisions. Experiments performed by Libet and his colleagues (see Libet, Wright and Gleason, 1982), and repeated a great number of times since, famously including the work of Soon *et al.* (2008), show that people can take certain types of rather unimportant decisions concerning the timing of actions a significant time before they are consciously aware of having taken them, suggesting that consciousness, and therefore conscious mental states, might have had no role in initiating these actions.

In these experiments subjects are seated; they are asked to make a movement with their finger at a time of their own choosing and to note the position of a rotating dot on a clock-face at the time when they are first aware of having taken the decision to make the movement. They are often, but not always, instructed "to let the urge to act appear on its own at any time without any pre-planning or concentration on when to act" (Libet *et al.*, *ibid.*, p 324). The time of the actual movement is determined by means of an electromyogram connected to the subjects' wrists. The start of neuronal activity associated with the movement, the initial rise of the so-called 'readiness potential', is obtained by means of an EEG (electroencephalogram). The experiment shows that the readiness potential begins to build up approximately 350 milliseconds (roughly a third of a second) *before* the subject is aware of the intention to move his/her finger. The implication often drawn from this is that if these findings regarding the gap between the build-up of the readiness potential and the awareness of the decision apply to this one type of decision they must apply to all other decisions, and that therefore consciousness must be epiphenomenal and free will must be a mere fantasy.

But it does not follow that Libet's result, although clearly true of this type of decision in these circumstances, is therefore necessarily true of all other types of decision. We already know that there are decisions, triggering actions, which are taken without being initiated by conscious thought, such as those that arise from activity in the procedural memory (like riding a bicycle, or playing a familiar piece of music on the piano, see Chapter 2, Section 3.3); there is also the multitude of decisions that are regularly taken on 'automatic pilot' (see footnote 24 on p 27). Libet seems to have identified another class of such decisions; or perhaps it is just a case of a decision taken on automatic pilot. In any case, this does not rule out the possibility that conscious mental states *are* necessary for the causation of certain classes of action; it may that the decision at the start of Libet's experiment, that one will *enable* decisions relating to the timing of actions to be taken without conscious intervention, itself needs to be taken consciously, just as it may be that conscious thought is needed to initiate actions when one is beginning to learn to ride a bicycle or play the piano. These experimental findings do not amount to a convincing case for the lack of mental causation, and therefore free will, nor do they establish the causal completeness of physics.

It is salutary to note that the substance of Libet's result was already known to William James (and probably to many other people; certainly, I discovered this useful trick myself as a child). Long before Libet appeared on the scene, James wrote the following enjoyable piece in his book entitled *The Principles of Psychology* (see Chapter 26, 1890, p 524):

"We know what it is to get out of bed on a freezing morning in a room without a fire, and how the very vital principle within us protests against the ordeal. Probably most persons have lain on certain mornings for an hour at a time unable to brace themselves to the resolve. We think how late we shall be, how the duties of the day will suffer; we say, "I must get up, this is ignominious," *etc.*; but still the warm couch feels too delicious, the cold outside too cruel, and resolution faints away and postpones itself again and again just as it seemed on the verge of bursting the resistance and passing over into the decisive act. Now how do we ever get up under such circumstances? If I may generalize from my own experience, we more often than not get up without any struggle or decision at all. We suddenly find that we *have* got up. A fortunate lapse of consciousness occurs; we forget both the warmth and the cold; we fall into some revery connected with the day's life, in the course of which the idea flashes across us, "Hollo! I must lie here no longer" – an idea which at that lucky instant awakens no contradictory or paralyzing suggestions, and consequently produces immediately its appropriate motor effects. It was our acute consciousness of both the warmth and the cold during the period of struggle, which paralyzed our activity then and kept our idea of rising in the condition of *wish* and not of *will*. The moment these inhibitory ideas ceased, the original idea exerted its effects."

Indeed, the mere fact that one is aware that these decisions are being taken without conscious intervention, and that this is worth remarking on (*e.g.*, by James), suggests that this is not the case with many of the other decisions that we take.

4.3 Conservation of energy

Papineau has a good account of the historical development of the idea that physics is causally complete in his book *Thinking about Consciousness* (Papineau 2002, Appendix: the history of the completeness of physics). In it he presents a line of thinking, additional to that of the inexorable march of physics, which might have convinced people that physics is, indeed, potentially complete in this sense; although it does not come close to establishing beyond doubt that this is so. Part of it concerns the principle of the conservation of energy.

The law regarding the conservation of energy is the generally accepted principle that energy cannot be created or destroyed through physical processes

(processes subject to the laws of physics) although the form in which energy is instantiated can change: kinetic energy can become potential energy and *vice versa*, for example, and mass can become some form of kinetic or potential energy and *vice versa*.[40] Papineau points out that if this principle applied *only* to activities relating to physics, then if mental states can cause physical (non-mental) events in the brain to take place, leading to actions, this would mean that mental states must be able to affect the motion of some electron or the outcome of some chemical reaction in the brain; this would inevitably involve a transfer of energy and therefore it would contradict the principle of conservation of energy. Does the principle of conservation of energy therefore rule out the possibility of mental states being causally efficacious in this way?

First, suppose that mental states although part of the material world, are instantiations of a property of matter that is not studied in the physical sciences, as in the case examined in this book. In this case it would seem reasonable to expand the principle of conservation of energy to include *all* the properties of matter, those not suited to study in the science of physics as well as those that are studied in physics. Then, so long as all the causal processes relating to mental states were consistent with the conservation of energy, the changes in potential or kinetic energy relating to mental causation at any point in time would simply be part of the totality of changes in the flows of energy taking place in the material world at that point in time; and all of these, taken together or separately, would be consistent with the conservation of energy; activating a decision would involve a transfer of energy from the mental state to the electron or chemical reaction that triggered the action. It would not have to be the case that the conservation of energy applied only to activities relating wholly to physics.

It is difficult to see any reason why conservation of energy should rule out the possible existence of a property of matter, not presently included in science, with causal processes relating to the way it operates (but for which there is not yet adequate empirical support). So long as any force that it is proposed exists is part of science (subject to causal processes that may be deterministic or probabilistic), as in the case considered here, there is no reason to suppose that

---

[40] Recent investigations in high energy physics (see Hesketh, 2016, pp 108-109) apparently suggest that, as a consequence of Heisenberg's Uncertainty Principle, a 'virtual' particle can "borrow a small amount of energy for a short time" thus bending the rules (indeed, this rule regarding the conservation of energy) and enabling "beta decay to happen".

it would break the appropriate conservation of energy principle – a point acknowledged by Papineau (see p 249).[41]

Next, suppose that substance dualism holds (see Appendix 1), and that mental states are outside the material world. Then, if mental causation were to hold it would be as if some cause outside our universe is making an electron move in a way that it would not otherwise have moved, or making a chemical reaction reach a conclusion that it would not otherwise have reached. Indeed, given the current state of knowledge, we cannot rule out the possibility that there is some mysterious force beyond our understanding that causes physical (non-mental) events to take place in our universe (see Chapter 8, Section 2.3, on libertarianism). If some inexplicable intervention caused a mass to accelerate (see the approach to laws of nature in Nancy Cartwright, 1983) we could calculate how large the force would have had to be, had physics as we know it applied, using the law of physics "force equals mass times acceleration":

$$F = ma$$

although the force in question in this case would be outside the science of physics. What would be happening in such a situation is that the total energy in the universe would be increasing (unless there were sinks occurring somewhere else). It is not the case that such a situation would run counter to the principle that energy cannot be created or destroyed through processes that are subject to the laws of physics. It seems highly unlikely that it will prove to be the case that creatures that are conscious emit more energy than they absorb, as would be the implication of mental states being a source of energy in this

---

[41] In this context, we should note this statement in Henry Marsh's excellent book on neurosurgery: "One quarter of the blood pumped every minute by the heart ... goes to the brain. Thought is an energy-intensive process" (*Do No Harm*, 2014, p 41). Kahneman (2011) also is impressed by the amount of energy thinking requires, saying: "... effortful mental activity appears to be especially expensive in the currency of glucose" (see p 43). While Ashcroft (2012) says: "The brain alone uses about 10 percent of the oxygen you breathe to drive the sodium pump and keep your nerve cell batteries charged. Perhaps somewhat surprisingly, it seems that merely thinking is energetically expensive." (p 40). None of which implies that the energy is spent on anything other than the phenomena already included in the science of physics, of course.

way, but it is unlikely that such a hypothesis has been tested with sufficient accuracy for the point to be established.[42]

Currently, there is no direct empirical evidence of a force that is related to mental causation. But it is not beyond all credibility that it might turn out to be the case that one day there will be convincing evidence of the existence of forces not currently studied in physics (see Chapter 7, Section 5.2), or even mysterious interventions beyond our current understanding, implausible though that might seem.

4.4 Conclusion

Of course, the fact that the causal completeness of physics is currently unproven is no reason to reject the proposition that it is the case, and it should be noted that among philosophers there is, currently, a broad consensus concerning its validity.

5 Arguments against the completeness of physics

5.1 The basic argument

It can only be the case that physics is *not* causally complete (in the sense that: "all physical effects are fully caused by purely *physical* prior histories") if two propositions hold true. First, there has to be something that exists that is "not physical", in the sense that there must be something that is not reducible to the properties of matter that are studied in the physical sciences; it must *not* be the case that all the facts relating to everything can be identified with facts that are suitable for study in the physical sciences. And second, that 'something' that exists and is not suitable for study in the physical sciences must be causally effective, it must be able to affect some of the things that are suitable for study in physics. So the questions that need to be addressed to make the case that

---

[42] Papineau (2002, p 252) recounts an experiment, performed in 1889, in which the energy flows relating to a small dog were measured and it was found that the energy the dog expended was the same as the energy contained in the food it consumed (given the accuracy of such experiments at that time). If such an experiment could be properly validated it would clearly lend support to any case someone might wish to make against the dual substance approach regarding mental causation.

mental states are causally effective, so that physics is not causally complete, are the following.

First, do mental states exist?

Second, how convincing is the proposition that mental states are not reducible to the properties suitable for study in the physical sciences?

Third, how convincing is the case that mental states are causally effective *per se*?

I argued in Chapter 2, Section 4 that each of these three propositions is knowable *ab initio* (see also Chapter 2, Section 2.3). If that is accepted, we know *ab initio* that physics is not causally complete.

Here I spell out the case for the second of these propositions in more detail. On the first, the fact that mental states exist is implied by Descartes' famous statement (1637): "*cogito, ergo sum*"; the mere fact that one can be aware of having a thought or a feeling is enough to establish for each of us privately, *ab initio*, that such a thing as a mental state does exist (see Chapter 2, Section 4.1 and Appendix 1). There is no need for anything more to be said. The third of these propositions, the case for mental states being causally effective, is presented in Chapter 7.

The important point to make about the possibility that mental states could be reducible to physics is the one made in Chapter 2, Section 4.2. If mental states were reducible to physics then, given that everything that is suited for study in the science of physics can be communicated perfectly in language (which has to be the case if experiments relating to the physical sciences are to be reproducible by others, see Chapter 2, Section 2.1), it follows that so long as the correct set of words is used to describe some experience, a sensory experience say (*e.g.*, tasting truffles), or an emotional experience (*e.g.*, what it feels like for X to be sad about the death of his mother), a person hearing and understanding those words would then know *exactly* what it is like to have that experience. Thus:

1. If mental states were reducible to the properties of matter studied in the science of physics, then,

2. every fact about a mental state would be of the sort suitable to be studied in the science of physics (from the meaning of 'reducible'), and then,

3. every fact about a mental state would be capable of being perfectly communicated from one person to another using language (from the definition of 'the science of physics'),

4. so there could be no epistemic gap (because everything we experience would be capable of being communicated perfectly to another person using language).

So then if, following introspection (or perhaps scientific experimentation, see below), we find that there *is* an epistemic gap, that we *cannot* communicate our feelings perfectly using language, it follows that mental states cannot be reducible to physics and the second requirement above is established.

The above argument is a case of *modus tollens*, that is: if A then B, and therefore, since not-B holds, not-A must be the case. The result therefore rests on two things, the plausibility of the assertion that there is an epistemic gap and the validity, or otherwise, of steps 1. to 4. above. Note that: a phenomenon is 'reducible' to the properties of matter studied in the science of physics if there are causal (nomological) relations that carry the implication that all the facts pertaining to that phenomenon can be identified with facts that are suitable for study in the science of physics (see footnote 2 on p 2); and, the science of physics comprises the results of our investigation of the properties of matter which are such that all the facts relating to them are public facts, facts that can be communicated perfectly between people using language (see Chapter 2, Section 2.1).

Since everything about physics can be perfectly communicated between people in language, and if mental states are reducible they are part of physics, the argument from step 1. to step 4. is sound. Therefore, we now address the question regarding the existence of an epistemic gap.

5.2 The existence of an epistemic gap

We now look at the reasons why we should accept the proposition that there is an epistemic gap.

First, we know *ab initio* that there is an epistemic gap, because we know *ab initio* that there are two different classes of fact and that one of them, the phenomenal facts, cannot be communicated perfectly in terms of language while the other, the public facts, can. As explained in Chapter 2 Section 2.1, the type of fact that is studied in the physical sciences is taken to be the defining factor regarding the physical sciences: experiments relating to the physical sciences must be capable of reproduction by other people and the results must be checkable against one another. This means that it must be possible for the facts relating to the physical sciences, the sciences that can be reduced to physics, to be communicated perfectly from one person to another using language. Thus, if someone tells you something related to these sciences that you did not previously know, such as: "the Eiffel Tower is up to 15 cm taller in summer than in winter", or "the earthquake of 16 December 1811 caused parts of the Mississippi River to flow backwards", or "the gravitational constant G is given by:

$$G = 6.673 \times 10^{-11} \text{ N m}^2 \text{ kg}^{-2}$$

(with a specified range of uncertainty)", you acquire new information, new facts. We know this from our own experience.

However, barring neurological stimulation (or magic, see Lewis, 1988, p 263) we know that it is impossible to acquire new "what it feels like" type facts (what it feels like to experience something) through verbal communication from others; it is necessary to have the experience oneself (for an opposing view see Lewis, 1988, summarised and discussed in Chapter 5, Section 2). For example, if someone tells you about some totally novel sensory experience that they have had you will not be able to acquire from them the new piece of "what it feels like" type information. Perhaps they took a new drug and were able to 'see' ultraviolet light; they might report the resulting "seeing experience" as being totally unlike any experience of seeing a colour or colour combination they had ever had before. But they would be unable to communicate to you, perfectly, in words, what such an experience was like.[43] Indeed, it is generally accepted that someone who has no eyes, or has always been colour-blind or

---

[43] A question which arises in this context is: if mental states were reducible to the science of physics, why have we not yet discovered how to communicate perfectly to others what it is like to have some experience (*e.g.*, a sensory experience the other person has never had) using language? The fact that we have not provides support for the proposition that mental states are not reducible to physics. This thought is summarised in the statement that, using introspection, we perceive that there is an 'epistemic gap' (see Chapter 2, Section 4.2).

who has never seen colours for some reason cannot discover what it is like to see red through being told what it is like by others, they must experience it themselves (see Nordby 2007 and Jackson 1982). Further, when a person loses a loved one for the first time they often express surprise at the nature of the experience of grief, in spite of having frequently come across others experiencing grief, both in life and in fiction. As James says (1890, p 226, see full quote below): "Absolute insulation [of one's feelings] … is the law" (my insertion)

The implication of the existence of two different types of fact is that there is a category difference between two different types of property of matter; instantiations of the properties of matter that are studied in the physical sciences give rise to facts that are capable of being communicated perfectly from one person to another linguistically, while instantiations of conscious mental states give rise to "what it feels like" type facts that cannot be communicated perfectly in that way. I therefore take it that anything that can be communicated perfectly in words from one person to another is the stuff of the physical sciences, and *vice versa*, everything that is studied in the physical sciences can be communicated from one person to another perfectly in words. Of course, this is not to say that feelings cannot be instigated in a person by the use of words. Obviously, a story recounted by a person, or a poem, can induce powerful emotions in another person.

Further support for the existence of an epistemic gap, if needed, comes from a variation on this. It arises from the fact that it is now well established that some creatures have phenomenal experiences that are quite different from ours (see Nagel, 1974). We know this because, for example, experiments have revealed that certain birds, dolphins, fish, rats and so on can experience magnetism (magneto-reception) in a manner that enables them to use information relating to the earth's magnetic field, both the direction and the dip (the angle between the horizontal and the magnetic field lines), in their daily lives (see Kremers *et al.*, 2014, and many more).

If the information content of sensations such as these consisted of public facts, as would have to be the case if mental states were reducible to physics, we would in principle be able to know what it feels like to experience magneto-reception if we chose the correct set of words to describe the experience even though we don't have the relevant sense organs and/or wiring in our brains.[44]

---

[44] Maybe one day a person could have a magnetism gene inserted when an embryo, and he or she might then be able to know what it feels like and attempt to tell the rest of us.

This suggests that the existence of sense organs and the existence of certain structures in the brain are relevant to the proposition that there is an epistemic gap. Suppose that we are correct when we assert that mind is a property of matter, and suppose further that the "what it is like" of a sensation arises as the result of some particular bit of the brain being stimulated. We would not then expect that a creature would have the capacity to "know what it is like" to experience such a phenomenon if it lacked the relevant bit of the brain, or, indeed, if it lacked the sense organ that receives the information and then passes it to the relevant bit of the brain. Thus, if the only way of knowing what it is like to experience something is through stimulation of some relevant structure in the brain, it is inevitable that there are epistemic gaps; any creature without some particular structure in its brain can never know what it is like to have it.

Finally, the fact that so many philosophers (and others) have signed up to the existence of an epistemic gap as a fact about phenomenal experience should be noted: they all believe that facts about phenomenal experience cannot be made available to others in the same way as can the facts about the properties of matter studied in physics. Could so many philosophers all be wrong?

Nagel (1974) describes the difficulties associated with imagining what it is like to be a bat, explaining that insofar as he can imagine it, it tells him: "only what it would be like for *me* to behave as a bat behaves" (p 439); his question is about what it is like for a bat to be a bat. He concludes that: "We cannot form more than a schematic conception of what it *is* like"; the wiring of the neurons in the bat's brain will be different from ours because their senses are different from ours, so even neurological stimulation will not suffice.

Searle explains his position on this in his 1983 paper entitled 'Why I am not a property dualist', saying:

> "… consciousness has a first-person ontology; that is, it only exists *as experienced* by some human or animal, and therefore, it cannot be reduced to something that has third-person ontology, something that exists independently of experiences" (*ibid.*, p 60, his emphasis),

and adds the comment: "It is as simple as that".

William James also has a view on this, writing (1890, *Principles of Psychology*, volume 1, p 226):

"... The only states of consciousness that we naturally deal with are found in personal consciousnesses, minds, selves, concrete particular I's and you's.

"Each of these minds keeps its own thoughts to itself. There is no giving or bartering between them. No thought even comes within direct *sight* of a in *another* personal consciousness than its own. Absolute insulation, irreducible pluralism, is the law. It seems as if the elementary psychic fact were not *thought*, or *this thought* or *that thought* but *my thought*, every thought being *owned*. Neither contemporaneity, nor proximity in space, nor similarity of quality and content are able to fuse thoughts together which are sundered by this barrier of belonging to different personal minds. The breaches between such thoughts are the most absolute breaches in nature."

and going on to say:

"Everyone will recognize this to be true, so long as the existence of *something* corresponding to the words 'personal mind' is insisted on ...".

Levine (1993, p 125) says: "After all, in order to know what it's like to occupy a state one has actually to occupy it"

Horgan (1984, p 149) says (of Jackson's fictional character Fred, who could see two totally different colours for what the rest of us call 'red', 1982):

"... I am quite prepared to concede that we do not know what Fred's red$_1$ and red$_2$ experiences are like, no matter how adequate a physical account we have of Fred's visual processes ...".

And these are in addition to the views of John Locke on the taste of a pineapple and David Hume on the: "idea of scarlet or orange, of sweet or bitter" (see Chapter 2, Section 3.2). There are a great many more such examples in the philosophy literature (see, for example, Ball, 2009).

6 The three anti-physicalist claims

There is no need for any of the three physicalist conundrums that have for some years been much debated in philosophy of mind, the knowledge argument, the conceivability argument and the hard problem (the existence of an explanatory gap), to present difficult issues for the causally effective property dualism proposition under examination in this book. Arguably, this is one of the more attractive features of this proposal from the viewpoint of modern philosophy.

6.1   *The knowledge argument*

Consider Jackson's 'knowledge argument' (1982 and 1986). Mary knows everything physical (non-mental) that can be known about seeing and about colours (in Jackson's words: "[s]he knows all the physical facts", 1986, p 392), but she has grown up without having ever actually seen colours herself. The knowledge argument proposes that Mary learns something new when she first sees colours, and therefore there must be something over and above the "physical facts"; and this means that "physicalism", as envisaged by Jackson at that time, is false.

But Jackson's "physical facts" consist of "information about the world we live in and about ourselves" that has been provided by "the physical, chemical and biological sciences" and the "information that automatically comes along with it" (1982, p 127; we should note that Jackson says here that he does not mean these "sketchy remarks" to constitute a definition of 'physical information'). His knowledge argument suggests that, if Mary does learn something new, there must be other facts, facts relating to what are known as '*qualia*' (Jackson believed in *qualia* when he wrote this paper, claiming that he was a "*qualia* freak"), which are different in some way from the so-called physical facts that Mary already knew. Therefore, the implication is that if these other facts exist, they must either relate to the properties of a different substance from matter or, and this is the possibility that I am examining in this book, there must be another property of matter over and above those properties that Jackson names as "physical". Jackson concludes the presentation of his knowledge argument saying:

> "It seems just obvious that she will learn something about the world and our visual experience of it. But then it is inescapable that her previous knowledge was incomplete. But she had *all* the physical information. *Ergo* there is more to have than that, and Physicalism is false" (*ibid.*, p 128).

Whereas Jackson's thesis that if Mary learns something new then "Physicalism" is false is clearly true of the type of physicalism Jackson was interested in at that time, reductive physicalism, it does not hold for the non-reductive type of physicalism. Jackson's argument does not have the implication that 'materialism' is false. If mind is a property of matter, with facts about conscious mental states (*qualia*, or phenomenal facts) analogous to, but different in nature from, the facts physicists refer to about non-mental states, it is obviously possible for Mary to learn new facts about seeing and about colour, even though she already knew all the facts the 'finished' physical sciences can produce about them, without physicalism in this broad sense, 'materialism', being false. These phenomenal facts relate to mental states – to the property of matter we know as 'mind'; and if mental states are instantiations of a non-reducible property of matter these phenomenal facts cannot be reduced to facts relating to the properties of matter studied in the physical sciences. So, there is no reason to assume that physicalism in the broad sense ("everything can be explained in terms of the properties of matter") is false just because when Mary first experiences what seeing red feels like she learns something she didn't know before.

In the world of Jackson (1982 and 1986) "Physicalism" is reductive; it is the thesis that there are no facts other than those that are of the type studied in the physical sciences, there is no information other than that which has been provided by what he calls "the physical, chemical and biological sciences". In this book, I propose that we know *ab initio* that "what it feels like" type facts, so-called 'phenomenal' facts, exist, and that we also know *ab initio* that these are different from the facts of physics because they cannot be perfectly communicated in words (see Chapter 2, Section 4.2). Jackson's conclusion is therefore just what we would expect.

The strange thing about the Mary story, and about the existence of the enormous number of academic papers written on the subject, is that this simple, totally obvious explanation of the knowledge argument (of the fact that our intuitions are at variance with the implications of the knowledge argument for what Jackson terms 'Physicalism') is rarely proposed and that no-one explains why this is so. The only person I have found who explicitly gives this explanation for the knowledge argument is Terence Horgan (1984), who argues that: "his [Jackson's] attack on Physicalism is fallacious, being an equivocation on two different senses of the phrase 'physical information'" (p 147). He says (pp 149-150):

"What I want to question is Jackson's supposition that a completely adequate physical account of a creature's visual processes gives us complete *physical information* about those processes. In one sense of 'physical information', this supposition is virtually a tautology: for, physical information is just the information that would be provided by a theoretically adequate physical account. But in another sense – the sense really required by the knowledge argument – the supposition is one that Physicalists can and should reject."

Horgan then distinguishes two relevant senses of the term 'physical information'. One he calls 'explicitly physical information'; he says this is information expressed "in overtly physicalistic language". In the framework that I develop in this book Horgan's explicitly physical information consists of information about facts relating to the material world that can be communicated perfectly using language. The other he calls 'ontologically physical information'; he says this is information expressed: "by other sorts of language – for instance, mentalistic language" (*ibid.*, p 150). In my framework, Horgan's ontologically physical information, which is expressed (presumably imperfectly) by mentalistic language, is information about facts of the "what it feels like" variety; it could be referred to as some sort of 'physical information' if the word 'physical' is interpreted in the "pertaining to matter" sense and if mind is a property of matter.

Chalmers' summarises the knowledge argument thus (1996, pp 140-146):

"[s]he knows all the facts couched in the terms of physics, but she lacks knowledge about the hidden (phenomenal or protophenomenal) essences of physical entities. If she had this knowledge, she would thereby know the phenomenal facts" (*ibid.*, p 143).

But in his terminology 'materialism' is synonymous with 'reductive physicalism', so he then says:

"… the very implausibility of the denial that Mary gains knowledge about the world is evidence that materialism is doomed" (*ibid.*, p 145).

Chalmers, like so many others, never explicitly acknowledges that it is logically possible that there are other properties of matter besides those studied in physics.

If we accept that there *are* facts of the "what it feels like" type (*qualia*) and that these cannot be communicated perfectly from one person to another using language, then there are facts that Mary could not have got to know in her black and white room. If we don't want to accept that the implication of Jackson's knowledge argument ("Physicalism is false") is that there must be "immaterial minds", there is another, perfectly obvious and plausible possibility: there could be another property of matter besides those studied in the physical sciences. It is difficult to see why this possibility is so universally ignored.

Perhaps the work of Lewis is relevant here. Lewis, in his 1988 paper 'What Experience Teaches', rules out the possibility of phenomenal information being associated with a property of matter different from those studied in physics by defining 'phenomenal information' as being *independent* of physical (pertaining to physics) information in the sense that: "[t]wo possible cases might be exactly alike physically, yet differ phenomenally" (p 84, and see Chapter 5, Section 2.2). But this definition of phenomenal information is unduly restrictive; it rules out the possibility of there being another property of matter besides those studied in physics (if some configuration of matter gave rise to a particular mental property, it would also give rise to a particular bunch of physical, non-mental, properties so these would be correlated with, they would not be independent of, the mental property). Perhaps this has not always been apparent to people considering the knowledge problem.

It is obvious that materialism, which can also be called "physicalism in the broad sense", is consistent with the knowledge argument; the knowledge argument clearly does not have the implication that *all* versions of physicalism are false (although it does, of course, have the implication that the type of physicalism Jackson referred to as Physicalism in those papers, 1982 and 1986, is false).

Finally, besides that of Horgan with which I agree, there are three other main explanations of the knowledge argument that arise in the philosophical literature; all three are predicated on the proposition that there is no such thing as a phenomenal fact, a fact of a different type from those that are studied in physics.

- First, there is the view that the knowledge argument is correct, but the conclusion that we draw from it, using our intuition, is just plain wrong. If Mary could know *all* the so-called 'physical' facts, and if there are *no* facts other than physical facts (despite our intuition to the contrary summarised in Chapter 2, Section 4.2), she would indeed have known all along what it would be like to see red. But, "… in any realistic, readily imaginable version she might know a lot, but she would not know everything physical" (Dennett, 1991, p 400); perhaps our intuition is leading us astray when it tells us that Mary must learn something new when she leaves her room; it may be that, in fact, if she did know *all* the 'physical' facts she would not learn anything new, after all.

- Second, there is the proposition that Mary does learn something new, but what she learns is not a new 'fact'; she acquires a new skill. This is Lewis' "ability hypothesis" (1988). The idea, in Nemirow's words, is: "some modes of understanding consist, not in the grasping of facts, but in the acquisition of abilities…. I understand the experience of seeing red if I can at will visualize red" (1980, p 475). But acquiring a skill takes time, practice and the reprogramming of the neurons in the cerebellum (see Chapter 2, Section 3.3); learning to visualize red doesn't take practice, so it is not analogous to learning a skill (the ability hypothesis is discussed in greater depth in Chapter 5, Section 2.4).

- Third, there is the proposition that what Mary learns is not a new 'fact', and nor is it a new ability; she has merely learned to think about seeing red in a new, different, way. In the words of Papineau (2002, p 51), she has acquired "a new *concept* of seeing something red" (his italics), a so-called 'phenomenal' concept, a different type of concept from the ones used in the science of physics. This is the approach to consciousness known as "concept dualism". But if Mary already knows what it is like to see red, why can she not acquire this concept from that knowledge; why does she need to *see* red to acquire this concept? This third explanation of the knowledge argument presupposes that reductive physicalism can exist in conjunction with the existence of an 'explanatory gap' (see Chapter 4, Section 5). I spell out the case against this, and therefore against concept dualism, in Chapter 4, Section 6.

All three of these seem remarkably unconvincing. The more plausible explanation is surely that phenomenal facts exist and relate to a property of matter different from those suitable for study in physics.

6.2   *The conceivability argument*

Now consider the conceivability argument. This concerns the possible existence of zombies: creatures that would be physically (that is, in all things that pertain to physics) identical to humans, and would behave in exactly the way a human would behave, but would be incapable of conscious experience (see Chalmers, 1996, pp 94-99). The idea is that if zombies are conceivable it must be conceivable that the arrangement of the matter that constitutes a person *could* give rise to the physical (pertaining to physics) characteristics of that person only, with no mental characteristics; and that if that were possible, physicalism in any sense, reductive or non-reductive, would be false (that is, 'materialism' would be false).

The conceivability argument has often been summarised thus:

    i. P_t & $\sim Q_t$ is conceivable

    ii.   If P_t & $\sim Q_t$ is conceivable, P_t & $\sim Q_t$ is logically possible

    iii.   If P_t & $\sim Q_t$ is possible, physicalism is false.

where P_t is the conjunction of all the physical truths about the universe (that is the facts about all the properties of matter that pertain to physics given the manner in which the components of that matter are arranged), while Q_t is some truth about a conscious mental state (see Chapter 5, Section 5 for Chalmers' summary statement). [45]

First, it should be emphasised that zombies, as well as being defined to be exactly like some human being in every physical (pertaining to physics) respect, so they *look* exactly like some human being, also *behave* in exactly the way a human behaves. But they lack consciousness: "There is nothing it is like to be a zombie" (Chalmers, *ibid.*, p 95). This means that the proposition that they could exist looks highly improbable if you sign up to our third fundamental proposition (see Chapter 2, Section 4.3). For if the existence of a zombie were to be conceivable it would have to be the case that it is conceivable that the zombie, a creature that would have no consciousness and therefore no feelings, could take the exact same decision in whatever circumstances obtain as would

---

[45] We should note at this point that some logical truths (*e.g.*, some advanced mathematical theorems) are so hard to prove that they are currently viewed by logicians/mathematicians as being both conceivably true and conceivably false, which raises questions relating to statement ii. in this argument. But this is not important to the argument that follows (see Chapter, 2 Section 2.3).

a person. But for a person, I have argued, we accept, *ab initio*, that many such decisions are determined by a complex array of feelings, and therefore require that the creature in question is capable of consciousness. And the zombie would have no consciousness and therefore no feelings. One might, therefore, be tempted to argue that it seems likely that P_t & $\sim Q_t$ is not possible, indeed one might even take the view that P_t & $\sim Q_t$ is not conceivable. The validity of the proposition that zombies are conceivable therefore seems dubious.

However, we could accept the first premise of the conceivability argument so long as the use of the word 'conceivable' is taken to imply that a statement is *not incoherent*, that the truth of the statement is not ruled out by *logic* (in general parlance the word conceivable means that, as well as not being incoherent, a proposition is nomologically conceivable; it does not run counter to the accepted laws of nature). The importance of this requirement is illustrated by considering any statement that is neither true nor false as a matter of logic; any statement that is contingent *a priori*. For example, suppose S is the statement "water is H_2O", then *a priori*, that is before we have examined the results of experiments, S is conceivable (therefore it is logically possible), but *a priori* not-S is also conceivable (therefore that, too, is logically possible); but it is not the case that both S and not-S can be false, as is implied by the third statement in the above argument. The conceivability argument, as Chalmers made clear, is *only* relevant for examining whether the truth or falsity of a proposition can be established through logic: if something *is* conceivable then its truth must be logically possible (but note the circumstances described in footnote 45 on p 63) although it still may run counter to a law of nature and so, in fact, be false. Perhaps we should rewrite the last line of the argument above to read:

"If P_t & $\sim Q_t$ is logically possible, it cannot be the case that physicalism is true as the result of logic."

The proviso about logic is important. The conceivability argument has only demonstrated that the proposition "physicalism is true" cannot be established *as a matter of logic*.

Indeed, Chalmers has claimed nothing more from his conceivability argument than that consciousness cannot supervene on the properties of matter studied in physics *as a matter of logic*. The conclusion drawn (above) from the conceivability argument is therefore only of interest to us if we had required that physicalism hold *as a matter of logical necessity*. The argument has not ruled out the possibility that, although zombies may be logically possible, they are nomologically impossible; it leaves open the possibility that physicalism holds as a matter of nomological necessity (see Chapter 2, Section 2.3). It remains possible that physicalism could hold as the result of a law of nature that ensures that mental states are instantiations of properties of matter, whether they are instantiations of properties that are suitable for study in physics, and therefore the type of physicalism that holds would be reductive physicalism, or of a property that is not suitable for study in physics, so it would be some form of non-reductive physicalism that holds.[46]

In conclusion, if our thesis that mental states are instantiations of a property of matter is correct, then once this is accepted, the proposition "P_t & $\sim Q_t$" would be deemed false, and therefore not conceivable; but this would not be because it is incoherent, it would be deemed false because it would run counter to a law of nature. It would be inconceivable in the sense of conceivability for which things are 'inconceivable' if they are considered impossible *either* for logical reasons (because they are incoherent) *or* because they are ruled out by a law of nature.

6.3 The hard problem

The hard problem of consciousness, labelled such by Chalmers (1995), is the problem of explaining how/why consciousness arises in the context of matter. This is also referred to in terms of the existence of an 'explanatory gap' (see Levine, 1983B and Chapter 4, Section 5). In Chalmers' words: "The explanatory gap comes from considering the question, Why, given that P is the case, is Q the case? ..." where P is: "the complete microphysical truth about the universe" and Q is: "an arbitrary truth about phenomenal consciousness" (Chalmers 2007, pp 169 and 168). If consciousness were reducible to the properties of matter studied in physics we would expect there to be causal relations that identify every fact about consciousness with facts that are suitable for study in physics, for mental states would be part of physics; but scientists and philosophers are unable to do this.

The proposal explored in this book is that there is a fundamental fact, akin to the fundamental facts regarding the existence of the properties of matter that

---

[46] The conceivability argument is akin to Descartes' argument in support of substance dualism, see Appendix 1. Note that Kripke (1972, p 97-105) has much to say on the possibility of contingent identities which is relevant to the conceivability argument (see Chapter 4, Section 4).

are studied in physics (see Chapter 2, Section 2.3), that ensures that if a certain type of material state is instantiated a certain type of phenomenal consciousness will be instantiated too (although the precise details relating to the particular material state remain to be discovered).[47] Ideas about how this might happen are: 'emergentism', the proposition that consciousness "emerges" if some particular combination of matter arises; 'panpsychism', the proposition that some fundamental form of consciousness has been everywhere in the universe ever since time began, since the Big Bang; and 'micropsychism', the proposition that, in Strawson's words: "… at least some ultimates are intrinsically experience-involving" (Strawson, 2008, p 71). If one of these proposals turns out to be the case, the question raised by "the hard problem" would be analogous to the question: Why is there such a thing as electric charge? The obvious answer would be, simply: it is one of the fundamental facts relating to the universe that this is so.

If the fact that mind exists is a fundamental fact of this sort, and if the endpoint of our search for explanations is the fundamental facts that make the world operate in the way it does, the answers to the 'why' questions, then it seems that we may have reached the final explanation. For if we think that mind is one of the fundamental properties of matter, just as is reckoned to be the case with electric charge, we would not, as scientists, ask how it can possibly be that mind arises in this way, which is what philosophers do when contemplating the so-called hard problem, we would simply accept that as being the case. Levine in fact provides that answer to his own question (2007, p 147): "… what is there to say in answer to why water is H_2O but that that's just the way it is? A similar answer, it is alleged, is appropriate in the psychophysical case".

I am therefore suggesting that one could say that there is an explanatory gap; we *cannot* explain how mind arises in the context of matter from the *micro-physical* truth about the universe (that is, we would need to postulate the existence of proto-consciousness, or something one might call a 'psychon', in order to explain it); but that this does not necessarily mean that there is a 'hard problem', for there is no need to suppose that it constitutes any sort of a 'problem', it could simply be what philosophers sometimes call "a brute fact".

---

[47] If you prefer the bundle theory approach to matter (see Chapter 2, Section 2.4) rather than the substratum view, you will postulate that a fundamental fact ensures that consciousness, or something that gives rise to consciousness, can be associated with the properties in the "bundle", as is the case for electric charge, or mass.

However, such an explanation of the existence of mind is unlikely to satisfy everyone. Christof Koch, in 2012, wrote: "The endpoint of my quest must be a theory that explains how and why the physical world is capable of generating phenomenal experience" (Koch, 2012, p 114-115). Perhaps philosophers tend to think of "matter" as being *defined* as "lifeless, consciousness-less stuff" and therefore see the hard problem as a problem simply because of their implicit definition of the word "matter" (see Chapter 2, Section 2.4).

4

Reductive physicalism

1 Introduction

As we have seen (Chapter 2, Section 2.5), it is often the case nowadays that when philosophers use the term 'physicalism' they mean reductive physicalism; this is an important aspect of current thinking. Therefore, although I have argued that this approach can be ruled out if we accept the definition of the science of physics proposed here along with the existence of an epistemic gap, in this chapter I explore the arguments in support of reductive physicalism.[48]

Place (1956) and Smart (1959) were among the first to take seriously the proposition that mental states can be completely understood in terms of facts relating to the properties of matter that are studied in physics; their work is discussed in Section 2. Section 3 then examines the different ways in which the

---

[48] As noted in Chapter 1, Section 1, a phenomenon is 'reducible' to the properties of matter studied in the science of physics if there are causal (nomological) relations that enable all the facts pertaining to that phenomenon to be identified with facts that are suitable for study in the science of physics (public facts). It has been suggested that there can be different types of reducibility, ontological (as above) and explanatory (the existence of a perfect linguistic explanation of a phenomenon, see Crane, 2001, pp 54-55). But with the definition of 'reducible' spelt out here, along with our definition of the science of physics (in terms of the reproducibility of experiments), ontological reducibility (as defined above) implies explanatory reducibility, and explanatory reducibility implies ontological reducibility, see Section 5 of this chapter.

"identity thesis" can be interpreted, while Section 4 summarises Kripke's famous argument concerning the identity thesis. In Section 5, I present Levine's argument for the existence of an explanatory gap, and this is followed, in Section 6, by a discussion of 'concept dualism'. Davidson's anomalous monism is addressed in Section 7.

Finally, we examine eliminative materialism and behaviourism in Section 8, before finishing with a brief conclusion.

2 Is consciousness a brain process?

2.1 Could the mind-brain relation be "the 'is' of composition"?

In this section I present reductive physicalism as it is proposed by Place (1956) and Smart (1959): the proposition that the states and processes of the (so-called) mind can be reduced to the properties of matter that are studied in the physical sciences; that is, that there are causal processes that enable all the facts relating to mental states to be identified with facts that are suitable to be studied in the physical sciences (see also Quine 1985, Dennett 1991, Lewis 1966, Papineau 2002, p 14, Tye 2009, and many more). Figure 3 below shows a comparison of reductive physicalism, in which there is no such thing as a mental property that is not a combination of physical (non-mental) properties (that is, mental states are fully explicable in terms of the physical properties of matter) and supervenience physicalism, in which mental properties are determined by physical (non-mental) properties of matter, but cannot be reduced to them. Using the words of C. D. Broad (1925) when describing "emergentism" (see Chapter 5, Section 9.2 for the complete quote) this can be described as the case in which: "… the characteristics of the [mental state] cannot, even in theory, be deduced from the most complete knowledge of the [physical properties upon which it supervenes]" (my insertions).

What U T Place (1956) was suggesting in his famous paper 'Is Consciousness a Brain Process?' was that it is not necessarily the case that: "sensations and mental images form a separate category of processes over and above the physical and physiological processes with which they are known to be correlated" (*ibid.*, p 44). He says that there was, at that time, an: "all but universally accepted view that an assertion of identity between consciousness and brain processes can be ruled out on logical grounds alone" (*ibid.*, p 46). Place began to doubt this when he discovered that to a physiologist (Sir Charles

Sherrington) the question was not seen to be a matter of logic. Instead Place found that what worried the physiologist was, in Place's words: "the apparent impossibility of accounting for the reports given by the subject of his conscious processes in terms of the known properties of the central nervous system" (*ibid.*, p 48). Place took this as indicating that, to the physiologist at least, such an account of conscious properties could, after all, be a practical possibility, and clearly, if that were so it couldn't be the case that it is ruled out by logic (if something is conceivable it is logically possible, see Chalmers, 1996; but see also Chapter 3, Section 6.2).

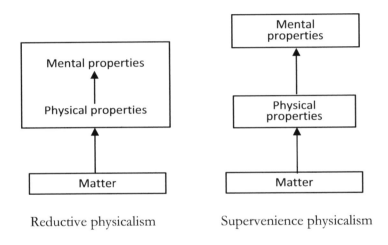

Reductive physicalism   Supervenience physicalism

Figure 3: Reductive physicalism and supervenience physicalism
In the case of reductive physicalism, the mental properties are simply a combination of physical properties by another name. In supervenience physicalism mental states are instantiations of a property that arises in the context of the physical properties but cannot be explained in terms of those properties (see Chapter 5, Section 3).

Place starts to spell out his proposal by describing a distinction that can be made between two different types of statement involving the word 'is'; two different types of statement relating to identities. He called these "the 'is' of definition" and "the 'is' of composition", citing "a square is an equilateral rectangle" as an example of the first, and "a cloud is a mass of water droplets

70

or other particles in suspension" as an example of the second; and he noted that in both cases it makes sense to add the phrase "and nothing else". These are both distinct from the 'is' of predication, he noted (giving "her hat is red" as an example), which does not concern identities and to which adding the phrase "and nothing else" would be false. These two types of statement are strikingly different, he says, for the 'is' of definition describes something that is, of course, necessarily true by definition, while the 'is' of composition is a contingent statement, the truth or falsity of which must be verified by observation (see Chapter 2, Section 2.3, and see also Section 4 of this chapter about the different types of statement that involve identities).[49] Two familiar numerical identities, those concerning water and H_2O, and light and a stream of photons, are examples of the use of the 'is' of composition.

Place then suggests that "consciousness is a brain process" *might* be an example of the 'is' of composition, and if it were, it would be analogous to the cases of water and H_2O or light and a stream of photons (see Chapter 4, Section 4.2). If this were the case it would be, as Place says, a reasonable scientific hypothesis, not necessarily true and not necessarily false; a hypothesis that we should be able to test empirically.

J. J. C. Smart (1959), who participated in the discussions surrounding Place's ideas, in Australia and elsewhere, took a slightly different approach from that of Place but it led him to the same proposition. He reckoned that sensations, or states of consciousness, were the only things that were being left out as developments in science increasingly enabled creatures to be understood in terms of complex physiochemical mechanisms saying: "Such sensations would be 'nomological danglers' …", and remarking that the laws by which they would dangle would be "odd". He said in this context (see also Chapter 5, Section 6.4): "I cannot believe that ultimate laws of nature could relate simple constituents to configurations consisting of perhaps billions of neurons (and goodness knows how many billion billions of ultimate particles) all put together for all the world as though their main purpose in life was to be a negative feedback mechanism of a complicated sort" (*ibid.*, p 143). He took the line that the issue should be decided on parsimony and simplicity, or, put another way, using

---

[49] 'Necessary' and 'contingent' are both words that can arise in significantly different circumstances, see Chapter 2, Section 2.2 and the footnote in Chapter 2 Section 2.3.

"Occam's razor"; and, in his view, this overwhelmingly favoured the identity thesis.[50]

Smart therefore signed up to the proposal that the relation between sensations and brain processes could be a case of the 'is' of composition, akin to that of a flash of lightning and an electrical discharge, saying: "... there are not two things: a flash of lightning and an electrical discharge. There is one thing, a flash of lightning, which is described scientifically as an electrical discharge to the earth from a cloud of ionized water molecules." (*ibid.*, p 146) and: "When I say that a sensation is a brain process or that lightning is an electric discharge, I am using 'is' in the sense of strict identity" (*ibid.*, p 145). But he also reckoned that: "there is no conceivable experiment which could decide between materialism and epiphenomenalism" (*ibid.*, p 155).

2.2 Why this is not a case of the 'is' of composition

It is perfectly easy to see that the proposed analogy between the mind state/brain state relation and the various cases cited of the 'is' of composition simply does not work.[51]

In the case of the 'is' of composition there are three descriptions identifying things in the analysis: first, the bundle of sensations received by a person in a certain set of circumstances; second, the thing "out there" that is generally thought by us humans to give rise to those sensations; and third, a thing "out there" which, although seemingly it might not have been the case, has actually been found to be what it is that gives rise to the sensations.[52] We humans identify the thing out there that gives rise to the "watery *qualia*" (what it looks like, feels like, tastes like *etc.*) as what we call 'water', but scientists have explained to us that it is a collection of H_2O molecules in their liquid phase. Hence 'water' is the exact same thing as 'H_2O molecules ...'. Therefore, the 'is' of composition does not involve our *experience* of water; it concerns two things we have identified as being out there, which it was originally thought might be

---

[50] We might note, for later use, that the same type of argument can be used in support of mental causation as an explanation for action, as in "Johnny went to get a drink because he was thirsty", where the alternative explanation of Johnny's actions relates to a multitude of chemical imbalances and electric currents involving neurotransmitters and muscle contractions, and requiring goodness knows how many billion billions of neuron interactions.

[51] See also Kripke (1972) and Section 4 of this chapter.

[52] By a thing "out there" I mean a thing that we believe exists in the world independently of a person being around to note its existence.

different, but which have now been found to be the same thing. These two things that are identical (that is, that are the same thing but have been given different names) in cases relating to the 'is' of composition are things out there; neither of them is a sensation experienced by a person. It is, very obviously, not the case that our experience of watery *qualia* is the same as – identical to – the thing that is this stuff called, alternatively, 'water' or 'H$_2$O molecules'. The same is true of lightning and electric discharges, and of all the other cases of the 'is' of composition that occur in the literature as well as any new ones that might be dreamt up.

In the case of the brain state/mental state relation there are only two descriptions identifying things. One is a collection of sensations (thoughts and feelings), the other is a thing out there (a collection of neurons and other stuff). How could that possibly turn out to be analogous to the 'is' of composition which requires that there are three things identified? If there are only two things identified in some analysis and the two are deemed to be identical it will be a simple identity of the type A = B (*cf.*, "Phosphorus = Hesperus"), two names given to the same thing (thus, whereas we call it "experiencing pain", neuroscientists call it "stimulation of the 'C-fibres'");[53] it could not be a case of the 'is' of composition. Any case of the 'is' of composition will take the form: "the thing which we perceive through sensations S and have named A, is identical to/is another name for, the thing scientists/others have named B".

2.3 *An issue relating to communication*

Both Place and Smart identify the communication of facts relating to mental states as being an important issue in the consideration of the relation between mental states and brain states. Place writes:

---

[53] Reference to 'C-fibres' in this context is of course figurative. In neurology, 'C-fibres' is the name given to a class of nerve fibre which carries signals from the periphery to the central nervous system; these nerve fibres do not occur in the brain and they carry other messages as well as those relating to pain. The reference here is not to those C-fibres. In this branch of philosophy of mind, the term 'C-fibres' is used figuratively and refers to the fact that damage, perhaps to the toe, is spoken of by philosophers as being experienced (as pain in the toe) as the result of stimulation of a fictional part of the brain called "C-fibres" (*nb.*, it is, of course, very well-known that damage to the neurons does not cause pain), see Puccetti, 1977.

"I am not trying to argue that when we describe our dreams, fantasies and sensations we are talking about processes in our brains. That is, I am not claiming that statements about sensations and mental images are reducible to or analyzable into statements about brain processes ... To say that statements about consciousness are statements about brain processes is manifestly false. This is shown (a) by the fact that you can describe your sensations and mental imagery without knowing anything about your brain processes or even that such things exist, (b) by the fact that statements about one's consciousness and statements about one's brain processes are verified in entirely different ways and (c) by the fact that there is nothing self-contradictory about the statement "X has a pain but there is nothing going on in his brain" (*ibid.*, 1956, p 44-45).

Place is suggesting that whereas he finds that *statements* about consciousness are patently not reducible to *statements* couched in the terms of the physical sciences, it could perhaps, nevertheless, be the case that mental states are reducible to physics, that *facts* about consciousness can be identified with *facts* relating to the physical sciences. What he is describing here is known nowadays as 'concept dualism', see Section 6 of this chapter.

Although Smart argues that sensations *are* brain processes (for reasons of parsimony) he also explicitly makes clear that in his view: "It is not the thesis that, for example, 'after-image' or 'ache' means the same as 'brain process of sort X' (where 'X' is replaced by a description of a certain sort of brain process)" (*ibid.*, 1959, p 144). Whereas Smart takes the view that the sensation associated with the after-image *is* a certain sort of brain process, he also sees the use of the term 'after-image' as picking out a different aspect of the sensation/brain process to that which is picked out by the term 'brain process of type X'.

Like Place, he is suggesting that there could be a distinction between the way in which *facts* about mental states and brain states relate to one another, and the way in which statements about those facts relate to each other.

2.4 *Conclusion on consciousness as a brain process*

If mind is a property of matter, and if the relevant bits of matter that give rise to this property are in the brain, then there is a sense in which consciousness is, indeed, a brain process, as Place proposed. However, consciousness could be said to be a brain process if *any* form of physicalism were to hold (so long as mind is a property of the matter in the brain rather than the matter in some

74

other bodily part); there is no need for reductive physicalism to be true for Place's point concerning consciousness being a brain process to be correct. Also, there remains a question as to whether, given that the relation between mental states and brain states is not a case of the 'is' of composition, it could nevertheless be the case that mental states are reducible to the properties of matter studied in physics.

Clearly, mental states could not be reducible to physical states (physical in the sense of "pertaining to the science of physics") if there were a category difference between what we mean by the term 'mental state' and what we mean by the term 'physical state'. As we have seen, all the facts relating to the physical sciences, the sciences that are reducible to physics, must be perfectly communicable from one person to another using language (because experiments relating to the physical sciences must be reproducible). And we know that it is impossible to acquire new 'what it is like'-type facts (what experiences that involve the senses are like) from others through language; information of this sort cannot be acquired through verbal communication with others, it is necessary to have the experience oneself or to submit oneself to neurological stimulation, see Chapter 5, Section 2. It follows that there *must* be a category difference between the non-mental properties of matter and mental properties of matter. Therefore, whereas there can be no argument with Place's assertion that mental states could be "processes in the brain", it seems that it is *not* the case that we can, as he suggests, abandon the proposition that: "sensations and mental images form a separate category of processes over and above the physical and physiological processes with which they are known to be correlated" (Place, 1956, p 44).

3 The identity thesis

As we have seen, reductive physicalism requires that there are causal processes which are such that all the facts relating to mental states can be identified with facts that are suitable for study in physics. Perhaps because of this, it is often known as 'the identity thesis'. However, 'the identity thesis' can also be interpreted as the proposition that there is a sense in which mental states can be said to be identical to brain states. In this section I look at some issues related to this.

3.1 *Can mental states be identical to brain states?*

Misunderstandings can arise from the language used regarding the identity thesis. For example, many philosophers nowadays apparently take the view that it could be the case that a mental state (a thing of which a person/creature could be conscious) is *identical* to a brain state, in the sense of these being two names for the same thing. But mental states consist only of thoughts and feelings. Thoughts and feelings are private and internal; they can be directly observed only by the person who experiences them. The brain, however, is a lump of matter; it occupies space and has mass and looks a certain way when extracted from the skull and set down upon a table; it has many properties at any point in time, such as electric currents and chemical reactions as well as weight and texture, that are public in the sense that, in principle, they could be examined and noted by any number of people. Therefore, a brain state is a situation regarding that lump of matter and a description of a brain state might include any or all the properties that obtain regarding that lump of matter at some point in time.

If mental states were strictly identical to brain states, the attributes of each would have to be the same; as Quine (1987, p 89) says: "A thing is identical with itself and with nothing else …". And whereas the proposition that thoughts and feelings are an *aspect* of a brain state is acceptable as a possibility to most of us, the proposition that chemical reactions and electric currents are an aspect of what we call a "mental state" is unacceptable, because what we refer to as a "mental state" consists *only* of thoughts and feelings and these are private and can *only* be accessed directly by the person experiencing the mental state.

If what the identity theorists assert is that brain states and mental states are identical, in the sense of these being two terms for the same thing, then, interpreting this statement strictly, and given the way the two terms are generally used, they are plainly in error. The fact that people *do* assert that they are identical may be related to a paper by Lewis, published in 1966, entitled: 'An Argument for the Identity Thesis', see below. But before proceeding we should note that the identity thesis interpreted in this way is very obviously a *logical* impossibility; the usual definitions of the terms 'mental state' and 'brain state' are such that they *cannot* pick out the same thing, they cannot have the same referent, just as a bachelor cannot be a married man.[54]

---

[54] As noted above, Place, to whom the proposition that mental states and brain states are identical is often attributed (but see Section 2.1 of this chapter) refers, in his seminal

3.2 Lewis on the identity thesis

Lewis, in his 1966 paper in support of the identity theory appears to disagree with the argument presented above, saying: "… it is pointless to exhibit various discrepancies between what is true of experiences as such and what is true of neural states as such" (p 19). The following is Lewis' argument in his own words:[55]

"The identity theory says that experience-ascriptions have the same reference as certain neural-state-ascriptions: both alike refer to the neural states which are experiences. It does not say that these ascriptions have the same sense. They do not; experience-ascriptions refer to a state by specifying the causal role that belongs to it accidentally, in virtue of causal laws, whereas neural-state-ascriptions refer to a state by describing it in detail. Therefore the identity theory does not imply that whatever is true of experiences as such is likewise true of neural states as such, nor conversely. For a truth about things of any kind *as such* is about things of that kind not by themselves, but together with the sense of expressions by which they are referred to as things of that kind. So it is pointless to exhibit various discrepancies between what is true of experiences as such and what is true of neural states as such. We can explain those discrepancies without denying psychophysical identity and without admitting that it is somehow identity of a defective sort" (*ibid.*, p 19, see later for Lewis' footnote).[56]

But if the identity theory holds, so the terms 'experiences' and 'neural states' both have the same referent, there would, of course, be no discrepancies between what is true of that referent when one term is used and what is true when the other is used. In the case of a numerical identity, the situation in which two terms pick out one thing, *all* the properties of the thing referred to *must* be the same, by definition, regardless of which term is used to

---

1956 paper 'Is Consciousness a Brain Process?', to "The all but universally accepted view that an assertion of identity between consciousness and brain processes can be ruled out on logical grounds alone …" (*ibid.*, p 45).

[55] Smart made a similar point, see Section 2.1 of this chapter.

[56] Kripke appears to support this point of Lewis', if somewhat half-heartedly, in his 1972 book *Naming and Necessity*, when he writes (pp 40-41): "… whether an object has the same property in all possible worlds depends not just on the object itself, but on how it is described. So it's argued."

describe it, because the thing is one thing referred to by two, different, terms. Therefore, despite what Lewis says here, it *must* be the case that if one can exhibit discrepancies between what is true of experiences and what is true of neural states, that is enough to establish that the identity between the two does not hold. So, is there something wrong with the argument put by Lewis, above? As we shall see, Lewis' argument is deceptive.

In the footnote relating to the above quote Lewis refers to Frege's paper: 'On Sense and Reference', saying "Here I have of course merely applied to states Frege's doctrine of sense and reference" (and he refers to Frege, 1892, translated by Geach and Black, 1960). So before examining Lewis' argument in greater depth we should check what Frege says on this point. Unsurprisingly, Frege does not present a "doctrine of sense and reference" that enables the 'referent', the thing that is picked out by two different names (or 'signs') that we humans have allocated to it, to differ in its properties depending on the 'sense' of the sign used to refer to it.

Frege starts his paper saying (1892, p 36):

"Equality gives rise to challenging questions which are not altogether easy to answer. Is it a relation? A relation between objects, or between names or signs of objects? In my ... I assumed the latter. The reasons which seem to favour this are the following: a = a and a = b are obviously statements of differing cognitive value; a = a holds *a priori* ... while statements of the form a = b often contain very valuable extensions of our knowledge and cannot always be established *a priori*. ... What is intended to be said by a = b seems to be that the signs or names 'a' and 'b' designate the same thing, so that those signs themselves would be under discussion; a relation between them would be asserted. But this relation would hold between the names or signs only in so far as they named or designated something. It would be mediated by the connexion of each of the two signs with the same designated thing."

He then sets up an example to illustrate his point (*ibid.*, p 37). He says: "Let a, b, c be the lines connecting the vertices of a triangle with the midpoints of the opposite sides. The point of intersection of a and b is then the same as the point of intersection of b and c." At this point Frege introduces the concept he calls the 'sense' of the sign, which was picked up by Lewis, above. Frege says:

"It is natural, now, to think of there being connected with a sign ...,
besides that to which the sign refers, which may be called the reference
of the sign, also what I should like to call the *sense* of the sign, wherein
the mode of presentation is contained. In our example, accordingly, the
reference of the expressions 'the point of intersection of a and b' and
'the point of intersection of b and c' would be the same, but not their
senses. The reference of 'evening star' would be the same as that of
'morning star', but not the sense" (*ibid.*, p 37).

Thus, Frege makes it quite clear that when one object is picked out by two or
more different signs, the 'sense' of the signs may differ, but the properties of
the one object to which both signs refer, the 'referent', will remain unchanged.

The caveat concerning Lewis' argument, quoted above, stems from his use
of the term 'as such'. Clearly, whatever is true of experiences *as such* would not
be necessarily true of neural states *as such* regardless of whether the identity
theory holds; each sign picks out just one aspect of, or one situation relating to,
what one might call a brain state. Lewis' argument is quite correct. If we
consider Hesperus *as such* we pick out the object in a certain position in the sky
at a certain time of day, and that is certainly not the same thing as Phosphorus
as such. But if we want to consider whether the object that is picked out by the
name "Hesperus" is the exact same object as that picked out by the name
"Phosphorus" we will need to seek discrepancies between the object(s) the two
names pick out. If the two names pick out the same object there will be no
discrepancies in the properties of the object picked out by the two,
different names.[57]

But the fact that this aspect of Lewis' argument is correct does not carry the
implication that it is pointless to exhibit discrepancies between what is true of
experiences and what is true of neural states. The identity theory states that
what is picked out by the term 'mental state' (or 'experiences') is the exact same
thing as that which is picked out by the term 'brain state' (or 'neural state'), and
addressing that question involves investigating the existence of discrepancies
between the *referents* of the two terms; what is true of mental states and what is
true of brain states. In the case of mental states and brain states, as usually

---

[57] The term "a lump of clay" could refer to the same object as the term "a statue of
David" depending on the circumstances of the reference, but "a lump of clay as such"
would not.

defined, there are indeed discrepancies; for example, brain states have mass and electric charges, while mental states have neither. There can therefore be no identity between mental states and brain states on the usual definitions.

The proposition that an object out there can change its properties because we change the name we use to describe it is clearly absurd.

3.3 Could a mental state be a property of a brain state?

Since it cannot be the case that the term "mental state" means the same thing as the term "brain state", interpreting these terms strictly as above, it may be that the identity theorists have something else in mind. For example, it clearly could be the case that, just as a cylinder can look like a circular disc from one angle and like a rectangle from another, so a brain state could be viewed as a mental state from one point of view, in that it could give rise to thoughts and feelings, and yet be viewed as being a mush of pinkish-white stuff with electric currents and chemical reactions from another.

It is logically impossible for a mental state *per se* (which by definition consists only of thoughts and feelings) to have *all* the properties of a brain state, since the brain is an object that has weight, chemical reactions and electric currents; so if a mental state is related to a brain state, and we are assuming in this book that that is the case, it could be that the brain gives rise to (instantiates) mental states; it could be that giving rise to a mental state is one of the many attributes of the matter incorporated into a brain. Therefore, a mental state could perfectly well be an instantiation of some property of a brain; consciousness could indeed be a brain process, as suggested by Place in 1956 (see Section 2 of this chapter). However, if this thought about the nature of mental states is correct, the mental state could be said to belong in a different category from that of the brain state: whereas a brain state would be the situation regarding *all* the properties of the lump of matter we call a brain, the non-mental properties *and* the mental properties, the mental state would be the situation regarding just one type of property of that lump of matter.

3.4 Could mental states be explicable in terms of physics?

Finally, what philosophers often seem to mean when they say that mental states are identical to brain states is that mental states are an aspect of a brain state and that this carries with it the implication that mental states are totally explicable in terms of the properties of matter studied in the sciences we call 'the physical sciences'.

But is it the case that if a mental state is an aspect of a brain state all the facts relating to mental states, facts relating to feelings and facts relating to thoughts, are the stuff of physics? Not necessarily, is the answer. There is an implicit assumption in this version of the proposition that mental states are identical to brain states, and it is that everything about what we *call* brain states is totally explicable in terms of the physical sciences. Clearly, it could also be the case, as is suggested in this book, that there is another property of matter, and that the facts relating to this other property of matter are different in some crucial way from those that are studied in the physical sciences, in which case the proposal that philosophers call 'non-reductive physicalism' (see Chapter 5) would hold.

If this were the case there could be an aspect to any state of a brain, namely the mental state that is associated with it, which is not suitable for study in the physical sciences, a view that is at variance with the meaning usually attributed to the assertion: "consciousness is a brain process". The identity thesis, then, would not hold.

4 Kripke on the identity theory

4.1 Introduction

Saul Kripke is an authority on identity statements, an issue he addressed in his book called *Naming and Necessity* (1972). At the end of his book he looks at the possibility that the relation between mind states and neural states could be an identity, a case of the 'is' of composition, as is proposed by the identity theorists Place (1956), Smart (1959) and Feigl (1958). He takes the case of a mental state, the sensation of pain, and the neural state associated with the experiencing of pain, named for convenience by philosophers "stimulation of the C-fibres" (see footnote 54). The idea under consideration, then, is that "the sensation of pain" *is* "stimulation of the C-fibres" in analogy with the case of, for example, water and H_2O, so these terms both refer to the one, same thing.[58]

Clearly, the sensation of pain is a private experience (no-one other than the person experiencing the pain can know exactly what it feels like) while the

---

[58] See also the discussion of this point is Section 2.2 of this chapter.

81

C-fibres being stimulated is an event out there in the world that can in principle be observed by others, for example, if they were looking at the screen attached to an EEG machine (electroencephalograph machine), so the proposal that the two are different names for the same thing looks an unlikely candidate to be the ontological basis of mind. Kripke approaches the question in the light of identities that arise for various reasons in differing situations, including that of the 'is' of composition, and then examines the case of pain and C-fibre stimulation to see if there is a valid analogy between this and the identities that involve the 'is' of composition (see Place, 1956, p 45).

4.2 Different situations that give rise to identities

In this section, I note three different situations in which identities arise, noted by Kripke (1972): I name these the 'happenstance' situation, the 'simple two names for one kind' situation, and the 'is of composition' situation.

'Happenstance' situations

First consider the identity that operates when the person who was the first Postmaster General (Benjamin Franklin) also invented bifocals (Benjamin Franklin was also an inventor), so either fact could be used to pick out the one person (Kripke, *ibid.*, pp 98, 145-6). Both these facts relating to Benjamin Franklin are contingent in the 'happenstance' sense (see footnote in Chapter 2, Section 2.3), because each of them could so easily never have happened.

A small perturbation to events could mean that any one of us did not do something that in fact we have done or, indeed, that any one of us would never have existed. This sort of identity is neither true by definition nor is it the direct result of a law of nature (although on a strict deterministic view of the world, the total of all the laws of nature plus some initial conditions could make it inevitable).

To my mind, this so-called identity with its happenstance type of contingency is akin to the 'equals' notion in an algebraic equation when two variables that can take a wide range of values happen to take the same value in some particular instance. Identity, represented mathematically with a three-barred 'equals' sign, indicates a different kind of relation in mathematics, namely that the two symbols pick out the same thing in all circumstances, as is the case in the other two situations that give rise to identities, presented below (and see Frege, 1892, p 36).

'Simple two names for one kind' situations

Next, consider the identity between the evening star called Phosphorus and the morning star called Hesperus (or the person called Cicero who is also the person called Tully, or the mountain called Gaurisanker which is also the mountain called Everest; see Kripke, *ibid.*, p 109). If we view the two names for the star as being two proper names for the same lump of matter (rather than taking the names to be summaries of time-position descriptors), then there would be a numerical identity holding between them so long as that lump of matter existed. But there would have been contingency of the "requires investigation" variety relating to *our understanding* of the truth of such a proposition as we wouldn't have known it until some work had been done by scientists on whether the proposition is true or untrue.

This sort of identity can hold for types, or kinds, as well as for tokens as in the above examples. Thus, the name of a kind, such as 'tiger' or 'gold' can be the subject of an identity between the name of the kind and a descriptor, which might be a scientific term for tigers or an element descriptor for a metal (Kripke, *ibid.*, pp 118-128). These are type-type identities and they too may be subject to contingency of the 'requires investigation' variety; we did not know that gold was an element until some scientist had proved it to be so.

Situations that involve the 'is' of composition

Third, consider identities that involve the 'is' of composition. Kripke uses as his example the identity between heat, the thing out there that gives rise to the sensory experience that we call 'heat' and the aspect of the motion of molecules that is relevant to something feeling hot to us humans (*ibid.*, p 131-34).[59] Here, I use the water/H_2O identity as my example of a composition identity. One might then describe the identity that involves the 'is' of composition thus:

- The name 'water' was originally given to the stuff out there that gives us humans a certain bundle of *qualia* relating to our senses of touch, sight, taste, *etc.*

---

[59] The word 'heat' has two meanings, referring both to the sensation of heat and to the temperature of an object "out there". It can be helpful, in this context, to use different terms for the thing "out there" that we perceive and the *qualia* that define our perception of the thing. Thus, we might call the thing we experience 'the perception of heat', and the thing out there that gives rise to our perception of heat 'a high temperature' (see also Section 5 of this chapter).

- In due course scientists discovered that, given the laws of physics that operate in our universe, the thing that gives rise to these sensations is a substance with molecules constructed from two hydrogen atoms and one oxygen atom (H_2O).

- Therefore, in our world, where a particular set of laws of physics and biology operates, an identity holds between this substance which consists of molecules of H_2O and the thing we call water. The two designators 'water' and 'H_2O' therefore pick out the exact same 'thing' as referent, so it is a case of 'numerical identity'.

Therefore, the stuff out there that leads to us experiencing the watery *qualia* is the exact same thing as H_2O, there is a numerical identity here. But, Kripke asserts, this relation is contingent (it is contingent *ab initio* in the 'requires investigation' sense). This is because *ab initio* there seems to be no necessity that this stuff that gives rise to the watery *qualia* is H_2O; scientists had to set up experiments in order to establish the point.

4.3 The possibility of a mental state/brain state identity

Now, finally, consider the relation between mental states and neural states. Following the work of Place (1956, see Section 2.1 of this chapter), Kripke examines the proposition that the relation between a mental state and a neural state (the sensation of 'pain' and stimulation of the C-fibres) is a case of the 'is' of composition, a relation *analogous to* the identity between light and a stream of photons, or water and a collection of molecules of H_2O. As we shall see, in the end he finds that it is *not* analogous to these identities. He therefore finishes his book with the following three sentences:

> "I suspect, however, that the present considerations tell heavily against the usual forms of materialism. Materialism, I think, must hold that a physical description of the world is a *complete* description of it, that any mental facts are 'ontologically dependent' on physical facts in the straightforward sense of following from them by necessity. No identity theorist seems to me to have made a convincing argument against the intuitive view that this is not the case" (1972, p 155).

84

So Kripke's intuitions at that time were *against* the correctness of materialism.[60] We will come back to this conclusion after examining his argument.

Here is the three-step argument put forward by Kripke to explain why there is *not* an analogy between the hypothecated identity relating mental states and neural states and the identities involving the 'is' of composition; he uses the heat/molecular motion identity as his example of the 'is' of composition (*ibid.*, pp 148-151):

- First, Kripke says: "the usual view holds that the identification of heat with molecular motion and of pain with the stimulation of C-fibers are both contingent" (*ibid.*, p 148).

- Second, he says: "When someone says, inaccurately, that heat might have turned out not to be molecular motion, what is true in what he says is that someone could have sensed a phenomenon in the same way we sense heat, that is, feels it by production of the sensation we call 'the sensation of heat' …, even though that phenomenon was not molecular motion", (*ibid.*, p 150). So the person would have experienced the same *qualia* as we experience in the presence of the molecular motion associated with a high temperature, the "sensation of heat", but he or she experiences it in the presence of something else. Note that "a high temperature" can continue to be associated with "molecular motion" in these circumstances; this identity can continue to hold. The change is that someone happens to be wired up in a different manner from the way in which we are wired up, so the *qualia* that we experience in the presence of a high temperature are experienced by this person in the presence of some other phenomenon. Different laws of biology operate regarding this person.

- Third, Kripke then asks whether there is something that is analogous to this story about heat and molecular motion that can apply in the case of the hypothecated identity between pain and stimulation of the C-fibres. He says: "Now can something be said analogously to explain away the feeling that the identity of pain and the stimulation of C-fibers, if it is a scientific

---

[60] Note that like so many others, Kripke makes no mention of the possibility that mental states could be instantiations of a property of matter different from those studied in physics, so whereas the identity thesis does not hold materialism in this sense, nevertheless, is true.

discovery, could have turned out otherwise?" (*ibid.*, p 151). The question he asks is: "is it analogously possible that stimulation of the C-fibers should have existed without being felt as pain?" (*ibid.*, p 151). But he finds: "Such a situation would be in flat out contradiction with the supposed necessary identity of pain, and the corresponding physical state, …" (*ibid.*, p 151).

If there were a pain/stimulation of the C-fibres identity that was analogous to the heat/molecular motion identity, Kripke notes, it would be possible to construct a story about pain and C-fibres that was analogous to the story about heat and molecular motion. He has shown in the above three-step argument that that is not possible (note the alternative presentation of the same point in Section 2.2 of this chapter).

It is in conclusion to the above argument that Kripke says (see above, and *ibid.*, p 155): "I suspect … that the present considerations tell heavily against the usual forms of materialism". But I think Kripke is wrong there. The identity could still hold; Kripke has only shown that it cannot be a case of the 'is' of composition. There still could be a simple "two names for one kind" situation resulting in an identity between 'pain' and 'stimulation of the C-fibres'.

4.4 Conclusion to Kripke's argument

My conclusion on Kripke's argument against the identity thesis is therefore somewhat different from that of Kripke.

The fact that this analogy with the water/H_2O identity does not hold, although interesting, is not the last word on the possible existence of the proposed identity. An identity could arise for a reason other than the 'is' of composition: it could perfectly well arise because of a "simple two names for one kind" situation (with us referring to something as "experiencing pain" while neuroscientists refer to that same thing, figuratively, as "C-fibres firing", a non-mental phenomenon). It would then be an identity analogous to the identity between Phosphorus and Hesperus, or gold and "the element with atomic number 79", instead of being a case of the 'is' of composition. Indeed, if we ask, as Kripke does in the case of stimulation of the C-fibres and the experience of pain (in step three above): "Is it possible that Phosphorus should have existed without the existence of Hesperus?", we find, as one might expect: "[s]uch a situation would be in flat out contradiction with the supposed necessary identity …" (to quote Kripke, *ibid.*, p 151, see step three above).

In my view, therefore, Kripke's result does not "tell heavily against" physicalism, of either the reductive, or the non-reductive, form. This is because ruling out the 'is' of composition is not enough; the identity could arise simply because we label the experience of pain in two ways, one relating to our feelings, the other coming from neuroscience. In this book, I reject reductive physicalism for quite different reasons (see Chapter 3, Section 5.1).

5 The explanatory gap

5.1 *The existence of an explanatory gap*

In 1983, Levine pointed out that people who believe in "materialism", by which he means that they believe that mental states are nothing more than 'physical' (non-mental) states of the brain, have a problem with what he called "the explanatory gap" (of course, the thought that motivates this problem was not new, see for example Nagel, 1974 and Kirk, 1974).

Levine starts arguing his case for the existence of an explanatory gap by reiterating Kripke's argument against physicalism (see Kripke, 1972, and Section 4 above). Levine says that this type of physicalist is committed to identity statements of the form:

"pain is the firing of C-fibers" (Levine, 1983B, p 354),

and notes that, according to Kripke's theory, if that statement is true it is *necessarily* true. Then he says that the same is the case for the following statement (note the alternative meanings of the word 'heat', in footnote 59 on p 83; Levine is presumably using the word in the "high temperature" sense):

"heat is the motion of molecules" (*ibid.*, p 354).

He then points out that there is what he calls "a felt contingency" (*ibid.*, p 355) about *both* these statements. But he suggests that there is an important difference between the two statements that relates to this "felt contingency", and argues that this is where the explanatory gap comes in.

Levine suggests that the difference between these two cases of "felt contingency", which he thinks explains the difference identified by Kripke, is that in the case of heat and the motion of molecules the statement: "expresses

87

an identity that is *fully explanatory*, with nothing crucial left out" (*ibid.*, p 357, his italics), while in the case of pain and the so-called 'C-fibre' firing the statement: "seem[s] to leave something crucial unexplained, there is a 'gap' in the explanatory import of [this statement]" (my insertions). More definitively, he says: "If there is nothing we can determine about C-fiber firing that explains why having one's C-fibres fire has the qualitative character that it does ... it immediately becomes imaginable that there be C-fiber firings without without the feelings of pain, and *vice versa*", and: "We don't have the corresponding intuition in the case of heat and the motion of molecules ... because whatever there is to explain about heat is explained by its being the motion of molecules" (*ibid.*, p 359).

It is this phenomenon, concerning explanations of mental states, that Levine calls "the explanatory gap".

However, in order to clarify the difference between the two cases Levine then seeks: "an account of what it is for a phenomenon to be made *intelligible*, along with rules which determine when the demand for further intelligibility is inappropriate" (*ibid.*, p 358), noting that there can be "primitive, brute fact[s] about the universe" (*ibid.*, p 358), and citing the gravitational constant 'G' as one such.

He then raises the key question relating to his suggestion that there is an explanatory gap: "[W]hy does the connection between what it's like to be in a particular functional (or physical) state and the state itself demand explanation, to be made intelligible?" (*ibid.*, p 358). In answer to his own question, he says: "Materialism, as I understand it, implies explanatory reductionism of at least this minimal sort: that for every phenomenon not describable in terms of the fundamental physical magnitudes (whatever they turn out to be), there is a mechanism that is describable in terms of the fundamental physical magnitudes such that occurrences of the former are intelligible in terms of occurrences of the latter" (*ibid.*, p 358-359, presumably his use of the word 'physical' here should be interpreted as meaning 'suitable for study in physics').

But, of course, if mind is a property of matter different from those properties that are studied in the science of physics, consciousness would, indeed, be a fundamental property of matter, and what it feels like to experience pain would, using Levine's own words, be a "primitive brute fact about the universe". In this case, therefore, although the so-called "explanatory gap" identified by Levine would certainly exist, it would not pick out something for which we require an explanation.

5.2 Does an explanatory gap imply an ontological gap?

Both the conceivability argument ("that there is no contradiction or incoherence in the extreme zombie hypothesis, the idea of a microphysical duplicate of one of us but with no consciousness", see Block and Stalnaker, 1999, p 29, and see Chapter 3, Section 6.2) and the knowledge argument ("that Jackson's Mary cannot deduce the facts about what it is like to see red from the microphysical and functional facts", *ibid.*, p 29, and see Chapter 3, Section 6.1) involve the notion of an explanatory gap. But both these propositions are often taken to carry the implication that "physicalism is false"; that consciousness is not ontologically reducible to the properties of matter studied in physics. The obvious question that arises from Levine's analysis is therefore: if there is an explanatory gap of the nature suggested by Levine, does this necessarily mean that there is also an ontological gap? Are Chalmers and Jackson right to assume that the conceivability argument and the knowledge argument carry the implication that there is an ontological gap – that mind, and therefore mental states, cannot be ontologically reducible to physics? Or could it be that the problem is merely that we humans are unable, for some reason (see below), to explain mental states in terms of physics in a manner that satisfies us while, in fact, they *are* ontologically reducible?[61]

Before examining Block and Stalnaker's treatment of this question, consider the likely response of one acquainted with physics. If something is ontologically reducible to physics, every fact about that thing must be related nomologically to facts that are suitable for study in physics, and of course it must be possible for these, both the facts and the nomological relations, to be communicated perfectly between people using language, given the fact that all experiments relating to physics must be repeatable by others. Therefore, anyone steeped in physics is likely to find the proposition that there is no ontological gap and yet there can be an explanatory gap (or *vice versa*) difficult to take seriously. This is, of course, the nub of the knowledge argument: If Mary knows all the microphysical and functional facts relating to seeing red, and if what it is like to see red is derivable nomologically from those microphysical and functional facts and Mary knows and understands all the natural laws involved, how could it possibly be that Mary is unable to work out from this knowledge what it is like to see red (see Chapter 3, Section 6.1)? She would be able to.

---

[61] See McLaughlin (2010) for a description of how type physicalism can be justified given the existence of an explanatory gap using inference to the best explanation.

However, Block and Stalnaker (1999) address this question of whether the proposition that the existence of an *explanatory* gap has the implication that there must be an *ontological* gap (note that Levine also, later, suggested that: "the explanatory gap is primarily an epistemological problem, not necessarily a metaphysical one", *Purple Haze*, 2001, p 10). Block and Stalnaker start by splitting the assertion that water is H_2O into two steps. First, they note that experts have given the name 'water' to the stuff out there referring to Jackson's description (1993, p 39), as that which: "falls from the sky, fills the oceans, is odourless and colourless, is essential for life". Block and Stalnaker summarise Jackson's description as "the waterish stuff". So, this definition can be stated as:

water = the waterish stuff.

Second, they take it that the fact that H_2O has the properties that affect our senses in a certain way (it is odourless, colourless, *etc.*) can be deduced from its atomic structure using the laws of nature that make up physics (in their words: "is ... derivable from microphysics", see Block and Stalnaker, 1999, p 12).[62] It follows that scientists should be able to tell us that the stuff they call H_2O must have the properties that will affect our senses in the manner Block and Stalnaker have designated for the stuff out there which they call "the waterish stuff"; therefore:

H_2O = the waterish stuff.

It follows immediately from these two statements, one a definition, the other the consequence of the laws of physics, that:

water = H_2O.

Block and Stalnaker (*ibid.*, p 12) then raise the question of whether the same analysis applies for consciousness; whether there is any reason why the facts relating to consciousness cannot be determined by the laws of nature that make up physics in spite of the fact that, as they put it: "the concept of consciousness

---

[62] These laws of nature cannot be known *a priori*, of course, they do not follow from the definitions of words, and they cannot be known from introspection; they are known to be true *a posteriori*, see Chapter 2, Section 2.3.

cannot be given an analytic definition in functional or physical terms" (*ibid.*, p 13). The question they are exploring, then, is whether reductive physicalism, ontological reduction of consciousness to the properties of matter studied in physics, can hold in spite of the fact that there is an explanatory gap. If that could be the case, how might it work?

Accepting the existence of an explanatory gap, if we wish to maintain the possibility that reductive physicalism holds there are various possibilities. First, it could be the case that whereas at this point in the development of science we are unable to derive what it is like to experience something from the laws of physics, as science develops further we may become able to do this; the explanatory gap that we perceive today may become closed in the future; clearly, this is a logical possibility. Second, it could be that the explanatory gap Levine has identified results from an inherent inability on the part of us human beings to fully comprehend consciousness (see van Gulick, 1985, McGinn, 1989 and others). Third, it is worth considering the possibility that, despite Levine's case for the perceived existence of an explanatory gap, we are, in fact, mistaken in thinking that there is one; although reductive physicalism holds and we perceive there to be an explanatory gap, it may be that in fact that is not the case (see Papineau, 2011). But fourth, it may be that there actually is no explanatory gap – not because there is a satisfactory explanation, but simply because we are wrong to assume that mental states are nothing more than 'physical' (pertaining to physics) states of the brain; maybe they are instantiations of another property of matter, one that is different from those suitable for study in physics and therefore one that it is, quite simply, impossible to 'explain' satisfactorily in terms of physics.

On the second of these, McGinn (1989) makes an excellent case for the possibility that: "we are cut off by our very cognitive constitution from achieving a conception of that natural property of the brain (or of consciousness) that accounts for the psychophysical link" (p 350). He introduces the concept of 'cognitive closure', saying: "A type of mind M is cognitively closed with respect to a property P (or theory T) if and only if the concept-forming procedures at M's disposal cannot extend to a grasp of P (or an understanding of T)". He then gives examples of what one might call perceptual closure (noting that the invisible parts of the electromagnetic spectrum are just as real as the visible parts although we are unable to perceive them) and of cognitive closure from the animal kingdom, citing monkey minds and the property of being an electron. "Nothing …", he says, "in the concept of reality shows that everything real is open to the human concept-forming faculty ..." (*ibid.*, p 351). Indeed, he says he finds it: "... deplorably anthropocentric to insist that reality be constrained by what the human mind can conceive" (*ibid.*, p 366) and adds that: "... in the case of the mind-body problem, the bit of reality that systematically eludes our cognitive grasp is an aspect of our own nature" (*ibid.*, p 366).

Papineau (2011) puts the case for the third suggestion, the proposition that, actually, there is no explanatory gap. He says: "The feeling of a 'explanatory gap' arises only because we cannot stop ourselves thinking about the mind-brain relationship in a dualist way" (2011, p 5). He lists many reasons which might explain why this is the case, and the more convincing of these are somewhat similar to McGinn's thesis.

First, he says that it could simply be that our culture implicitly assumes that dualism is the case, so we are all brought up to take it for granted. But Papineau is not convinced by this; he feels that there is: "some feature of our cognitive architecture that forces the intuition of dualism on us" (p 15).

The next reason he gives for why we might think there is an explanatory gap when there isn't one, he calls 'the antipathetic fallacy'. The idea is that people might implicitly assume that introspection ought to reveal the true nature of consciousness. But when we think about a phenomenal experience, such as the experience of seeing something red, we typically recreate that experience in our imaginations. So, introspection does not reveal mental states to be physical. So people conclude that mental states could not be physical. Therefore, Papineau says, people think that the statement: "The experience of seeing something as red = such-and-such neural activity in V4", cannot be true (*ibid.*, 2011, p 16). But Papineau finds this unconvincing because people who have not thought much about the mind-body issue would then be less likely to take a dualistic view, and this appears not to be the case.

Then, he says, there is the possibility that we have two distinct cognitive systems, one for thinking about mental processes and the other for thinking about physical processes, as described by Paul Bloom is his book *Descartes' Baby* (2004). Paul Bloom, a psychologist at Yale University, has been exploring the development of intuitions relating to moral responsibility by looking at morality in babies. He says:

"We can explain much of what makes us human by recognising that we are natural Cartesians – dualistic thinking comes naturally to us. We have two distinct ways of seeing the world: as containing bodies and as containing souls. These two ways of seeing the world interact in surprising ways in the course of development of each child, and in the social context of a community of humans they give rise to certain uniquely human traits, such as morality and religion." (Bloom, 2004, p xii).

The proposition here is that there *is* an explanatory gap and that it results from our inability to switch information between our two cognitive systems (as opposed to the alternative proposition, namely that there are two different types of information: public facts and private facts).

Papineau's final suggestion for why we think there is an explanatory gap when there isn't follows from a thought of Melnyck (2008). Melnyck points out that, in Papineau's words: "… what happens when we accept any identity claim of the form a = b is that we 'merge the files'" (*ibid.*, p 17). So, what if for some reason we cannot merge the files of mind-brain identities? If phenomenal concepts and physical concepts are realised in different parts of the brain it may be that we cannot merge the files. Perhaps this could explain why we think there is an explanatory gap.

Block and Stalnaker conclude that, although there does appear to be an *explanatory* gap, this does not necessarily mean that there must be an *ontological* gap; they think that it still could be the case that mental states are simply instantiations of the physical (non-mental) properties of neural states. And if that were the case, concept dualism would be a natural approach to take to the problem of the nature of mind (see Section 6 of this chapter, below).

5.3 Conclusion on the explanatory gap

But given that experiments in physics must be repeatable by others, if any property of matter is suitable for study in the physical sciences that property must be such that every fact relating to it is perfectly communicable linguistically by one person to another. So, if the way things feel when they are experienced were ontologically reducible to physics, it *would* then be possible to explain to other people, satisfactorily, in the vocabulary used in physics, *exactly* the way they feel.

So given that Levine is right, and that there is this "explanatory gap", if consciousness relates to matter there *must* be another property of matter besides those studied in physics, and what it feels like to experience something must be an instantiation of that other property of matter. And the fact that that is so must be, in Levine's terminology a "primitive, brute fact".

6 Concept dualism

What Place and Smart were suggesting, see Section 2 above, was in fact an early version of the approach to reductive physicalism that nowadays takes the name 'concept dualism' and was later enunciated by Loar (1990/97), Papineau (2002) and others. As Loar puts it as he sets out the rationale for concept dualism at the beginning of the 1997 version of his paper: "... the present objective is to engage anti-physicalist arguments and entrenched intuitions to the effect that conscious mental qualities cannot be identical with ordinary physical properties, or at least that it is problematic to suppose that they are so".

Papineau, spelling out the idea carefully in his book (2002), proposes that there are two different types of 'concept' that can be used to refer to conscious properties: 'phenomenal concepts' and 'material concepts'.[63] In Papineau's words, "The general idea is that when we use phenomenal concepts, we think of mental properties, not as items in the material world, but in terms of *what they are like*" (his italics, *ibid.*, p 48). To elucidate "what they are like" he suggests we think of what it would feel like if the dentist's drill slips and hits the nerve in a tooth. 'Material properties', on the other hand, are the familiar physical (non-mental) properties that are associated with objects in the external world, such as stones, or houses, or dogs. Examples of material properties associated with a dog might be "hairy", or "four-legged", but they could also be something physical related to the condition of the dog's neurons at some point in time. The material concept associated with a conscious property would be a description of what happens physically (non-mentally) when the creature

---

[63] The word 'concept' has a range of different meanings. Here, I take a 'concept' to be an abstract idea that picks out the fundamental characteristics that define a set of objects. I take it, therefore, that the term 'concept' is used to pick out those specific bundles of entities stored in the long-term memory that turn up together in the working memory on a regular basis because they are relevant to some set of material or abstract, real or imaginary objects (see Margolis and Laurence, 2014, for a further discussion of the meaning of 'concept'). In such a case it is convenient, for communication purposes, to attach a verbal label, or name, to such a bundle; we call the bundles that have labels 'concepts'. The words 'red', 'dog', 'tree', 'stone', 'happiness', 'unicorn' can be viewed as being labels that pick out concepts. The essential inclusion in the bundle of some element relating to "what it is like to experience something" is necessary if a concept is to be classed as a phenomenal concept ('red' and 'happiness' are phenomenal concepts; 'stone' is not; for 'dog', 'tree' and 'unicorn' the question of whether they pick out a phenomenal concept would depend on the context).

experiences the conscious property at issue, that is, what happens physically, inside the creature's body, when it 'sees' the colour red or 'feels' thirsty. Papineau emphasises that: "Material concepts are those which pick out conscious properties *as* items in the third-personal, causal world" (his italics, p 48).

However, Papineau also signs up to the proposition that everything can be reduced to physics, saying: "I believe that in the end the materialist argument wins", and by 'materialist' Papineau means physicalist in the narrow sense, he means that everything pertains to the science of physics (*ibid.*, p 14). The reason is that he accepts the requirement that "physics is complete" in the sense that all physical effects are fully caused by purely physical (non-mental) prior histories, but he also assumes both that conscious mental states can be the cause of physical effects and that there is no "over-determination". Therefore, he claims that mental states must be physical:

"Many effects that we attribute to conscious causes have full physical causes. But it would be absurd to suppose that these effects are caused twice over. So the conscious causes must be identical to some part of those physical causes" (*ibid.*, p 17, but see Chapter 5, Section 7 below).

Concept dualism therefore rests on two assumptions:[64]

1. Conscious mental experiences can be reduced to physics/contemporary brain science – as Papineau says of Mary when she emerges from her black and white room: "There are no new experiential properties in the offing" (*ibid.*, p 51)

2. Conscious mental experiences, however, can be referred to in two quite different ways, one using phenomenal concepts (that pick out what it is like to experience things, so phenomenal facts must exist) and the other using

---

[64] In Loar's words (1997): "It is my view that we can have it both ways. We may take the phenomenological intuition at face value, accepting introspective concepts and their conceptual irreducibility, and at the same time take phenomenal qualities to be identical with physical-functional properties of the sort envisaged by contemporary brain science." In Papineau's words (2002, p 47): "Conscious properties are identical to material properties ...", and "I think that we have two quite different ways of thinking about conscious properties ... I shall call these two kinds of concepts 'phenomenal' concepts and 'material' concepts."

material concepts (that pick out the physics that takes place when we experience those things).

In concept dualism, therefore, we have two, quite different, ways of thinking about mental properties – in the one case we can describe them using phenomenal concepts (such as "red"), and in the other we can describe them using only physical concepts, concepts that have no phenomenal content (perhaps noting the wavelength of the light reflected by the object); and along with making a distinction between these two types of concept, it is assumed that reductive physicalism holds.

But we need to be clear about the definitions relating to this issue:

i.   from the definition of 'phenomenal fact', one person/creature has privileged access to phenomenal, or private, facts; they are not available on an equal basis to everyone (see Chapter 2, Section 3.2);

ii.   from the definition of 'physics', facts relating to the properties of matter studied in physics are public facts, equally available to any number of people (see Chapter 2, Section 2.1); and,

iii.   from the definition of 'concept', a concept is a bundle of entities, or a single entity, drawn from the long-term memory (see the footnote 63 on p 94).

It then follows that if the concept dualists' first assumption, namely that conscious mental experiences can be reduced to physics/brain science, is correct, there would be no phenomenal facts, so conscious mental experience would include no phenomenal facts. And if that were the case there would be no phenomenal facts in a person's long-term memory. Therefore, there would be no phenomenal facts that could be used to construct phenomenal concepts. For if the inclusion of some element relating to what it is like to experience something is necessary for a concept to be classed as a phenomenal concept (as follows from the definition of 'concept', see footnote 63 on p 94), and a concept cannot generalise or abstract from facts that simply don't exist, there can be no phenomenal concepts. So, the first of the concept dualists' two assumptions implies the negation of their second assumption: if there are no phenomenal facts, as must be the case if everything can be reduced to physics, there can be no phenomenal concepts.

On the other hand, if we suppose (as Papineau does) that conscious states do: "involve awareness, feelings" (2002, p 1), and that the concept dualists' second assumption is fine, then given that we accept both that all the facts relating to the properties of matter studied in physics are public facts and that the facts regarding phenomenal experiences are private, phenomenal facts, so there is a category difference between the facts relating to the properties of matter studied in physics and the facts regarding phenomenal experiences, it must be the case that everything cannot be reduced to physics, so the concept dualists' first assumption does not hold. The second of the concept dualists' assumptions implies the negation of the first. Concept dualism is internally inconsistent.

But this depends on the definitions of 'phenomenal', 'physics' and 'concept' that I use in this book. Perhaps others would disagree with those. Let us try another way of putting it that depends only on a concept being a bundle of facts and the proposition that it is conceivable that there could be different types of fact (see Chapter 2, Section 2.1). Then, if the concept dualists' first assumption holds, any fact relating to a conscious mental experience could be replaced by facts of the type used in the physical sciences and these would *fully* describe it; that being so, all the facts available for forming concepts would be of same type in which case the concept dualists' second assumption cannot be the case. If the concept dualists' second assumption is true, so there are two *distinct* types of fact available for forming concepts, then it cannot be the case that one of these types of fact can be fully described in terms of the other (they would not then be distinct), and this must be possible if mental experiences are reducible to physics, so the concept dualists' first assumption cannot hold.

Whichever way you play this one, it seems to me that you arrive at an inconsistency. What the concept dualist wants is that phenomenal experience exists and that phenomenal experience can be totally reduced to physics; but that runs counter to what we normally mean by the terms 'phenomenal experience' and 'physics'.

Presumably the concept dualists would disagree with some part of this simple argument. But since the existence of phenomenal facts seems obvious (and is the first of the fundamental propositions in this book), the existence of an epistemic gap also seems obvious (and is the second of our fundamental propositions), and since physics is defined in such a way that it does not include the study and analysis of phenomenal facts, I shall leave the subject there apart from one final comment. The motivation for concept dualism appears to be to enable something that one might call physicalism, or at any rate something that is not substance dualism, to exist in the light of Jackson's knowledge argument; the concept dualist wants to avoid the necessity of signing up to the existence of two substances. But property dualism of the type explored in this book, achieves this objective in a perfectly simple and straightforward manner. We don't need concept dualism for this.

7 Davidson's anomalous monism

7.1 Introduction

Davidson, in his 1970 paper 'Mental Events', presents an approach to the relation between brain states and mental states which he calls 'anomalous monism' (page references are to the 2001 reprint of Davidson's 1980 book *Essays on Actions and Events*). He starts by referring to his desire to reconcile freedom with causal determinism, then he says: "*Autonomy* (freedom, self-rule) may or may not clash with determinism; *anomaly* (failure to fall under a law) is, it would seem, another matter" (*ibid.*, p 207, his italics).[65] In his paper, he takes it that: "both the causal dependence, and the anomalousness, of mental events are undeniable facts"; his aim, in this 1970 paper, appears to be to explain how this can be the case (*ibid.*, p 207).[66]

As presented in his 1970 paper, Davidson's anomalous monism contains many propositions that appear at first sight to be at variance with each other. However, it also contains several useful ideas that I use elsewhere in this book, so I need to include a summary of it.

7.2 Davidson's three principles

Davidson starts his paper (1970, p 208) by setting down three basic principles, namely:

1. Principle of causal interaction: at least some mental events interact causally with physical events.

---

[65] See Chapter 8 for a discussion of compatibilism (free will combined with universal causation) and libertarianism (free will combined with failure to fall under a law).
[66] Davidson wrote another paper on anomalous monism, 'Thinking Causes' (1993), in which he responded to the critics of this one.

2. Principle of the nomological character of causality: where there is causality, there must be a law: events related as cause and effect fall under strict deterministic laws.

3. Principle of the anomalism of the mental: there are no strict deterministic laws on the basis of which mental events can be predicted and explained.

As Melchert (1986, p 265) remarks, these are: "apparently at odds with each other". There have been several attempts to reconcile them, a notable one being that of Honderich (1982) in which mental events are identical to physical events according to 'token' identity, not 'type' identity; so the *same* mental event is 'identical' to a *different* physical event each time it occurs ("… we have token-identity but not type-identity", p 60). This is very obviously at variance with the normal meaning of the term 'identity', see also Section 4 of this chapter.

Suppose that events, things that happen "out there", are subject to 'strict' (presumably that means non-probabilistic) deterministic causal processes, and that we set these down, in words, as laws (Davidson decrees that laws are linguistic, *ibid.*, p 215); this would be in keeping with Davidson's Principle 2. Then, accepting his Principle 1 as holding, there are many reasons why it might be impossible for us to set down in words the causal processes that relate to the occurrence of a mental event, an event that has mental characteristics as well as physical characteristics, and which would therefore enable Principle 3 to hold. Perhaps mental characteristics arise without causes ("failure to fall under a law", as may be the case in libertarianism, see Chapter 8, Section 2.3), or perhaps the causal processes that underlie mental events are not 'identified', in the statistical sense, so they cannot be understood by us and set down in words.[67] It also might be the case that there are causal processes that determine mental events but they are stochastic, and therefore cannot be represented by "strict deterministic laws" because Davidson's use of the term 'deterministic' could

---

[67] As in the "parameter identification problem" in statistics (if there were a set of simultaneous equations containing more variables than there were equations, for example).

rule out the existence of stochastic laws.[68] Davidson's three principles are not necessarily inconsistent.

7.3 Is it some type of dualism that Davidson has in mind?

On first reading, it is not clear to me what type of theory Davidson has in mind for his anomalous monism. For example, Davidson says: "That there is a categorical difference between the mental and the physical is a commonplace" (*ibid.*, p 223) suggesting, with its overtones of Ryle (1949), that he might view some sort of ontological dualism as obtaining.

But he also says: "Although the position I describe denies there are psychophysical laws, it is consistent with the view that mental characteristics are in some sense dependent, or supervenient, on physical characteristics" (*ibid.*, p 214), which suggests that what he is describing may be a form of non-reductive physicalism. The following quote seems to confirm the view that anomalous monism is a case of non-reductive physicalism: "… we can pick out each mental event using the physical vocabulary alone, but no purely physical predicate, no matter how complex, has, as a matter of law, the same extension as a mental predicate" (*ibid.*, p 215). All this seems to make it clear that anomalous monism is a case of non-reductive physicalism; the brain state that is associated with the mental characteristics of some event can be referred to by citing the physical characteristics upon which the mental characteristics supervene, or which correlate with the mental characteristics, but the mental characteristics of the event cannot be described in terms of these physical characteristics. For this to be the case, it surely must be the case that mental characteristics are not ontologically reducible to physical (pertaining to physics) characteristics.

However, towards the end of his paper Davidson finds that a mental event *is* a physical event. The proof goes thus: "Suppose m, a mental event, caused p, a physical event; then, under some description m and p instantiate a strict law. This law can only be physical …. But if m falls under a physical law, it has a physical description; which is to say it is a physical event" (*ibid.*, p 224). But if the mental event has a physical description, and *is* a physical event, how can it

---

[68] We should also note that, given the way Davidson's third principle is worded, it does not rule out the possibility that there are strict deterministic laws on the basis of which the physical effects of mental events can be predicted and explained. But that doesn't seem to be Davidson's intention, and one could argue that it is ruled out by the name given to that principle.

be the case that "no purely physical predicate, no matter how complex, has, as a matter of law, the same extension as a mental predicate" (see above)? Davidson says that anomalous monism: "... rejects the thesis, usually considered essential to materialism, that mental phenomena can be given purely physical explanations" (*ibid.*, p 214); so it may be that it is a case of concept dualism.

Of course, it turns out that Davidson does have concept dualism in mind (see Section 6 of this chapter). In his later paper (1993) Davidson says: "AM [anomalous monism] holds that mental entities ... are physical entities, but that mental concepts are not reducible by definition or natural law to physical concepts" (*ibid.*, p 3, my insertion). This is, in my view, an untenable position: if 'physical' is defined as "suitable for study in physics" and facts ('concepts') are suitable for study in physics only if they can be perfectly communicated between people verbally, Davidson's position is incoherent.

7.4 Conclusion on anomalous monism

So Davidson's anomalous monism is a case of concept dualism, and given our definition of physics and given the existence of an epistemic gap, it cannot hold. However, there are several ideas in Davidson's paper that are worth noting and, indeed, I refer to it quite frequently in this book, which is why this brief summary of it is included.

First, there is his use of the term 'supervenience', which has proved so handy in non-reductive physicalism. Next, he suggested that "laws are linguistic", making a clear distinction between the causal processes "out there" and our attempts to encapsulate them in language (or mathematics) which is useful. Then there is the implication of the proposition that if a set of mental characteristics supervenes on some set of physical characteristics, so you can't have the physical characteristics without also having the mental characteristics, it could be impossible to discover which it is that does the causing; this is relevant to our desire to assess the possibility that mental states can be causally effective. It suggests that there could be an unusual situation here regarding the question of which it is of the mental characteristics, which are a property of matter, and the physical characteristics that are also associated with that matter, that is "doing the causing" on any occasion. Indeed, it suggests that it may not be possible for us, ever, to discover which it is; this issue is addressed in Chapter 5, Section 7.3.

Finally, there is the distinction Davidson makes between those causal processes that relate to physical characteristics, which he assumes can be described by "strict deterministic laws", and such causal processes, if any, as may apply to mental characteristics. For one could interpret Davidson's paper as proposing that there *are* causal processes applying to mental characteristics but that the type of causal processes involved is different from that which applies to physical characteristics, so any "laws" that may encapsulate them cannot be described as "strict deterministic laws". He could then have been suggesting that mental characteristics are 'anomalous'; because he requires his 'laws' to be strict and deterministic, and he views mental characteristics as being associated with stochastic causal processes (see Chapter 5, Section 7.3). But given his subsequent paper, it seems that that is not what he intended.

8 Eliminative materialism and behaviourism

Eliminativism and behaviourism are two related approaches to the nature of mind that were developed in the middle of the twentieth century. Both minimise or eliminate the significance of mental states in the scheme of things.

The aim of any approach called 'eliminativism' is to make the case that something that we think might exist does not exist. So the aim of eliminative materialism is to argue that something relating to consciousness does not exist. The most radical suggestion, that of eliminating consciousness itself, was touched upon briefly by C D Broad (1925, p 5) when he considered what he termed: "Behaviourism, taken quite strictly", and judged it "silly" in the sense that it is a theory which "only an inmate of a lunatic asylum would think of carrying into daily life" (*ibid.*, p 5). Nevertheless, Georges Rey reiterated the possibility of radical eliminativism more recently, saying: "I certainly cannot rule out the possibility that I am not conscious right here, now …" (1983, p 22, seemingly a rather strange statement, what could he have meant by 'conscious'?). Further, both Dennett (1988, Chapter 12) and Lewis (2008) have suggested that '*qualia*' is a word without a meaning, a view apparently also held by many other philosophers. But as Descartes pointed out so succinctly, it is just plain obvious, to any person, that conscious mental states do exist.

Behaviourism comes in various flavours. 'Psychological' behaviourism is a theory that assumes that human behaviour is learned through positive and negative feedbacks. It is viewed as beginning with the work of Pavlov (see, for example, 'The Experimental Psychology and Psychopathology of Animals', for which he was nominated for a Nobel Prize in 1903). A classic paper in psychological behaviourism is that of Watson (1913), while arguably the most influential contribution to the approach is that of Skinner (see, for example, Skinner 1974).

However, according to Graham (2016) and others (*e.g.*, Smith, 1986, Putnam, 1963, p 326, or Mace, 1948), 'logical' behaviourism, also known as 'analytical', or 'philosophical' behaviourism, "traces its historical roots to" the logical positivism developed in Vienna in the early-to-mid twentieth century. Logical behaviourism is a theory about the meaning of mental terms. The philosophers in Vienna at that time were developing the philosophy of science; given the fact that science deals only with statements that can be verified experimentally they proposed that mental concepts should be viewed as picking out behavioural tendencies and that mental terms, such as 'believe', should therefore be replaced by the behaviour with which they are associated. Science depends on experiments and on the observations generated by the experiments, which are public and available to all. If mental phenomena were to be subject to a science analogous to physics, they needed to depend on observations that are equally available to all. Therefore, these people proposed, behaviour must be what matters for a science of the mental. As Hempel said (1945): "all psychological statements which are meaningful, that is to say, which are in principle verifiable, are translatable … into statements which do not involve psychological concepts but only the concepts of physics" (p 18), while Carnap (1932, p 166) maintained that: "Every psychological term is translatable into a statement about the physical state of the body of the organism" (see also William O'Donohue and Richard Kitchener, 1998). Underlying this was the idea that it is fundamental to science that people can report their experiments and the results of their experiments to others, in language, in order to ensure reproducibility.

Thus, behaviourism as a theory of mind arose following the search for a scientific approach to mental states. It had the great advantage that it allowed philosophers to abstract from the difficult question of mental causation; physical inputs of various sorts led to physical outputs – behaviour.

However, whereas behaviourism is fine when it is dealing with psychology, with scientists examining the behaviour of other people, as a theory of mind it ignores the fact that we also have direct access to our own minds, and the fact that we believe that what goes on in our minds is relevant to what we do, to our behaviour. Analytical behaviourism takes it that assertions concerning mental states only have meaning if they are translated into statements about behaviour or "dispositions to behave in some manner". The ontological question at issue in this book (whether mental states are properties of a substance different from matter, reducible to physics, or non-reducible, *etc.*) simply doesn't arise for a behaviourist. But this is not because there is no such thing as a mental state (behaviourists refer to "mental states" when they maintain that assertions relating to them can be translated into statements about dispositions to behave), it is because for analytical behaviourism, questions relating to the ontology of mental states are irrelevant.

Gilbert Ryle was an influential proponent of behaviourism. His book, *The Concept of Mind* (1949), published when interest in behaviourism was at its height, held that mental states should be viewed as being nothing over and above the person's actions, the behaviour which is initiated. Behaviourism was also taken up with enthusiasm by the American philosopher Carl Hempel (1949) and was influenced by the thinking of Wittgenstein (1922). A difficulty often cited regarding behaviourism comes from Putnam (1963): it is the proposition that any mental state (on the usual definition) can be associated with different types of behaviour depending on the characteristics and the situation of the individual experiencing it; it may be that a person who is experiencing pain will strive to behave as though he or she is not experiencing pain.

Behaviourism is of little interest to us here. Descartes' first fundamental finding in his Meditations, the proposition that the one thing that we know for sure is that consciousness, that is, awareness of feelings and thoughts, exists. Since this is so, there is more to mental states than the behaviour with which they are associated. Each of us can make direct observations regarding our own mental states, and that is the aspect of mental states that I hope to elucidate in this book. Behaviourism ignores that fact.

Other forms of eliminative materialism relating to consciousness concern language. Sellars (1956) suggests that a person's understanding of his/her own mind does not actually come from direct experience, instead it is picked up from the culture of the community he or she lives in. It certainly seems likely that some of the terms we use to describe mental states have no clear, precise referent; we have already noted that the word 'consciousness', although useful for communication purposes, has no precise referent. Also, different languages pick out slightly different mental concepts. Elimination of some of the terms we use to describe the so-called mental states to which we refer, is clearly a possibility.

More radically, Feyerabend (1963) suggests that the type of discourse that one might call mentalistic language could be eliminated in favour of physical language, saying: "There is ... not a single reason why the attempt to give a purely physiological account of human beings should be abandoned"

(1963, p 65); thus, a person looking at a patch of red paint on the wall might describe the situation in terms of what he/she thought was happening in the parts of the brain related to seeing. Quine wrote: "the bodily states exist anyway; why add the others?" (1960, p 264). Rorty sees this as a possible consequence of the establishment of 'materialism', writing: "… the sort of empirical results that would show brain processes and sensations to be identical would also bring about changes in our way of speaking" (1965, pp 24-25). Paul Churchland and Patricia Churchland take this proposition further, suggesting that: "our common-sense conception of psychological phenomena constitutes a radically false theory, a theory so fundamentally defective that both the principles and the ontology of that theory will eventually be displaced, rather than smoothly reduced, by completed neuroscience" (see Paul Churchland, 1981, p 67, for example). But to be helpful as a means of communication, replacing mentalistic language with physical language would require that we had all already experienced every possible feeling, so we knew what it felt like when some obscure structure in the brain was stimulated, and we would have to know exactly what happened in the brain when we had had the experience. Although logically possible, the proposition seems totally unrealistic and anyway does not get around the fact that if someone has not had some experience it is impossible to communicate to them in words exactly what it is like.

9 Conclusion on reductive physicalism

Reductive physicalism presupposes that phenomenal facts can be ontologically reduced to facts that are suitable for study in physics; but our definition of physics together with our second *ab initio* proposition, concerning the existence of an epistemic gap, carry the implication that this is not possible. None of the work examined in this chapter that offers support of one kind or another for reductive physicalism has been found to stand up to scrutiny, given those two constraints. Therefore, I conclude that reductive physicalism cannot hold, so long as those two constraints hold.

5

Non-reductive physicalism

1 Introduction

In 1974, in his paper 'What is it Like to Be a Bat?', Thomas Nagel spelt out the reason why he sees the mind-body problem, the problem of the relationship between mind and body, as being different from problems such as that relating to water and H_2O, and rejecting what he dubbed: "the recent wave of reductionist euphoria" (*ibid.*, p 435). He says:

> "If physicalism is to be defended, the phenomenal features must themselves be given a physical account. But when we examine their subjective character it seems that such a result is impossible. The reason is that every subjective phenomenon is essentially connected with a single point of view, and it seems inevitable that an objective, physical theory will abandon that point of view" (*ibid.*, p 437, Nagel uses the word 'physicalism' in its narrow sense).

The final sentence of this quote brings to mind the "epistemic gap", the existence of which is the nub of the case for non-reductive physicalism.

A reason that is sometimes given for the rejection of the idea that mental states, although (presumably) arising in brains, could have a different nature to the things that are studied in physics is the proposition that if a mental state arises in the context of a brain state, it must surely be the case that anything the mental state can do could just as well be done by the 'physical' aspects of the brain state in question. Quine (1985, p 5) argues that: "… a dualism of mind and body is an idle redundancy." He points out that corresponding to some mental state will be a bodily state which might be specified as "the state of accompanying a mind that is in that mental state". Turning that around, so the mental state is the state accompanying the body that is in that bodily state then suggests that, in Quine's words: "The mind goes by the board, and will not be missed". Chalmers (1996) takes a similar view, asserting: "The physical world is more or less causally closed" (p 150), and then saying: "The very fact that experience can be coherently subtracted from any causal account implies that experience is superfluous in the *explanation* of behaviour, whether or not it has some subtle causal relevance" (1996, p 158-159, his italics).

I suggest here that the ability to experience feelings enables the use of an effective mechanism for the taking of certain types of decision, and that this type of decision could not be taken in the same way, using a maximising type of law of nature (see Section 4.3 of Chapter 2), in the absence of a gadget such as 'feelings' (see Chapter 6). If the mind were to "go by the board" the ability to take decisions in this way would also "go by the board", but it would be sorely missed.

In Section 2 of this chapter we address this important question of the existence of phenomenal facts; Lewis, in his famous 1988 paper, makes the case against their existence. Then, in Sections 3 to 6, we examine some variations on the theme of non-reductive physicalism starting with supervenience physicalism in general (see Figure 1a in Chapter 1, Section 1), then looking at Kim's approach in his 2005 book *Physicalism, or Something Near Enough* and Chalmers' 'naturalistic dualism' (see Chalmers, 1996), both special cases of supervenience physicalism, and finally we examine property dualism as presented in this book, which does not assume supervenience (Figure 1b in Chapter 1, Section 1). Non-reductive physicalism accepts, however, that mental states are outside physics, and therefore that the physical sciences are, in a sense, incomplete.[69] In Section 7 we look at the possibility of dual causation, the case

---

[69] As we have seen (Chapter 3, Section 4), in philosophy the 'completeness of physics' is generally defined in terms of causal completeness, that is, as: "all physical effects are fully caused by purely *physical* prior histories" (here 'physical' means "non-mental"); this definition of 'completeness' does not rule out the possibility of a physical event causing an event outside physics to occur, so it does not rule out the possibility that mental states are outside physics.

in which we do not reject from the start the possibility of 'over-determination'. Next, there is a summary of functionalism, in Section 8.

Finally, in Section 9, we examine the alternative hypotheses concerning the manner in which consciousness arises (is instantiated) in the context of matter, namely emergentism, panpsychism and micropsychism.

2 The existence of phenomenal facts

In his interesting 1988 paper, 'What Experience Teaches', David Lewis sets out a number of arguments designed to suggest that we should reject the idea that there is such a thing as phenomenal information, information that is not reducible to the type of information studied in the physical sciences (the distinction between the two being, of course, that the type of information studied in the physical sciences can be communicated perfectly between people linguistically while in order to know a phenomenal fact, what something is like to experience, it is necessary actually to have the experience). In this section, I examine his arguments to see if any of them can make a convincing case against our thesis that mind is a non-reducible property of matter, which of course carries with it the implication that phenomenal facts *do* exist.

2.1 Is experience the best teacher?

Lewis starts by trying, ever so gently, to shake one's faith in the idea that phenomenal information can only be learned through experience. First, he suggests that maybe either neurosurgery or magic might enable the learning of what an experience is like (with neurosurgery viewed as a possibility, but raising a question about the interpretation of what exactly is learned, while the proposition that magic could enable this learning to take place simply ignores the existence of the laws of nature). Or, he says, possibly some new type of science lessons or science learning? After which Lewis concludes (*ibid.*, p 79): "It is not an absolutely necessary truth that experience is the best teacher about what a new experience is like. It's a contingent truth … we just might be in for surprises".

Here I take the view that although Lewis is right when he says that it is not an "absolutely necessary truth" in the sense in which logical truths are necessary, nevertheless we are not in for a surprise: I suggest that we know *ab initio* that phenomenal information can only be learned from experience (see Chapter 2, Section 4.2 and Chapter 3, Section 5).

2.2 Lewis' hypothesis of phenomenal information

Lewis then spells out what he calls "the hypothesis of phenomenal information" (*ibid.*, p 84) as the hypothesis that: "… besides physical information there is an irreducibly different kind of information to be had: *phenomenal information*." He says:

> "The two are independent. Two possible cases might be exactly alike physically [in terms of their non-mental properties? materially?], yet differ phenomenally. When we get physical information we narrow down the physical possibilities, and perhaps we narrow them down all the way to one, but we leave open a range of phenomenal possibilities. When we have an experience, on the other hand, we acquire phenomenal information; possibilities previously open are eliminated; and that is what it is to learn what the experience is like" (my insertion).

But by spelling out his hypothesis in this way Lewis has restricted the meaning of the term phenomenal information to cover *only* such information as is independent of all so-called "physical information". For information to rank as phenomenal information in Lewis' sense it has to be *independent* of physical information: it has to be possible for two "cases" to be exactly alike 'physically' while differing phenomenally. But if mind is a property of matter, if two cases are exactly alike regarding the *matter* involved they will also be exactly alike in terms of their phenomenal properties. When we narrow down to one the physical possibilities, the possibilities regarding the *physical properties*, we also narrow down the phenomenal possibilities to one (apart from in the exceptional case in which a change in the matter produces a change in the mental state but no change in the physical properties). It is only in the case of *ontological dualism* (see Appendix 1) that phenomenal information and physical (non-mental) information would be independent in the manner suggested here by Lewis.

By defining phenomenal information as he does, Lewis rules out the possibility that that there might be phenomenal information associated with a property of matter not suitable for study in physics; and he gives no justification for doing this.

Lewis then demonstrates that if phenomenal information of the type implicit in what he calls the hypothesis of phenomenal information exists in the context of Jackson's knowledge argument, materialism cannot hold.   If 'materialism' holds, he says, any two possibilities that are exactly alike 'physically' (by which he means alike in terms of the *matter* involved) will be alike in every way; and this is true.   So, he says, if there were another kind of information, different from the type of information that arises in physics, which picked out one of the two possibilities but not the other, 'materialism' (as he defines it) would not hold; and this is also true.   But this does not rule out the possibility that there is another type of information, different from the type of information that arises in physics because it is what we know as 'phenomenal' information, and that this type of information arises in *each* of his two possibilities because there is another property of matter that is not studied in the science of physics and this type of information relates to this other property.

Throughout this paper Lewis never explicitly considers the possibility that phenomenal information could be information about an instantiation of a property of matter that is different from those that are studied in physics apart, perhaps, from when, in the middle of his presentation of this particular argument, he refers to phenomenal information as "… something … which is alien to this world – an alien kind of thing, or maybe an alien fundamental property of nonalien things" (*ibid.*, p 89), and the words "an alien fundamental property of nonalien things" clearly could be used to describe mind being a property of matter.

2.3 *Betting against the truth of physics*

Next, Lewis suggests that phenomenal information is a peculiar sort of information. With physical (non-mental) information, when you don't know some piece of information you typically have some idea of what the relevant alternative possibilities are. With phenomenal information, if you don't know what it's like to have an experience, you also have no idea of the alternative possibilities (*ibid.*, p 94). Which is true, up to a point (think magneto-reception), but is not relevant to the possibility of the existence of such information.

Then, more seriously, he makes his case against the possibility that physics as we know it could be at fault, saying (*ibid.*, p 95):

"if something nonphysical sometimes makes a difference to the motions
of physical particles, then physics as we know it is wrong. Not just silent,

not just incomplete – wrong. Either the particles are caused to change their motion without benefit of any force, or else there is some extra force that works very differently from the usual four. To believe in the phenomenal aspect of the world, but deny that it is epiphenomenal is to bet against the truth of physics. Given the success of physics hitherto, and even with due allowance for the foundational ailments of quantum mechanics, such betting is rash!"

Lewis is quite correct: this would be betting against the truth of physics as we know it today. But I think he exaggerates the odds against such a bet turning out to be correct. In this book, I suggest that maybe there could be another force relevant to science, as well as the 'usual four', see Chapter 7, Section 5.2, but if there were, there is no reason why it should have to work "very differently from the usual four". Such a force might operate only inside the brains of certain higher order creatures and it seems highly unlikely that scientists would have tripped over it at this point in the development of our understanding if they were not actually looking for it. It is unlikely that it would have much effect on any of the macro-truths that are currently believed because of physics as we know it today (although it would have had a profound effect on the events that have taken place in the world). Perhaps more likely, Lewis' "something nonphysical" could, instead, have its effect on the motions of physical particles through one of the already known forces. Alternatively, quantum mechanics or dark matter may be involved (see Chapter 7, Section 5.2). The question of whether experiments could throw light on this proposal is addressed in Chapter 7, Section 5.3.

The idea that a mental state could affect the motion of a particle is potentially an exciting development for science as well as being a bet against the truth of physics as it is understood today; both physics and neuroscience would be fundamentally changed. But, after all, science is developing all the time.

2.4 The ability hypothesis

David Lewis suggests that the question regarding the existence of phenomenal information, illustrated so vividly by the knowledge argument (see Chapter 3, Section 6.1), can be explained by what he calls the "ability hypothesis". In a nutshell, the ability hypothesis says that, although Mary knows everything there is to know about seeing red from studying the relevant physics and neuroscience *etc.* in her black and white room, it is only when she sees the colour red that she acquires the *skill* of being able to visualise red (in Lewis' words, the skill of being able to: "remember and imagine and recognise" red, *ibid.*, p 99). This hypothesis was originally proposed by Nemirow (1980) who said: "some modes of understanding consist, not in the grasping of facts, but in the acquisition of abilities.... I understand the experience of seeing red if I can at will visualize red" (p 475).

So we start by supposing, with David Lewis, that there is no such thing as phenomenal information; why then do we have this intuition that Mary would learn something new when she leaves her black and white room and first sees the colour red?

The proposal that Mary learns a new ability concerns the way in which a person can "know how" to do something. We know quite a bit about "knowing how" (see Chapter 2, Section 3.3, where I make the point that different types of knowing can be expressed verbally in many ways). We know that learning how to perform a skill, such as riding a bicycle or playing a piano sonata involves neuronal changes that take place in the cerebellum and we know that it involves encouraging the growth of new neuronal connections through repeating actions; it involves practice (see, for example, Kandel, 2006, p 202). Lewis was aware of this, so he said: "Information very often contributes to know-how, but often it doesn't contribute enough. That's why music students have to practice" (*ibid.*, p 100). But learning what it is like to see red is not like that. Once a person has seen red, they know what it is like; no practice is needed, suggesting that it is not a skill of the same type as riding a bicycle or playing a musical instrument.

Finally, the way Lewis describes his ability hypothesis it reads very much as if it is a description of "what it feels like" under another name, a different terminology. He explains that: "... knowing what an experience is like just *is* the possession of these abilities to remember, imagine and recognise" (*ibid.*, p 100). But surely, knowing what an experience is like just *is* knowing a phenomenal fact; and it is only once the phenomenal fact is known by the person, that the person can remember, imagine and recognise it. Lewis says: "These abilities to remember and imagine and recognise are abilities you cannot gain (unless by super-neurosurgery, or by magic) except by tasting Vegemite and learning what it's like" (*ibid.*, p 99). Quite so. If there actually *is* such a thing as phenomenal information; we don't need Lewis' ability hypothesis to explain Jackson's knowledge argument.

2.5 *Conclusion on Lewis' argument against phenomenal information*

Lewis says that "for materialists it is essential to reject it [his hypothesis of phenomenal information]" (*ibid.*, p 97, my insertion), and that is correct. For if his hypothesis of phenomenal information were true of the world, given the way in which it is worded, materialism would not hold. But this does not mean that we should reject the proposition that phenomenal facts exist (using the term 'phenomenal' as it is usually understood), or that we should reject the proposition that these phenomenal facts either supervene on physical facts or relate to instantiations of a property of matter that is different from those that are studied in physics. After all, we know that mental states exist (if we know anything we know that, see our first fundamental proposition, Chapter 2, Section 4.1), and we know that what it is like to experience our mental states is impossible to communicate perfectly to another person in language (see our second fundamental proposition, Chapter 2, Section 4.2); and if that is the case we know that phenomenal information, what some experience feels like, exists and is different from public information.

Of the four points Lewis produces that support the proposition that there is no such thing as phenomenal information:

- the idea that some new type of "science lessons" could enable the accurate communication of phenomenal information runs counter to our experience; we know from our own experience that in order to know what some sensation feels like it is necessary to experience it;

- the 'phenomenal information' of Lewis' "hypothesis" is not the type of phenomenal information we are concerned with in this book; he stipulates in his definition of the term that phenomenal information must be "independent" of physical information, that the term only applies to the situation in which two cases can be exactly alike physically (materially) and yet differ phenomenally, and that restriction does not apply to the type of phenomenal information we are concerned with here;

- he is correct when he asserts that admitting the existence of phenomenal information raises issues relating to physics as we currently view it, but contrary to his view, the problems that might arise seem unlikely to cause any great upset to physics as it is currently understood; and,

113

- Lewis' "ability hypothesis" provides a possible, but implausible, explanation of how the situation described in the knowledge argument might arise *if there were no such thing as phenomenal information*. It is implausible because it does not comply with what is known about the process of acquiring skills (the necessity for repetition, so new neuronal connections develop). So, it seems more likely that if there were no such thing as phenomenal information the 'Mary' situation would simply not arise.

3 Supervenience physicalism

The term 'supervenience physicalism' describes the type of non-reductive physicalism most often cited in the recent philosophy literature.[70] The formal definition of supervenience has it that a set of properties 'A' is said to 'supervene' upon another set of properties 'B' if and only if no two things can differ with respect to their A-properties without also differing with respect to their B-properties. In David Lewis' words, "We have supervenience when there could be no difference of one sort without differences of another sort" (1986, p 14). In the case of supervenience physicalism, an A-property would be some type of mental state (an instantiation of the property of matter we have called 'mind') and the B-properties would be the physical (non-mental) properties associated with the collection of neural states that arise in the context of that mental state; supervenience physicalism says that there cannot be a difference in the mental state without there also being a difference in the associated physical (neural) properties of the brain.

However, there is a question as to why a supervenience relation between mental properties and physical properties might arise. If the supervenience relation is deemed 'necessary', as is generally the case, it could hold as the result of logic (as in "economics supervenes on the behaviour of people regarding the production, distribution and consumption of goods and services", which is true because of what we mean by the term 'economics'). If it is not necessary as the result of logic, it could be necessary because of the existence of a law of nature

---

[70] Apparently, it was Davidson who first used the term 'supervenience' in the context of physicalism. He said: "[M]ental characteristics are in some sense dependent, or supervenient, on physical characteristics. Such supervenience might be taken to mean that there cannot be two events alike in all physical respects but differing in some mental respect, or that an object cannot alter in some mental respect without altering in some physical respect" (Davidson, 1970, p 214).

which ensures that some mental property arises whenever a particular configuration of physical properties arises (see Chapter 2, Section 2.3): that is, there could be a law of nature that says that the B-properties give rise to (instantiate) the A-properties, as in Figure 1a (in Chapter 1, Section 1, see the arrows). If that were the case, the mental properties would arise *because* the physical properties are instantiated, and obviously, every time the particular configuration of physical properties occurs the mental property will then occur too. Then, assuming supervenience physicalism holds would simply involve assuming that mental states are properties of some combination of the physical properties of matter because a law of nature requires that that is so (rather than being instantiations of a property of matter different from the physical properties of matter, see Figure 1b in Chapter 1 Section 1).

But supervenience as defined above can also arise because of features that just happen to be the case regarding matter, instead of as the result of a necessary relation between mental properties and physical properties. This could arise in the case of property dualism, see Figure 1b, where mental properties are a property of matter and have a similar ontological status to the properties studied in physics; mental characteristics arise because there is a law of nature that says that every time some configuration of *matter* (the type of matter and/or its arrangement) arises the mental property in question will also occur. But if it so happened that matter was such that it was not possible to change its configuration in such a way as to change the mental state without *also changing the physical properties*, then it would be the case that there could be no change in the mental characteristics without a change in the physical properties. But in this case, there would be no law of nature *directly* connecting the mental characteristics with the physical properties of matter; the supervenience would appear to have an element of happenstance.

I take the term 'supervenience physicalism' to refer to the thesis that mental properties are determined by the physical properties of matter as the result of a law of nature, as in Figure 1a; one might call this 'nomological supervenience'.[71] This seems to be the case in most specifications of supervenience physicalism, see Kim (2005, p 33), Papineau (who finds: "the notion of supervenience more

---

[71] If it was possible to change the constitution of matter in such a way as to change the mental characteristics but not the physical properties, the proposition that mental states are instantiations of a property of matter different from those studied in physics but of a similar ontological status could be considered to constitute a counter-example to Kim's statement that: "[m]ind-body supervenience can usefully be thought of as defining *minimal physicalism* ..." (2005, p 13).

trouble than it's worth", 2002, p 36), Wilson (2005, p 433), Gardner (2005, p 191), and many more.

If materialism is true, so there is only one substance and it is 'matter', and if mental states are instantiations of something that derives from matter in some way (as do physical, that is, non-mental states), then whether consciousness is reducible or non-reducible, emergent, panpsychic, micropsychic or identical to non-mental properties, it would certainly be the case that there cannot be a change in the mental state without there also being a change regarding the matter itself (although, of course, there might be no change to the physical properties).

Before leaving the subject of supervenience we should note that the term 'supervenience' has another meaning in philosophy besides the value-neutral one described above (see Horgan, 1993). The notion of supervenience nowadays often carries with it the idea that the thing that does the supervening is in some sense a 'higher level phenomenon' than the thing on which it supervenes. And, further, the supervenience of mental states on neural states is often taken to imply that consciousness 'derives from' or 'is grounded by' the non-mental properties of neural stuff in some special, mysterious way rather than that it is simply another property of the material stuff, as some non-mental property of matter such as electric charge might be a property of some material stuff. I can see no reason why there should be value judgments relating to 'higher' and 'lower', or to 'first level' or 'second level' associated with the supervenience relation. The first meaning given here of the term supervenience ("no difference in A without a difference in B") clearly does not necessarily imply the other – the "hierarchical values", or "mysterious grounding" relation – although there are many situations in which both might hold.

4 Physicalism, or something near enough

Jaegwon Kim finds, in his book *Physicalism, or Something Near Enough* (2005, p 1), that: "… although we cannot have physicalism *tout court*, we can something nearly as good".

Kim sets down what he identifies as the two big problems of theory of mind: the first being: "how mentality can have a causal role in a world that is fundamentally physical", and the second being: "can we give a reductive physicalist account of consciousness?" (*ibid.*, p 1). He sees the first as requiring that causative mental states are reducible to physics because, like so many others, he signs up to the philosophers' specification of the causal completeness of physics. However, he views some types of mental state as being "functionalizable" (*ibid.*, p 165), in the sense that they should be: "characterizable in terms of their causal work". So he takes it that it is these types of mental state that must be reducible to physics. In his view, there are insurmountable problems with causation operating from one 'substance' to another, so he rules out the possibility of causally effective mental states that are instantiations of some property of another substance ('immaterial minds'). Because he has accepted both the causal completeness of physics and the exclusion argument,[72] the possibility of there being another property of matter, one that is not suitable for study in physics but that *can* interact causally with the properties of matter studied in physics, never arises.

On the second big problem Kim finds that there are reasons why we should reject the proposition that all mental states can be wholly accounted for in terms of physics. He says: "As far as we now know, the only way to create a system with conscious experience is to duplicate an appropriate animal or human brain" (*ibid.*, p 169). Where a mental state is not functional, as with sensory states (or *qualia*), Kim therefore accepts that these could be irreducible.

His conclusion, after careful analysis, is that: "intentional/cognitive properties are reducible, but qualitative properties of consciousness, or 'qualia', are not" (*ibid.*, p 174). But if this is the case *qualia*, which would be instantiations of something outside physics, cannot have any effect on the intentional/cognitive properties because those are reducible to physics, and they would not be reducible to physics if the phenomenal information of the *qualia* influenced them. So, *qualia* are epiphenomenal.

Kim's proposal is problematic if we accept that we know, *a priori*, that it is *qualia* that are the key to the taking of those complex decisions in which the effects of the alternative choices are not directly comparable, see Chapter 2, Section 4.3. So the idea that the "qualitative properties of consciousness", the *qualia*, are epiphenomenal, with its implication that feelings must therefore have no effect whatsoever on a person's actions, is not a proposition that is acceptable in the light of our third fundamental proposition (for example, if Kim were correct, it would not be because you don't like the taste of spinach

---

[72] The exclusion argument says that where a mental property that appears to be causally effective supervenes on some set of physical properties, it will be the physical properties that cause the behavioural effects; there will be no causal work left for the mental state to perform.

that you choose not to eat it, it would be the result of something to do with your physical, that is non-mental, attributes; a situation somewhat reminiscent of Leibniz, 1695, see Appendix 1).

5 Naturalistic dualism

An approach that is somewhat similar to the one I develop in this book is that of naturalistic dualism (see also Chapter 7, Section 2), put forward by Chalmers and presented in his book *The Conscious Mind* (1996).

A fundamental feature of Chalmers' naturalistic dualism is his rejection of reductive physicalism. He takes this to follow from the proposition that one cannot, based on logic alone, rule out the possibility of the existence of zombies – creatures that are physically identical to conscious creatures in every way but have no consciousness (see also Chapter 3, Section 6.2). This means that, indeed it is simply another way of saying that, consciousness cannot be *logically* supervenient on the physical. He then concludes that: "the failure of logical supervenience directly implies that materialism is false: there are features of the world over and above the physical features" (*ibid.*, p 123).

He spells this argument out thus (p 123, my insertion):

1. In our world, there are conscious experiences.

2. There is a logically possible world physically identical to ours, in which the positive facts about consciousness in our world do not hold.

3. Therefore, facts about consciousness are further facts about our world, over and above the physical facts.

4. So materialism [by which Chalmers means 'reductive physicalism', see below] is false.

So Chalmers takes it that the implication of this argument is that reductive physicalism is false. But if reductive physicalism *did* hold in our world, there would be nomological relations such that all the facts about consciousness could be identified with public facts (see footnote 2 on p 2), and these facts about consciousness would then also hold in any other world that had the same laws of physics as operate in our world. So the above argument does not rule out the possibility that reductive physicalism holds, but this would be the case because of nomological considerations rather than because of logical considerations. However, reductive physicalism can be ruled out on other grounds (see Section 5.1 of Chapter 3), so the point that Chalmers is making does hold good.

Also, somewhat confusingly, Chalmers calls the approach that he rejects 'materialism'. The reason he uses the term 'materialism' to describe reductive physicalism is that, he says: "the existence of further contingent facts over and above the physical [non-mental] facts is a significant enough modification to the received materialist world view to deserve a different label" (*ibid.*, p 126, my insertion).

Chalmers takes it that, given that we know that we *do* have conscious experiences, there *must* be something other than that which is studied in physics: "The physical facts incompletely constrain the way the world is; the facts about consciousness constrain it further", he says (1996, p 123, but this is a comment reminiscent of Lewis' argument, see Section 2.2 of this chapter). He also finds it plausible that if, for example, his own physical [material?] structure were precisely replicated, his conscious experience would be replicated also. So he says, see page 124: "... it remains plausible that consciousness supervenes *naturally* on the physical. It is this view – natural supervenience without logical supervenience – that I will develop". Chalmers therefore endorses the proposition that, given the laws of physics and biology that operate in our world, consciousness might supervene on the physical (the non-mental? that which pertains to physics? matter?) in our world and it is this proposition that he names 'naturalistic dualism'. He says, however: "conscious experience involves properties of an individual that are not entailed by the physical [non-mental?] properties of that individual, although they may depend lawfully on those properties" (p 125, my insertion).

Chalmers does not take his argument to imply that materialism in the sense that: "there is only one substance and we call it matter" is false. His approach is consistent with the existence of something that one could call 'physicalism in the broad sense' or 'materialism' because there is nothing in his approach that requires a second substance; there is nothing in it that prevents it being the case that everything pertains to matter. It remains logically possible that there is a law of nature, a law of the type referred to in the last paragraph of Section 2.3 of Chapter 2, that says that if matter exists then consciousness, or at least proto-consciousness, exists (just as electric charge, or mass, or extension in space exist).

119

So Chalmers' approach is similar to the one proposed here in that, as with the property dualism proposed in this book, Chalmers takes it that conscious experience is a fundamental feature of the world, that is, that it is not reducible to something else that is more basic.

Chalmers also says that where there is a fundamental property, there must also be laws of nature, and that these natural laws will relate 'experience' to the properties of matter studied in physics. But then he assumes that any such laws will not interfere with the so-called completeness of physics (all physical effects are fully caused by purely *physical*, non-mental, prior histories) which he takes to be an established, irrefutable truth about the world. So he takes the view that these laws would only specify how this thing called 'experience' *depends* on the processes studied in physics; in his scheme there are no laws that describe how mental states can *influence* non-mental states because he takes it that the mental is epiphenomenal.

Chalmers suggests that experience may be: "a fundamental feature of the world, alongside space-time, spin, charge and the like" (p 126). But his assumption that mind supervenes 'naturally' (not logically) on the 'physical' lends itself to the assumption that it is the physical properties on which the mental properties supervene that do the causing; that "the physical domain is causally closed" (1996, p 161). He says: "Where we have new fundamental properties, we also have new fundamental laws. Here the fundamental laws will be *psychophysical* laws, specifying how phenomenal (or protophenomenal) properties depend on physical properties" (p 127). And he adds: "These laws will not interfere with physical laws; physical laws already form a closed system. Instead, they will be *supervenience laws*, telling us how experience arises from physical processes."

Therefore, although Chalmers' approach to the ontology of consciousness is similar to that presented in this book, his approach to mental causation differs fundamentally.

6 Property dualism

6.1 Introduction

In this section, I describe the approach I call 'property dualism', explaining what it is (Section 6.2 below), how it relates to supervenience physicalism (Section 6.3), and noting the main references to it in the philosophy literature

(Section 6.4). The question of whether, given property dualism, mental states can causally affect physical states (those relating to the properties of matter studied in physics) is discussed in Chapter 7.

6.2 *What is property dualism?*

As we have seen, many modern philosophers believe that there is only one substance (matter), denying the possibility that there might be immaterial minds that animate material bodies. But while some also identify mental states with physical (that is, suitable for study in the science of physics) states, taking it that mental states can are reducible to the properties of matter studied in physics, others acknowledge the possibility that there could be two different classes of property of matter, 'physical' properties and 'mental' properties with the mental properties fundamentally different in kind from the 'physical' properties. The position in which there are two different types of property and they both have the same ontological status is the one that I call 'property dualism' in this book.

Here I assume that there is just one kind of substance, matter (see Chapter 2, Section 2.4) and that mind is a property of this stuff called matter, a property that is different from the properties of matter that are studied in the physical sciences but has a similar ontological status to those properties (see Figure 1b in Chapter 1, Section 1). Further, I suggest (Chapter 2, Section 4.3 and Chapter 3, Section 5) that there are reasons for taking seriously the possibility that mental states can be causally effective *per se*, and I assume that the interactions mental states have with the properties of matter studied in physics are governed by causal processes, so every event has a cause, that is, 'universal causation' holds (deterministic or probabilistic, see Chapter 2, Section 2.2 and Chapter 8, Section 2). This approach, which I call 'causally effective property dualism', is consistent with science being 'complete' in the sense that it would encompass all the causes and all the effects, mental as well as physical, of all the causal processes including, therefore, all mental/physical causal interactions.

The fact that this approach has mental states not reducible to the properties of matter studied in the physical sciences has the implication that, just as there are facts relating to the properties of matter that are studied in the physical sciences such as the direction of motion and the momentum of some body, or its mass or charge, so there are facts of the "what it feels like"-type (what it feels like for a person to see red or to be hungry) known as phenomenal facts or *qualia*, that relate to this other property of matter (see Chapter 2, Section 3.2). And just as there are causal processes regarding the properties of matter that are studied in the physical sciences, so one might expect there to be causal processes regarding the effects mental states have on the properties of matter studied in physics as well as causal processes regarding the effect the properties of matter studied in physics have upon mental states (see Chapter 6).

Property dualism thus assumes the existence of a single substance but assumes that this single substance could have two, very different, *types* of property. Our bodies have both physical properties such as extension and weight, and mental properties such as thoughts and feelings. It is not just that we might talk of mental states and physical states in different ways; the idea is that there is an ontological difference between the two. And it is not just that mental properties are a kind of strange spin-off from the physical properties, so they make no difference whatsoever to anything physical that happens now or in the future because they are epiphenomenal: mental properties can affect physical properties; mental properties make a difference in the world.

According to property dualism, mental states cannot be fully explained in terms of the properties of matter studied in the physical sciences (neither ontologically nor linguistically), and nor do they arise only because of the existence of the properties of matter studied in the physical sciences; mental properties have the same ontological status as non-mental properties.

6.3 *Property dualism compared to supervenience physicalism*

Supervenience physicalism can be viewed as being a special case of property dualism. In property dualism, mental properties arise in the context of some configuration of matter (some arrangement of different types of particles *etc.*), and this configuration of matter will also give rise to some collection of physical properties, see Figure 1 in Chapter 1. We would therefore expect to find that there is a correlation between a mental property and some set of physical properties.[73]

In the case of supervenience physicalism, however, a change in a mental property requires that there is also a change in the set of physical properties. But in the case of property dualism it is possible that there could be a change in the mental property, and therefore a change in the matter (a change in the

---

[73] Of course, much of the matter associated with a brain state, along with its physical properties, will be irrelevant to the mental state. Also, it may be that two or more mental states that arise in association with different configurations of matter could be indistinguishable mentally to the person concerned.

types of particle involved or in the manner in which they relate to each other), but no change in the physical properties. This is because it is logically possible that two different configurations of matter which instantiate (give rise to) the same collection of physical properties could instantiate different mental properties.[74] This difference between supervenience physicalism and property dualism is more obvious in the case of the bundle theory approach (see Chapter 2, Section 2.4). If supervenience physicalism were the case, the same mental property would always arise in the context of some particular bundle of physical properties; in property dualism, however, there could be two bundles of properties that were identical in their physical properties but differed in their mental properties.

The more important difference between supervenience physicalism and property dualism is simply that if supervenience physicalism holds there is a clearly defined collection of physical properties that might have done the causing; if mental properties have the same ontological status as physical properties this is not necessarily the case; and anyway, it might be expected that mental causation would hold simply because all the other properties of matter are causally effective.

6.4 References to property dualism in the literature

In many ways, causally effective property dualism seems to be the simplest and most obvious assumption to make regarding the nature of mental states (states which have the "what it is like" characteristic), that is, regarding the nature of 'mind', although few philosophers have supported this proposal in recent years. Smart, in 1959, must have perceived the possibility that consciousness might be 'merely' another property of matter and he rejected it in favour of the identity thesis when, speaking of "states of consciousness", he wrote:

---

[74] This might arise if there were two varieties of some element of the collection of matter that gave rise to a mental state which were the same in every way except regarding the aspect relating to the mental state to which they, in combination with the rest of the matter, gave rise; so all the physical aspects remained unchanged. Two bits of matter would then differ in their mental properties but not in their physical properties. This would be similar to the situation in which the charge, or the spin of a fundamental particle can differ without any difference in the particle's mass, for example.

"I cannot believe that ultimate laws of nature could relate simple constituents to configurations consisting of perhaps billions of neurons (and goodness knows how many billion billions of ultimate particles) all put together for all the world as though their main purpose in life was to be a negative feedback mechanism of a complicated sort" (p 143, and see also Chapter 4, Section 3.1).

I suggest in this book that the approach that Smart is rejecting here, that mind is a property of matter that relates to neurons and that what it amounts to is a form of negative feedback system (a form of homeostasis, see Chapter 6, Section 4), deserves serious consideration. Galen Strawson (2006) also must have had something along the lines of this approach in mind when he rejected the approach Smart was advocating back in 1959, writing: "... real physicalism can have nothing to do with *physicsalism*, the view – the faith – that the nature or essence of all concrete reality can in principle be fully captured in the terms of *physics*" (p. 4, his italics).

Although the possibility of property dualism is allowed by modern philosophy, few modern philosophers have considered this option sufficiently plausible for it to be worth setting pen to paper and writing an article or a book exploring the implications of it. However, dubbed "interactionism", a term usually used to describe the situation in which mind is a property of a different substance from matter and causal effects operate between mind and matter, this approach *is* included in Chalmers' classification of views on the metaphysics of consciousness (2002); it comes under the heading "Type D Dualism".

There are four approaches in the literature that come close to the causally effective property dualism presented here. First, there is Chalmers' 'naturalistic dualism' (1996), a form of supervenience physicalism (see Section 5 of this chapter). The difference is that, as explained above, if mind is a property of matter different from those studied in physics but of similar ontological status, this lends itself naturally to a causal role for mental states (all the other properties of matter are causally effective so why not this one). Chalmers' approach, which assumes that mind supervenes 'naturally' on the physical, is therefore combined with the assumption that, as Chalmers says: "the physical domain is causally closed" (1996, see p 161). Chalmers therefore takes it that epiphenomenalism pertains: that there is no causal role whatsoever for mental states regarding the physical world.

The second approach with similarities to causally effective property dualism is functionalism (see Section 8 of this chapter), the only approach in the recent literature that does not deny that something that could be called "effective mental causation *per se*" exists. The heart of functionalism is that the key feature of something that can be called a 'mental state' is the *function* it plays; so, effective mental causation *per se* is a given with functionalism. However, in functionalism a mental state is, *by definition*, that which performs a certain function (rather than the feelings and thoughts which are normally associated with the term "mental state") and this leads to a range of highly fanciful consequences.

Third, McGinn describes an approach somewhat like this in his 1982 book (*The Character of Mind*, Chapter 2). He presents an excellent description of the case in which mental states are instantiations of a property of matter that differs from, and is not reducible to, the properties of matter studied in physics (1982, pp 27-33). But he makes no reference to mental causation, and he does not identify this approach as having any advantage over any of the other approaches he considers or as being the one that should be pursued. Also, he later suggests that: "the mind-body problem brings us bang up against the limits of our capacity to understand the world" (1989, p 354).

Finally, Galen Strawson (*e.g.*, 1994, 2008) is one of the few modern philosophers who view "experiential phenomena" as relating to matter in a similar way to that of non-mental phenomena. As noted above, he takes the view that what he calls 'real physicalism' can have nothing to do with reductive physicalism. He starts from what he views as being a fundamental fact: the fact that the one thing the existence of which is more certain, more real to us than that of everything else, that which we call "conscious experience", is 'physical'. The result is that it seems very odd to him that anyone might find it strange that something that is 'physical' is capable of 'experiencing' things. He refers to Eddington who wrote, in his book on the nature of the physical world: "But what knowledge have we of the nature of atoms which renders it at all incongruous that they should constitute a thinking object?" (1928, p 259).

However, although Strawson signs up to the basic ontology of property dualism, to the best of my knowledge he does not address the issue of mental causation.

7 The rejection of 'over-determination'[75]

7.1 The issue

We have seen in Chapter 4, Section 3 that it is often suggested that the only way to reconcile mental causation with the completeness of physics (as defined in 2. below) is to be a 'type identity theorist', that is: "to identify mental properties with physical properties" (Crane, 1995, p 230). Whereas we may come across some situations that appear to involve psycho-physical causal processes (mental states *per se* causing physical events), a type identity theorist would reckon that it must be the case that this is either because the mental properties are identical to physical properties, or it is because the mental state is supervenient on a physical state and it is that physical state that does the causing; as Kim says: "at some point, purely physical causal processes take over" (Kim, 1984, p 264).

Many have spelt out the assumptions underlying the problem of mental causation in broadly the same way, see Crane (1995, p 229), Lewis (1966), Papineau (2002, pp 17-18), Kim (2005, pp 21-22) and others. They say:

1. There is mental causation

2. All physical effects are fully caused by purely *physical* prior histories

In Lewis' case the first premise is "… the definitive characteristic of any experience as such is its causal role" (*ibid.*, p 19) and the second "all phenomena [are] describable in physical terms" (*ibid.*, p 23). From these he goes straight to the conclusion that: "From the two premises it follows that experiences are some physical phenomena or other" (*ibid.*, p 24). Crane, Papineau and Kim, however, add a third assumption:

3. There is no over-determination

In this section I examine this third assumption. Obviously, its implications depend on what you mean by 'over-determination'. If the meaning of over-determination, on the face of it a mildly pejorative term, relates only to

---

[75] In the early part of this section I ignore the proposition that feelings are relevant to the outcome of certain types of decision (see Chapter 2, Section 4.3).

'coincidence' (as in simultaneous bullet killings), then the proposition that there is no over-determination on a regular basis is acceptable. But if the term over-determination means 'dual causation' we might not wish to rule it out without further consideration. Here, I look at some of the possible implications of this thought.

7.2 Dual causation

The first two assumptions above can, of course, be reconciled without signing up to the identity theory; logic allows another alternative. There could be a strict one-to-one relation of nomological necessity between the two types of property of the matter involved in a brain state, the physical properties and the mental properties, a relation that does not require mental characteristics to be identical with physical characteristics, but which does mean that you can't have one of these two things, the mental state and the physical state, without the other also obtaining.

If this were the case, an event in a creature's brain that gives rise both to a mental occurrence and to the instantiation of a physical (neurological) state, and which causes a physical event (an action) to take place, may cause the action because of the mental characteristics, operating through a psycho-physical law as in point number 1 above, or through the laws of the physical sciences by the physical prior history, as in point number 2 above, see Figure 4 below.

In Figure 4 the long arrows represent laws of nature describing a causal process as understood by us humans. The upper, dashed, arrow represents a psycho-physical law. Psycho-physical laws deal in both psychological concepts (such as "feeling hungry") and physical concepts (such as "opening the refrigerator" or the movement of an electron in a neuron). The lower arrow, undashed, represents a physical law; physical laws deal solely with physical (non-mental) concepts. If the action is caused both by the mental characteristic through a psycho-physical law and by the physical characteristic through a physical law, then the two laws, as well as the two sets of properties of matter, must be inextricably bound together; you can't have one without the other. The action in Figure 4 is caused by the brain event, and the brain event has two different types of property associated with it.

So, does the existence of these two 'causes' give rise to an unacceptable type of over-determination? The answer is: not necessarily. This is because one of these mental/neural characteristics cannot occur without the other also occurring; there would have to be a law of nature that ensures that whenever

127

some mental characteristic acts as a cause of some physical event, operating through a psycho-physical law, a neuronal characteristic operating through the laws of physics also acts as a cause of that event (and *vice versa*). There could be one causal event which has two aspects to it; it is that causal event which we observe giving rise to the event that constitutes the effect, the action, but we humans might regard each of these aspects of the causal process as being individual laws of nature (as Davidson, 1970, says, laws are linguistic).

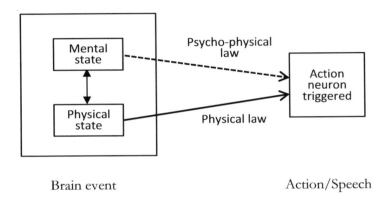

Brain event   Action/Speech

Figure 4: An event with two causes

Here, a brain event involves both a physical (neuronal) state and a mental state; you can't have one without the other. We humans have laws of nature associated with each; so you can't have one of these laws operating without the other also operating.

There would then be no reason why we should not use the laws relating to mental events when we identify the thing that causes the action (as in "Joe went to get a glass of water because he was thirsty") rather than the laws relating to physical brain events (involving a multitude of highly complex biological and chemical reactions, electric currents *etc.*). Indeed, to do otherwise would seem to be like trying to "explain" the sequence of pictures on a television screen by specifying the patterns of dots, rather than by citing the story-line depicted (see also Smart, 1959, discussed in Chapter 4, Section 2.1).

In fact, the question of the mechanism through which mental states could have direct physical effects has meant that the physical has tended to win out in the causality stakes. For example, Honderich (1982, p 64), examining

Davidson's anomalous monism, considers the possibility that it is: "a mental event as physical which causes an action".

However, people have generally tended to view physics as consisting of "strict deterministic laws" (prior to quantum mechanics) while some have doubts as to whether there are any sound psycho-physical laws at all – that is, laws that relate mental states to action (*e.g.*, Davidson, 1970, p 208). If there were a fundamental difference of this sort, deterministic versus probabilistic, between the laws of physics and the laws of psycho-physics, we would indeed be able to discover which was the law that caused the action. This issue is addressed next.

7.3 Laws of physics and psycho-physics

An obvious problem with the proposition that both the mental and the physical characteristics of some mental event could equally be viewed as being the cause of a subsequent event, is that laws involving physical causes are often thought of as being deterministic (100 percent certain in their outcome) or near-deterministic, while laws with mental causes often appear to be highly stochastic; the predictions they give rise to seem to have a large element of uncertainty attached to them (see, for example, Davidson, 1970, who reckons that: "there are no strict deterministic laws on the basis of which mental events can be predicted and explained", p 208)

Where physical laws are concerned, it used to be taken for granted by many that they had no random component attached to them at all, and that the outcome of a causal process would therefore be determined with 100 percent certainty. During the last century, however, with the development of quantum mechanics, it seems that there could be a stochastic component in the laws of physics, depending largely on the magnitudes of the objects under consideration. In most cases, any stochastic component a process might possess is likely to be an extremely small proportion of the total signal – this is certainly the case for physical macro-events such as those involving billiard balls and the like; but there are also cases for which the random element associated with quantum mechanics could be significant. Whether this might be so for neuronal events depends on the nature and magnitudes of the structures involved. [76]   We therefore cannot rule out the possibility that quantum uncertainties could inject a degree of randomness into the micro-behaviour of neurons in some circumstances, thereby having a potentially significant effect on the macro-behaviour of the organism (see Hameroff and Penrose, 1996, who propose that this might be the case, and Tegmark *et al.*, 2000, who maintain that according to their calculations: "there is nothing fundamentally quantum-mechanical about cognitive processes in the brain", p 4202).

Where mental laws are concerned, as with the physical laws underlying a person's behaviour, if one could know the full gamut of mental states to which another person is subject, along with all the psychophysical causal processes and the magnitude of any inescapable uncertainty associated with them, we might find that the stochastic element was extremely small, or there might not be any uncertainty at all.   In that case one would be able to predict with reasonable or total accuracy the way in which a person would behave in any circumstances.   However, quite apart from the current state of psycho-physical science, we can never know exactly what it is like to be another person, so the uncertainty of us humans regarding psycho-physical causal processes is unlikely ever to be reduced to a level comparable to that of the laws of physics.

It seems that we cannot rule out the possibility of dual causation on the basis that the perceived uncertainly of predictions relating to mental processes is greater than that relating to physical processes.

---

[76] The famous two-slit experiment demonstrates that if a particle or atom is fired towards a screen that has two slits in it, with a detection screen beyond, it is uncertain where it will hit the detection screen. The probability of it hitting the detection screen at any specified point does not just depend on which slit it "goes through", as common sense would suggest, it also depends on the relation between the positions of the two slits (Jönsson, 1974). It is as if the one particle somehow goes through both slits. This can be the case with quite sizeable particles. Recently, a group based in Vienna fired a "buckyball" molecule (60 carbon atoms in a cage-like structure), which has a diameter of around 1 nanometer (10^{-9} of a meter), through the double slit apparatus and demonstrated that these particles have no problem in, as one might say, sailing through both slits simultaneously (Arndt *et al.*, 1999). The buckyball is similar in diameter to the width of the DNA double helix. A typical axon is around a micrometer (10^{-6} of a meter) in diameter, with some much larger and others much smaller. This suggests that quantum effects in brains may be improbable, but is a possibility that cannot be totally ruled out (see also Chapter 7, Section 5.2).

7.4 *Conclusion regarding 'over-determination'*

On the grounds considered above, there seems to be no reason why we should reject over-determination in the sense of dual causation regarding mental and physical properties. If it is the case that whenever a mental state arises a physical state arises also, there is no reason why we humans should not postulate a law of nature corresponding to each of these two aspects of an event. And on the face of it, it could be that we would then be unable to identify either one of these laws of nature as being the *actual* cause.

However, so long as we sign up to Proposition 3 in Chapter 2, Section 4.3, this situation does *not* arise. Given that we know, *ab initio*, that it is the mental state that determines the outcome when a complex decision between alternative actions is being taken; the proposition that the physical aspects of the mental state can "make the judgment" regarding which option will be best for the creature concerned, while not ruled out by logic, just seems too implausibly farfetched on practical grounds.

8 Functionalism

8.1 *Functionalism as a theory of consciousness*

Functionalism starts from the idea that what matters about the mind is what it makes happen, its function. It is often specified in terms akin to input-output tables (see Block, 1978), so that given the physical and mental state of some organism (or 'thing') along with some input, functionalism simply decrees that there will be a specified output and a new physical and mental state for the organism (or 'thing'). The difference between functionalism and behaviourism is that on the behaviourist view a stimulus (that is, a physical input) gives rise to behavioural outputs whereas, on the functionalist view a stimulus *plus* a mental state input gives rise to behavioural outputs *plus* a mental state output. This enables functionalism to deal with the counterexamples to behaviourism in which a person burns his/her finger but does not exhibit classic pain behaviour because of a mental state that suppresses it.

Accepting the proposition that what matters about mind is what it makes happen, the functionalists take the view that it is sensible to *define* 'mental state' in terms of the function that is involved. This means that two mental states are deemed to be the same, in functionalism, if they play the same role (but note that one *experience* of a 'mental state', so defined, may then feel very different from another *experience* of the same so-called 'mental state'; the meaning of the term 'mental state' has been fundamentally changed, so we should keep an eye out for problems arising). Once that definition has been accepted, the function played by the so-called 'mental state' in making some particular thing happen could just as well be played by any gadget other than a mind so long as that gadget was wired up in such a way as to perform the same function. So computers can have these things called 'mental states', as can thermostats. Indeed, a particular 'mental state' could be "made of" anything (the population of China, see Block, 1978; beer cans and ping-pong balls, see Chalmers, 1996 p 249) just so long as the "fine-grained functional organisation of the parts" is the same.

Then, since we normally think of what we call "mental states" as being a thing that can have consciousness associated with it, a question arises as to whether the so-called gadget, perhaps the population of China, gives rise to consciousness (see Block, 1978). But, as we have seen, in functionalism, it is not the case that mental states would be associated with 'experience'; the definition of 'mental state' is quite different from the usual one. Indeed, it is obvious that the 'mental states' of functionalism can be multiply realised in terms of the matter involved (see Section 8.2 below); but it clearly does not follow from this obvious fact that the same thing would be the case for mental states that are defined in the usual way, as "what it feels like" to experience something (see Section 3.1 of Chapter 2).

Functionalism has its so-called 'mental states' dependent on matter and it assumes that the things it calls 'mental states' can be causally effective. To that extent we can pick no argument with it in the context of this book. Beyond that, to propose that all that matters about the mind is what it makes happen runs counter to personal experience; and, more seriously, to name what might be called a 'functional state' relating to a creature its 'mental state' is clearly at variance with the normal meaning of mental state. And then, as we have seen, because people assume that if something is called "a mental state" the normal meaning of the term *also* applies, it has given rise to fantastical notions, such as the possibility that the population of China, taken as a whole, might experience consciousness!

8.2 *Putnam's multiple realisation argument*

In Putnam's influential paper 'The Nature of Mental States' (1967, reprinted in Rosenthal, 1991, pp 197-203) he addresses the question "Is pain a brain state?" arguing *against* a positive answer in the broad context of the functionalism approach. In this book, I am putting the case for mental states such as pain being properties of the matter associated with the brain, so in this section I examine Putnam's case against that proposition.

Putnam argues that: "pain is not a brain state, in the sense of a physical-chemical state of the brain (or even the whole nervous system), but another *kind* of state entirely." He says: "I propose the hypothesis that pain, or the state of being in pain, is a functional state of a whole organism" (p 199 as reprinted in Rosenthal, 1991). He then lays down a challenge for a hypothetical "brain-state theorist" who maintains that pain is a brain state. Putnam says that to "make good his claims" the brain-state theorist must "specify a physical-chemical state such that *any* organism (not just a mammal) is in pain if and only if (a) it possesses a brain of a suitable physical-chemical structure; and (b) its brain is in that physical-chemical state" (*ibid.*, p 200). Putnam points out that "the physical-chemical state in question must be a possible state of a mammalian brain, a reptilian brain, a mollusc's brain (octopuses are molluscs, and certainly feel pain), *etc.*" (*ibid.*, pp 200-201).

Before proceeding, we should note that the fact that a wide range of physical states exists to fulfil any *function* is a common-place in evolution theory. In biological terms, this is something that occurs right across the animal kingdom, and is known as 'convergent evolution': it is the situation in which similar, but genetically unrelated, structures evolve in different organisms to perform some function, or in which organisms that aren't closely related evolve similar traits to adapt to similar environments. As Putnam himself points out, there is a limited set of effective solutions to some challenges, and this means that in some cases one solution will develop independently again and again.

There are lots of examples of convergent evolution, here are a few of them.

- *Wings.* Wings have developed in many different forms. It is thought that the last common ancestor of both birds and bats, which have significantly different wing structure, did not have wings. Although there are obvious, significant, differences between the wing structure of birds and bats, they have to be broadly similar in construction due to the physical constraints to which any type of wing construction is subject.

- *Sight.* Seeing is achieved through a variety of different physical mechanisms. One of the most famous examples of convergent evolution is the camera eye, which arises both in squid and in vertebrates. It is thought that the last common ancestor of squid and vertebrates had a simple photoreceptive spot. However, the eyes of the squid do differ from vertebrates' eyes in that the squid's eye has the blood and nerve vessels entering from the back of the retina, while in vertebrates these enter from the front. Most insects have a totally different form of eye from that of vertebrates, they have a compound eye which has a much faster 'flicker fusion rate' (the frequency at which a flashing light appears steady); this allows the insect to absorb changes in what it sees far more quickly than humans and makes it more difficult for humans to catch them.

- *Anteaters.* The giant armadillo in North America, the giant anteater in South America, the giant pangolin in Africa and the spiny anteater in Oceania all have similar looking heads. This is because they have all evolved to hunt in tall grass and eat ants. But they are not close relatives; their evolutionary origins are all quite different.

- *Antifreeze.* Fish have antifreeze mechanisms both in Antarctica and in the arctic. But the genes that control the mechanisms are quite different. Independent episodes of molecular evolution seem to have taken place in each location, but both have had the same result in terms of function.

- *Consciousness.* More controversially, it has recently been suggested that evolution might have had at least two attempts at consciousness, because the consciousness of octopuses, although using the same building blocks as that of humankind (neurons), makes use of a very different technology (system of connections).[77]

It seems likely, therefore, that the reason why there is a range of physical-chemical states of a brain associated with avoidance behaviour (for example), is that if a creature were unable to experience something that caused it to take

---

[77] See Godfrey-Smith, 2017.

avoidance action when threatened with damage to its physical state it is very unlikely that the species would have survived.

This suggests that we would *expect* evolution to produce a number of *different* mental states (using the term now to pick out feelings and thoughts, its normal meaning) that play the role of causing a creature to take avoidance action, that is, to be in the functional state Putnam associates with the one term 'pain', and there seems to be no reason why these mental states (these feelings) should not be qualitatively quite different, so there would be $pain_1$, $pain_2$, ..., $pain_n$, where n is a large number, and each of these mental states could arise in the context of a brain state with its own, individual physical-chemical structure. This would be the case in different types of organism but, indeed, it seems likely that there are also a great number of different types of mental state playing the role of pain, from time to time, in any one type of creature. The fact that we humans have one generic name for all these states does not mean that every time we use that word we are referring to the exact same mental state. Thus, it does seem likely that one so-called functional state could be associated with a great number of substantially different brain states, as suggested by Putnam; but if that is the case, surely it is likely that each of these brain states is associated with a different mental state (defined in the "what it is like" sense rather than in Putnam's function-related sense). There seems to be no good reason for assuming that the mental state, in the usual sense of the term, associated with each of the different brain states will be exactly the same just because the function it performs is the same.

Now let us look, briefly, at Putnam's proposal. Putnam asks the question: "Is pain a brain state?", arguing that it is not, because "another hypothesis is more plausible" (*ibid.*, p 199). But, of course, it all depends on what you mean by 'pain'. If pain is *defined* to be a 'functional state', as Putnam suggests, then pain is *not* a brain state, as is illustrated by the examples of functional states noted above. But if pain is taken to be a psychological, or mental state of the "what it feels like" variety, then the question is the same ('Is Consciousness a Brain State?') as that addressed in some depth by Place (1956) and Smart (1958), see Chapter 4, Section 2.1.

Had Putnam been making the case that there is one, single, unique, *feeling*, named by us 'pain', and asserting that this coexists with a whole range of different *brain* states across creatures, or across species (an idea that has come to be known as 'multiple realisation'), and had he been successful in making that case, then clearly this would have implications for the approach to mind known as the identity thesis (see Chapter 4, Section 3), and possibly for physicalism in general, too. But it seems that that is not what he was suggesting. He was merely suggesting that a single *function* can be performed by a whole range of different *material* states; a very plausible suggestion with which we have no cause to argue.

In conclusion, multiple realisation of functions seems highly likely to arise because of convergent evolution, and a great many of the different things we call 'mental states' (feelings and thoughts) could perfectly well be involved in the same function, as are a great many physical states; different versions of the things we usually call 'mental states' could be involved in a single 'functional state' (referred to by Putnam as a 'mental state'). Putnam's point about multiple realisation, which is true of functional states, is not relevant to the proposition investigated in this book, which is about the thoughts and feelings that we call 'mental states'. However, it should perhaps be noted that, although there is not, and never could have been, any means of testing whether Putnam's proposal of multiple realisation of 'mental states' (meaning functional states) was in fact also true of 'mental states' (meaning thoughts and feelings, or psychological states), many respected philosophers of mind have signed up to it (see, for example, Yablo 1992, pp 249-50).

9 Emergentism, panpsychism and micro-psychism

9.1 Introduction

If we are to espouse the proposition that there is another property of matter besides those studied in the science of physics there is a question as to how this property arises. Does this property arise only when some particular combination of matter occurs in nature (a proposition known as 'emergentism', see Broad, 1925)? Could it be implicit in matter wherever and whenever matter arises (known as 'panpsychism')? Or could 'micropsychism' be the case, as Strawson suggests when he says: "Micropsychism is not yet panpsychism, for as things stand realistic physicalists can conjecture that only some types of ultimates are intrinsically experiential ..." (see Strawson, 2008, p 71)? I briefly consider each of these possibilities in this section.

When considering these possibilities, we should bear in mind that 'matter' is often implicitly defined as "non-experiential stuff" or "non-mental stuff", which could be viewed as carrying with it the implication that the proposition that matter gives rise to consciousness is incoherent (see Section 2.4 of

Chapter 2). Many philosophers reject emergentism, and maybe that is because given their implicit assumptions about the nature of matter they find it implausible, perhaps even incoherent. But it *must* be the case that matter gives rise to consciousness if mind is a property of matter, the proposition we are examining in this book. So here we view matter as being, at the very least, capable of giving rise to phenomenal experience.

9.2 Emergentism

Emergentism is the proposition that new properties of matter might emerge in some way from combinations of matter, or combinations of properties of matter, and that these new properties of matter might have characteristics that could never, even in principle, be derived from knowledge of the things from which they emerge. C D Broad, in his book *Mind and its Place in Nature* (1925) defined emergentism thus:

> "Put in abstract terms the emergent theory asserts that there are certain wholes, composed (say) of constituents A, B, and C in a relation R to each other; that all wholes composed of constituents of the same kind as A, B, and C in relations of the same kind as R have certain characteristic properties; that A, B, and C are capable of occurring in other kinds of complex where the relation is not the same as R; and that the characteristics of the whole R(A,B,C) cannot, even in theory, be deduced from the most complete knowledge of the properties of A, B, and C in isolation or in other wholes which are not of the form R(A,B,C)."

He then notes that "The mechanistic theory [the identity theory] rejects the last clause of this assertion." (p 61, my insertion).

As mentioned above, many philosophers reject emergentism, perceiving it to be an incoherent situation, perhaps implicitly taking 'matter' to be defined as "non-experiential stuff". But emergentism is not incoherent, it *is* conceivable: if scientists were to announce, some day in the (perhaps) far distant future, that they had created a conscious creature by combining simple chemicals into some structure, we might view it with astonishment, and we might seek alternative explanations, but it would not be immediately apparent that what they were saying was incoherent, that they *must* be lying.

137

9.3 *Panpsychism*

One alternative to emergentism, given property dualism, is the proposition that this basic element of consciousness, 'proto-consciousness', has existed everywhere and always alongside the properties of matter studied in physics. This proposition is known as panpsychism. If we opt for the bundle theory (see Chapter 2, Section 2.4) there would be no substratum, only a bundle of properties. In that case, given panpsychism, this fundamental element relating to consciousness would presumably have existed in the universe since time began, unlike in the case of emergentism, but as is the case in the set of beliefs known as Vedānta (see Appendix 1).

But, although this remains conceivable as a possible explanation of consciousness, it is difficult to see why we should assume that some form, consciousness is everywhere, always. The other properties of matter turn up in different combinations in connection with the fundamental particles, with one or two sometimes missing in individual cases; the neutron and the neutrino have no charge, the photon and the neutrino (perhaps) no mass, and so on.

9.4 *Micro-psychism*

Galen Strawson says he believes that: "… experiential phenomena cannot be emergent from wholly non-experiential phenomena" (2008, p 70). Like many others, he finds unacceptable the idea, presented succinctly in Broad's definition of emergentism (above), that some combination of constituents of matter could possess characteristics totally different from those of the constituents taken on their own or in other combinations. He therefore puts the case for what he calls 'micro-psychism', the proposition that at least some 'ultimates', that is, some fundamental physical entities, are intrinsically experiential. The general idea could be expressed as the assertion that these fundamental entities (fundamental particles?) perhaps have a property, or behave in a manner, that could be identified as 'proto-consciousness', some kind of building block that is then able to result in consciousness in complex creatures. Strawson says: "… if experience like ours … emerges from something that is not experience like ours …, then that something must already be experiential in some sense or another" (p 70).

Strawson then takes the view that if micro-psychism were found to be the case, then in the future: "… the idea that some but not all physical ultimates are experiential might look like the idea that some but not all physical ultimates are spatiotemporal ..." (*ibid.*, p 71). But one could argue instead that it would look like the idea that some but not all physical ultimates have charge (*e.g.*, neutrons) or have mass (*e.g.*, photons) or respond to the electromagnetic force (*e.g.*, dark matter), so one might expect that some but not all fundamental particles would carry proto-consciousness; alternatively, one might suggest that proto-consciousness could be associated with the quantum mechanics that describes the way the particles behave (*e.g.*, collapse of the wave function).

So perhaps proto-consciousness is one of the properties that is already known to be associated with fundamental particles; after all, what do we imagine proto-consciousness would look like when viewed in a laboratory? We noted earlier (Section 4.3 of Chapter 2) that consciousness, feelings, are associated with decision-taking, and that decision-taking requires a maximisation law of nature (choose A_i to maximize $F(A_1, A_2, \ldots, A_n)$), while the laws of nature associated with macro-physics (see Section 2.2 of Chapter 2) are generally linear in form (if A then B given C). Perhaps there is a law of this form relating to the behaviour of some fundamental particles. Or perhaps proto-consciousness is associated with the behaviour of the particles, with quantum mechanics, for example with the collapse of a wave function (see Hameroff and Penrose, 1996).

If proto-consciousness were already to exist at the micro-level, and to be incorporated into the brains of creatures that developed early in evolution, it could be that consciousness as we experience it, along with complex mental states, has developed in the brains of more sophisticated creatures during the later stages of evolution. The "what it feels like" element that arises in any particular circumstances would then be the feeling that results in behaviour likely to promote survival of the individual and the species in those circumstances. In this case one might argue that both micro-psychism and emergence were involved. Individual mental states, with their characteristic and non-deducible "what it feels like", would 'emerge' given the existence of laws of nature of the type noted in Section 4.3 of Chapter 2 associated with proto-consciousness along with the pressures of survival implicit in the evolutionary process.

If that were the case, the feelings associated with any particular mental state would be impossible to deduce, even from complete knowledge of the physical (non-mental) components of the brain; mental states would be instantiations of a property of matter that is different from those that are studied in the physical sciences.

9.5 *Conclusion*

Something along the lines of one of these options, or a combination of them, *must* obtain if property dualism is to hold. It seems that the most probable is micro-psychism, since all the other properties of matter are associated with fundamental particles in some way, combined with the 'emergence' that evolution would then supply.

6

The role of consciousness

1 Introduction

In this chapter we look in more depth at Proposition 3 in Section 4.3 of Chapter 2, the idea that we know from introspection that the ability to experience feelings is necessary for practical reasoning: the taking of effective multi-variate decisions (decisions in which the expected outcomes of different choices are not directly comparable because the issues they involve are not commensurable). There are two consequences of that proposition that deserve further examination. The first is that enabling this type of decision to be taken could be the reason why consciousness has taken the world by storm; that is, enabling these decisions could be the *role* of consciousness. The second is that this proposition would have several consequences regarding the structure of the brain, and these can be checked against our current knowledge of brain structures. I examine both these issues in this chapter.

In the next three sections I examine the first of these consequences. I spell out the possibility that the role of consciousness is to enable the taking of multi-variate decisions in Section 2. In Section 3, we consider in more depth whether this proposition is justified given our general understanding of how decisions are taken. Section 4 then notes that this type of decision-taking can be viewed as being nothing more than a rather sophisticated extension of the biological principle known as homeostasis.

141

Then I address the second consequence: several aspects of this hypothesis can be checked against our current knowledge of neuroscience, see Section 5:

- If the hypothesis is true, and if materialism holds (there is just one substance and we call it matter), then there must be some part of a person's body, most likely in the brain, that performs this task of action selection. The evidence currently available suggests that this function, which I am suggesting in this book involves a mental state of taking a decision triggering a physical action, is performed within the basal ganglia. The basal ganglia have a multitude of connections both to the sensory and to the planning areas of the cerebral cortex, as well as to the motor neurons (see Section 5.1).

- If this is where the mental causation occurs, damage to the basal ganglia or its connections, perhaps because of illness or accident or perhaps for genetic reasons, would prevent the mental causation taking place; and we would expect that if it was not possible for a person's feelings to influence their actions, the person would be unable to take sensible and effective multi-variate decisions. It appears that this is so (see, for example, the case of Phineas Gage, in Section 5.2).

- Next, having consciousness, and therefore being able to take effective decisions of this sort, will increase the likelihood that a creature survives and flourishes, and therefore species with this ability would be expected to flourish in evolutionary terms. This means that we would expect that the creatures from which we are descended evolutionarily would also have consciousness of some sort, and that they also, therefore, and their other descendants, would possess a structure in their brains in which the taking of a decision can affect the physics, namely, brain parts that perform the function that the basal ganglia seemingly perform for vertebrates. And, indeed, there is evidence suggesting that this is so (see Section 5.3).

- Also, we would expect these other creatures to behave in a manner consistent with being able to experience feelings that are like ours. Of course, we can never know for certain what it is like to be another creature, but there is evidence that suggests that other creatures might well have feelings much like ours (Section 5.3).

Finally, in Section 6, I note the implications of this assumption regarding the role of consciousness for the ontology of mind.

2 A role for consciousness

One of many important issues relating to consciousness concerns the reason why it has come to be such a striking characteristic of humans, possibly other vertebrates and perhaps other creatures also, given that it remains unclear exactly what role it plays. The most obvious explanation for the huge success of creatures with consciousness would be if, whatever its role turns out to be, that role is of key importance in terms of survival and so has been selected for in the process of evolution. Obviously, if mental states (states of which a creature can be conscious) play a role that is beneficial to survival, creatures capable of experiencing mental states would have an advantage in the fight for survival over others that were not capable of consciousness; evolution would then favour those capable of consciousness and this would explain why they have flourished.

A commonly held view amongst philosophers (see, for example, Rosenthal, 2008) has it that anything that could be done by a creature because of it being capable of consciousness could also be done without involving consciousness. Indeed, Harnad, who subscribes to the view that consciousness plays no key role in facilitating survival, has set a challenge to those who propose some adaptive advantage for consciousness, requiring that they explain why the same advantage could not be gained in the absence of consciousness "with *exactly the same causal mechanism*" (his emphasis, 2000, p 3). This proposition has been named 'conscious inessentialism' (see Flanagan and Polger, 1995). If this proposition were correct, consciousness would either be epiphenomenal, with no effect whatsoever on behaviour, or, if it did have some effect on behaviour, it would be possible to acquire the advantage it delivered in other ways in the absence of consciousness. There would then be no *need* for it to be selected for by an increased propensity to survive. If this were so, consciousness would presumably be a spin-off from some other property, one that *is* essential to survival; it would be an inescapable by-product of the other property but would have no key functional role of its own. Gould and Lewontin (1979), for example, warn against taking it that something is important for survival in case this might, as they put it, "invert the proper path of analysis", making an analogy with the architectural spandrels of San Marco which are adorned with a design "so elaborate, harmonious and purposeful that we are tempted to view it as the starting point of any analysis" (p 582). And Jackson (1982, p 134) points out that the weight of the polar bear's heavy coat might be viewed as being a hindrance to survival, evidence against the efficacy of evolution, if one were unaware of the enormous importance of having a warm coat to the polar bears' survival.

The idea in our third fundamental proposition (Chapter 2, Section 4.3) is that some of the information needed for practical reasoning is phenomenal information – facts of the type: "it would feel like *that* to experience X". And a creature must be capable of consciousness if it is going to be able to experience feelings and store what those feelings are like in its long-term memory. It is important to note that it is not necessary that these decisions are taken consciously in order that consciousness is required for the process to take place; it could be that the process, when not a conscious process, uses material that was conscious at some point in the past and has been programmed for automatic response or is stored in a long-term memory and can be used in unconscious cognitive analysis. Clearly, this proposal meets Harnad's challenge in that, if it were correct, it would be necessary for the taking of this type of decision that the creature *can* experience consciousness; conscious inessentialism would not hold.

Importantly, if it turns out that feelings are necessary for the taking of this type of decision there must be some way in which the phenomenal information, what the feelings that are key to this decision-taking process *feel* like, can influence a physical (suitable for study in physics) property of matter; the decision is going to cause a physical effect to occur, such as the movement of a limb, or speech, so mental causation must be effective (see Chapter 7, Sections 4 and 5). So the proposition that the ability to be conscious of phenomenal information is *necessary* for the taking of this type of decisions – the fact that we know, from introspection, that the way we feel about the alternative options affects which action we choose to perform when we take these decisions – has important implications for the ontology of consciousness and for the completeness of physics (as we shall see in Chapter 7, Section 3, although physics would not be complete in these circumstances, science could still be complete).

There have been several proposals for the role that consciousness might play that are quite dissimilar to the suggestion in this book. For example, Baars (2002) suggests that what is special about consciousness is that it "facilitates widespread access between otherwise independent brain functions" (p 47) and several people support the suggestion, notably Morsella (2005). Nichols and Grantham (2000, p 668), perhaps in a similar vein, suggest that "phenomenal consciousness serves the function of integrating information in the service of reasoning and action".

Penrose considers the possibility that: "awareness might be of an advantage to a predator in trying to guess what its prey would be likely to do next by 'putting itself in the place of that prey'" (1989, p 529). Nicholas Humphrey comes up with the suggestion that consciousness gives a creature: "the ability to *understand, predict and manipulate the behaviour* of other members of his own species ...", without which, he says, "a person could hardly survive from day to day" (2008, p 77). This raises the question of whether a species such as ours, along with many others, could get into the situation of mutual dependence which he describes so vividly in the absence of consciousness, and suggests that there may be a further evolutionary role for consciousness over and above that of facilitating multi-variate decisions: that of enabling the benefits of living in herds to be accessed in the interest of survival.

Many people have proposed roles for consciousness that are like the suggestion in this book, although they generally take a different view from mine regarding the ontology of consciousness, and they often see consciousness as *assisting* effective decision-taking rather than actually being essential to it. Peter Carruthers is one of several people who think that consciousness plays a role in the enabling of what he calls "increasingly flexible behaviours". He suggests that the "evolutionary gains ... come from the increasingly flexible behaviours which are permitted" because of "conceptual representations of the environment generated by perception" and "reasoning in the light of those representations" (2000, p 125); but he takes mental states to be "physical states of the brain" (p xiii). Daniel Dennett says that there is a role for consciousness in providing an answer to the "Now what do I do?" question (1991, pp 177, 188), but he envisages that consciousness is a 'functional' phenomenon, with the implication that any physical set-up with a similar structure to the relevant parts of the brain could perform the same role in decision-taking as that of the mind (see also Chapter 5, Section 8). Armstrong (1968), like Carruthers, subscribes to the view that "mental states are nothing but physical states of the brain" (p xi), and he suggests that "in a problem-situation various possible situations may be tried out 'in the imagination' in order to see which response will best fit the agent's purpose" (p 163). Dehaene and Naccache (2001, p 11) suggest that consciousness is required for, among many other things, "the spontaneous generation of intentional behavior", but also remark that: "Within a materialistic framework, each instance of mental activity is also a physical brain state" (p 3). Clearly, although closely related to the proposal made here, none of these will pass Harnad's challenge, because they all see the relation between consciousness and the physical (pertaining to physics) as being such that it is the physics that does the causing.

The idea here is that consciousness is *necessary* for a broad class of decisions regarding what to do next, rather than just being helpful as in the suggestions noted above. If this is correct, the reason why the ability to experience feelings, and to anticipate experiencing them, has developed through evolutionary adaptation over the aeons would be because it enables creatures to choose the best, or a near-best, action quickly and efficiently given the set of alternative actions available in some situation.

3 The role of feelings in practical reasoning

The term used by philosophers to pick out the ability of a person/creature to select the most desirable action from the set of available options when taking a decision is "the will". Having a 'will' therefore enables a person to perform practical reasoning and to implement the action that practical reasoning picks out as being the one with the most desirable consequences, the one to choose. Practical reasoning is the process people use when they solve the action selection problem, that is, when they set about deciding what to do next.[78] Where a range of options for action is available, each with a number of possible consequences, practical reasoning involves the consideration of each option in terms of its pros and cons and then the determination of which is most desirable, or the picking of one that seems acceptable if time is short, through a process of "qualitative evaluation". Qualitative evaluation involves feelings.

3.1 The action selection problem

Some decisions are taken by reflex, an automatic response to some stimulation that bypasses the decision-taking parts of the brain; others are programmed into the neural connections in the brain, either before the creature is born or later, during the creature's life. In both of these cases the action initiated by the

---

[78] This process is similar to the one economists call 'cost-benefit analysis' and psychologists and neuroscientists call 'action selection'. Descriptions of practical reasoning, broadly similar to the one here, can be found in any text on decision theory. An early explicit use of practical reasoning is Pascal's Wager, described in his *Pensées* (1660, Section 233).

creature is an automatic consequence of the situation (typically it is of the "if A then B, given situation C" type, although there may be probabilities involved) and it requires no conscious intervention or deliberation. The driving notion in this section is the fact that there are other important types of situation in which a creature is faced with a variety of possible courses of action each with a range of likely outcomes, probably including a large dose of uncertainty given the facts available to the decision-taker, and that in order to choose the most desirable option the creature has to take a view about what the consequences of each option might be like to experience, what they might *feel* like. We call such a decision a 'multi-variate decision' because the decision involves assessing very different types of pleasure or pain (sensory pleasure against risk of pain, benefits to others against future benefits for ourselves, *etc.*) to distinguish it from the other types of decision in which, for example, more of something may be obviously better than less. Choices of this sort vary widely in degree of urgency. The ability of a creature to survive and flourish, and therefore the survival of its species, can depend on it being able to make a quick and effective decision regarding the available courses of action.

An example of the simplest type of multi-variate decision taken using practical reasoning is that of Peter Rabbit (see Beatrix Potter 1902, *The Tale of Peter Rabbit*). Peter Rabbit is hungry. He needs to decide whether to eat the grass on the heath, which doesn't taste that good, or whether instead to go into Mr McGregor's garden to eat the delicious lettuces, but with a risk of being chased, shot, and put in a pot. He must trade familiar varieties of taste against degrees of risk and fear of pain and death when deciding on his course of action.

3.2 *What does practical reasoning involve?*

The key feature of practical reasoning arises in a situation in which there are various actions that might be chosen and each one results in a somewhat different bundle of outcomes: if the most desirable, or a reasonably acceptable, outcome is to be identified, then (see Watson, 1975, p 346, and Chapter 2, Section 4.3) each of these bundles of likely outcomes needs to be 'evaluated' in some way so the one considered most desirable, all things considered, can be chosen and initiated. This evaluation process requires the chooser to imagine what the outcomes might *feel* like, so he/she needs to access memories relating to feelings; and to be able to access memories relating to feelings, to experiencing something, requires that the creature in question has the capacity to feel, that is, it means that the creature must be capable of consciousness.[79]

Decisions of this sort, multi-variate decisions, require the following. First, the creature must be able to identify the alternative courses of action available in some situation and the range of likely outcomes these actions could give rise to. Then there needs to be an assessment of the feelings, the satisfactions and pains, which are likely to be associated with each of these outcomes. Many feelings have an aspect to them, known to psychologists as 'motivational affect' (effectively, an incentive effect) according to which a situation is viewed as being desirable (positive) or undesirable (negative) in some degree; 'motivational affect' is valenced, in the sense that it is experienced in varying degrees on a continuum and may be positive or negative. The 'motivational affect' associated with the likely outcomes of a proposed action indicates the desirability, the net intensity of the likely satisfaction or pain expected if that action were initiated, and according to psychologists it is this that determines the outcome of the decision regarding what to do next.[80] In his 1980 paper, Zajonc promotes the role of 'motivational affect' (as opposed to cognitive analysis, but accepts that both are necessary for decision-taking) saying, for example: "People do not get married or divorced, commit murder or suicide, or lay down their lives for freedom upon a detailed cognitive analysis of the pros and cons of their actions" (p 172). If this is correct, it would be the 'motivational affect' associated with the consideration of an option that indicates its desirability and thus it is this that gives rise to a person's actions.

The final step in decision-taking, then, is a comparison of the net intensity of the 'motivational affect' associated with each of the actions available; this will enable the most desirable (or, if time is short, an acceptable) option to be identified; a 'motivational affect comparison' function is required, therefore, in order that a person can perform the necessary task of comparing the 'motivational affect' he or she experiences when contemplating the alternative options available and pick the option perceived to be most desirable. It is

---

[79] Note that if this is correct, a philosophical zombie would be unable to take decisions using practical reasoning, because a zombie has no consciousness and so is unable to 'feel' things. If this is so, and if, as seems likely, decisions taken using silicon do not pick out the same choices as decisions based on feelings, taken by living creatures, the existence of a philosophical zombie who behaves exactly as some human would behave in all circumstances is not conceivable, see Chapter 3, Section 6.2.

[80] This may be what Crane had in mind when he wrote his book *Elements of Mind* (2001) and spoke of 'intentionality'.

difficult to see how macro-physics, which operates using laws of the "if A then B given C" variety, can perform this task. What is needed is a process that can solve the problem:

$$\text{"choose } A_i \text{ to maximise } F(\ldots), \text{ given C"}$$

(see Chapter 2, Section 4.3). Since it is consciousness that enables us to experience feelings, it could be that the existence of consciousness is in some way related to whatever process it is that makes it possible for this function to be performed.

If this is the case, one could argue that we should guard against falling into the *reverse* of the spandrels fallacy: to us, the effect of consciousness is so important that it might lead us to, as Gould and Lewontin (1979) put it, "invert the proper path of analysis" (p 148). Whereas one might imagine all sorts of mysterious, weird and wonderful reasons for the existence of something that means as much to us as consciousness does, in fact the reason for its existence could simply be that it enables the taking of the multi-variate decisions that will enhance the likelihood of a creature, and its kind, surviving. The suggestion in this section is that for the first, basic, creatures to evolve into more complex and sophisticated creatures it was *necessary* that this function could be performed, necessary that there was some way in which this role of "choosing" could be fulfilled by the creature. The idea is that macro-physics on its own, seemingly dependent on laws of the type "if A then B given C", could not do it. But it turned out that this other property of matter could. So this other property of matter, 'mind' or 'consciousness', has proliferated in our world. Seen by a Martian, or by some hypothetical sensate being outside our human race, consciousness would then look as if it was merely a gadget that is successful in increasing the likelihood of survival of the creatures that live on this planet.[81]

The theory of multi-variate decision-taking has been developed over a great number of years (see, for example Pascal, 1660; Von Neumann and Morgenstern, 1947; Luce and Raiffa, 1957; Markovitz, 1952; Kahneman, 2011). Originally it was thought that the "expected value" of some measure of the benefit or pain associated with the outcomes was the key factor that determined

---

[81] It may be overly speculative to suggest that if a law of nature with this structure were found to operate on a micro-level it could be that this is the 'proto-consciousness' that enables the complex decisions of sophisticated creatures.

the choice, but then it was realised that uncertainty can be highly significant in determining what people choose (both in the form of the variance of the outcomes, see Markowitz, 1952, and in terms of the skew, where there may be a small probability of a very good or a very bad outcome, indicated by the third moment of the probability distribution, see Kahneman and Tversky, 1979). It is likely that there is still much to be understood about risk perception, however. Significant discrepancies arise between risk perception as reported by the general public and predictions of risk based on experts' views of technology and statistical theory when risks of different sorts are compared, as when the risk of death from a nuclear accident is compared with the risk of death from a road accident (see Slovik, 1987). Also, a paper by Greene *et al.* (2001) has shown that activity in areas of the brain related to emotion is significantly increased when there is personal involvement in the question at issue compared to when there is not. This may be relevant to the famous trolley dilemma (Foot, 1967), where the decision concerns whether to allow five people to die or to kill one (other) person by turning a switch, and its partner, the footbridge dilemma (Thomson, 1976), where to save the five people it is necessary to push one (other) person to his/her death. It seems likely that the differing results in these two thought experiments arises because the chooser factors in the expectation of being badly afflicted personally after the footbridge dilemma, both by painful memories and by public opprobrium; this would be less of a problem in the case of the trolley dilemma.

In any case, people's feelings regarding the outcomes of their actions, which derive from their 'values' (the person's dispositions to experience certain types of feelings in certain circumstances), are viewed as being a key factor in the assessment of the alternative possible actions in decisions which depend on the use of practical reasoning.

3.3 Multi-variate decision-taking and awareness

A question that now arises concerns the extent to which awareness is involved in the taking of these decisions, and whether awareness is necessary at the time the decision is being taken. The answer seems to be that whereas decisions of this sort can be, and frequently are, taken without awareness of any sort being involved, this can only the case if the results of previous analysis of similar issues relating to the same feelings are already available in the memory.

Several reasons have been cited in the literature that suggest that consciousness is not necessary for the taking of this sort of decision. First, we now know that conscious capacity is severely limited in that the working memory, where cognitive processes of this sort are worked out consciously (see Appendix 2, Section 2.3), can only hold seven items, plus or minus two, at a time (Miller, 1956). So, we know that much of the processing needed before a multi-lateral decision is taken must be done unconsciously (see also Dijkaterhuis and Nordgren, 2006, on unconscious thought). But since feelings are a necessary part of such decision-taking, and a creature must be capable of consciousness to experience feelings, this processing must be informed by conscious analysis that has taken place previously.

Next Rosenthal, who subscribes to the proposition that the taking of decisions of this sort does not necessarily require consciousness, suggests that for consciousness to be necessary for practical reasoning it must be the case that intentional action only results from conscious volitions (2008, p 829). But this may not be the case. A creature that has experienced the relevant feelings, and can store information about them in its memory, is able to use that information in unconscious analysis as well as in conscious analysis. It is not necessarily required that such decisions are always taken in the spotlight of consciousness, although given that it is our feelings that determine the outcome of the choice process, the ability to experience consciousness must be a necessary concomitant for these decisions to happen; the memory of previous conscious experiences stored in a creature's long-term memory store can be used to take decisions of this sort without consciousness being needed at the time the decision is taken.

Then there are two experimental results that may be deceptive in suggesting that decisions can be taken without awareness of feelings occurring. First, as we saw earlier (Chapter 3, Section 4.2), the work of Libet *et al.* (1982) shows that certain rather trivial decisions concerning the timing of actions can be taken before the subject is aware of having taken them, so consciousness can have played no part in the triggering of these decisions. But of course, it does not follow that *all* our decisions are taken in that manner.

Second, the famous case of the 'hand-shaking' experiment, reported by Édouard Claparède (1911) is often interpreted as indicating that decisions can be taken without consciousness. In this experiment, the subject was unable to remember the situation surrounding the pain she had experienced on a previous occasion, when the psychologist had concealed a pin in his hand before shaking hers, because she suffered from a form of amnesia. But always afterwards she was reluctant to shake his hand. This has often been interpreted as implying that knowledge (*i.e.*, of the situation on that previous occasion) that is not available to consciousness can nevertheless inform decisions. But whereas it certainly seems to be the case that multi-variate decisions can be taken without conscious awareness, this is not necessarily the correct interpretation of Claparède's experiment. The subject could well have become programmed to experience 'motivational affect' when offered the psychologist's hand, while having no memory trace whatsoever of the circumstances that had originally given rise to the pain.

If practical reasoning is the way in which this type of decision is taken, feelings can be viewed as being instantiations of the mechanism which enables certain types of creature to take multi-variate decisions effectively and which thereby enhances the likelihood of their survival.

4 Practical reasoning as a form of homeostasis

To survive, and therefore to reproduce, organisms must maintain a relatively stable situation regarding several aspects of their internal environment such as the pH level in their blood, their temperature and their blood pressure. The mechanism by which this is done is the negative feed-back process known as 'homeostasis', named such following the work of Claude Bernard published in 1865. Homeostatic control mechanisms have three components. First, they have a sensing component that monitors and responds to changes in the environment; this is known as the 'receptor'. Second, they have some sort of a 'control centre' that determines whether action is required. Third, they have an 'effector'; this is a mechanism which operates to correct any significant deviation from the acceptable range by initiating a change in the behaviour of some muscle or organ or some-such.

However, in the more sophisticated creatures several of the feedback mechanisms necessary for survival, and for quality of life, are the result of intentional behaviour, that is, they follow from an action taken by the organism seemingly triggered by an awareness of some imbalance (see Panksepp, 2011, who identifies certain 'primal affects' along with their 'comfort zones' and potential negative effects on survival). 'Motivational affect', the emotion/feeling that drives an intentional action can therefore be viewed as being the trigger for a form of homeostasis (as suggested by Paulus, 2007); cognitive processes are involved in determining the range of possible actions and informing the choice, and motor neurons ensure that the muscles respond to implement the chosen action. It is fundamental to this process that the experience of an emotion that has 'motivational affect' and therefore an incentive effect associated with it is involved, causing the person/creature to decide to perform an action. Thus, a person/creature will seek something to eat when it is hungry, something to drink when it is thirsty (the internal feedback system regarding osmosis and thirst, that depends on the hypothalamus, can only deal with small variations), somewhere to rest when it is tired and somewhere warm when it is cold. For instance, reptiles, which don't have an effective internal temperature adjustment system, often choose to lie on a sun-heated rock in the morning to increase their body temperature.

A person, and perhaps a creature, may also be concerned to maintain the welfare of loved ones and their own self-esteem, and therefore their moral behaviour, within acceptable ranges.

Thus consciousness, enabling the experience of a great variety of feelings and thoughts, can be regarded as an essential part of a sophisticated biological development of the homeostasis type.

5 In support of action selection by practical reasoning

If the role of consciousness, and of 'motivational affect', is to enable the effective taking of multi-variate decisions relating to actions, so this is the reason why consciousness has been so successful in evolutionary terms, there should be some evidence amongst our current understanding of neuroscience that supports this proposition. In this section I report my findings from a search for three types of such evidence: evidence relating to the part of the brain that facilitates this type of decision-taking; evidence relating to what happens when that part of the brain is damaged; and, evidence that suggests that other creatures descended from the same evolutionary ancestors as us have similar brain structures, that these might play a similar role in facilitating decision-taking, and that these creatures might therefore experience feelings broadly similar to those which we experience.

5.1 *The physical correlate of action selection*

It is currently thought that the neural correlate of action selection is the basal ganglia. The basal ganglia are part of the limbic system, a collection of structures which includes the hypothalamus, the hippocampus and the amygdala as well as the basal ganglia, and is located below the cerebrum in humans. Ever since the publication of Papez' 1937 paper on the hypothalamus and its connections it has been generally accepted that the limbic system is associated with feelings and emotions.

There is a range of evidence supportive of the view that the basal ganglia are associated with decisions relating to actions. First there was the discovery, some years ago now, that Parkinson's disease involves a deterioration in certain types of neuron in the basal ganglia, and then that in Huntingdon's disease an abnormal form of a protein causes some of the cells in the basal ganglia to malfunction (Marsden, 1981 contains much useful background information on the role of the basal ganglia). Next, the key inputs to the basal ganglia come from the cerebral cortex, which is responsible for processing sensory input, and for reasoning and planning; the output from the basal ganglia, after first returning to the cerebral cortex, travels *via* the thalamas to the brain stem and then on to the muscles that trigger actions. It has been known for some time that the primary motor cortex has axons which extend all the way to the basal ganglia (see Mink, 1996). These findings support the proposition that the basal ganglia are the structures in the brain in which decisions concerning actions are taken. The idea is that whereas the possible actions are identified in the cerebral cortex, it is within the basal ganglia that it is decided which action, out of the set which the cortex has identified as being available, is the one likely to produce the most desirable outcome and so is the one that should be executed.

Redgrave *et al.* (1999) have proposed a model in which systems in the brain that are associated with emotions that often give rise to powerful motivation, such as those concerned with eating or hunting or sleeping or reproducing, compete for access to the motor resources that are needed for any one of these to achieve their ends. Somehow, the causal mechanism assumed to operate in the basal ganglia (the mechanism that enables a mental state to influence the physics) must enable the selection of the action related to the most pressing needs.[82] Redgrave *et al.* identify three methodologies that could solve this action selection problem; one has a pre-ordained priority order across the competing initiating systems, the second postulates inhibitory bilateral connections between each pair of systems and an excitatory link to the shared motor resource, while the third has a central selection mechanism that inhibits access

---

[82] A useful definition of the selection problem is the following: "... simply stated, the selection problem is: at any time, which functional system, or sensory event, should be put in a position to direct the shared motor resources – the final common motor path?" (see Redgrave *et al.*, 2011, p 140).

to the motor neurons for the systems that are not preferred and disinhibits access for the one that is favoured. They identified the third as being the most likely one, partly because it is the most efficient (it requires fewer connections for each competing system and for a new entrant), and partly because it is the only system that enables the selection mechanism to evolve without the changes having any effect on other aspects of the control mechanism. Unlike in most other regions of the brain, in the basal ganglia the great majority of neurons use a neurotransmitter that is inhibitory in nature (GABA), so the selection process probably involves ensuring that the inhibition of those channels that are not selected is maintained or increased while the selected channel is disinhibited to enable access to the necessary motor resource. In a later paper (Redgrave *et al.*, 2011) it is argued that: "… the re-entrant looped architecture of the basal ganglia represents biological solutions to [the] fundamental behavioural problems of selection and reinforcement" (p 138).

The proposal that it is the basal ganglia that is the brain structure within which this important function takes place gains support from an increasing number of psychology experiments. Structures in the basal ganglia have been found to be active when choices are made see for example Knutson and Greer (2008), who were seeking the neural correlates of anticipatory affect – the feelings people experience when anticipating outcomes that matter to them. Further, it now seems likely that the bit of the basal ganglia that assesses the intensity of motivation is the caudate nucleus. Delgado *et al.* (2004) conducted an experiment in which the only thing that varied was the intensity of the motivation: they asked their subjects to guess the values of a series of cards with the feedback varying between simply recording their success or failure or recording a monetary reward when they succeeded and a monetary charge when they failed. The magnitude of the response in the caudate nucleus varied significantly depending on the type of reward offered.

It seems likely, therefore, that it is within the basal ganglia that the mental influences the physics – that this is where mental causation takes place, and current knowledge suggests that the caudate nucleus may be the bit of the basal ganglia where the *valence* (the intensity) of the 'motivational affect' (the incentive effect) associated with each of the alternatives is assessed.

5.2 What if the ability to experience 'motivational affect' is damaged?

Direct evidence relating to the mechanisms we humans use when we are taking decisions of this sort is available from the effect of certain brain lesions on people's behaviour; these lesions may arise as the result of accident or illness, or following the medical treatment of brain conditions.

There is one brain lesion that seems to leave all the cognitive aspects of a person's abilities intact and working perfectly well, but which means that the person is unable to take multi-variate decisions effectively. The lesion in question is the one relating to the well-known case of Phineas Gage, who had an iron bar 3 cm thick pass through his head following an accidental explosion when building a railway in the US in 1848. Afterwards he appeared at first to have experienced no damage whatsoever to his mental abilities. But it turned out that he had suffered a puzzling change to his personality that meant that he was no longer able to hold down a job and that his marriage and all his other relationships broke down. The case puzzled the doctors. Many years later, in the early 1970s, Antonio Damasio, a professor of neuroscience in California, was invited to examine a patient, known as 'Elliot', who had had a tumour removed and this had left him with disabilities that had the same effect on his life as Phineas' had had on his. So Damasio was able to perform tests on Elliot designed to enable him to discover exactly what it was that caused his problems and also what had caused the problem in the well-known case of Phineas Gage (see Damasio, 1994 and also see John Darrell Van Horn, 2012).

Elliot performed perfectly, in the laboratory, on every mental test that had at that time been invented. So the doctors created a new set of tests relating to decision-taking in social situations; these included listing the possible options for action, predicting the consequences of these actions, devising strategies to achieve objectives, and analysing the options in moral dilemmas (for example, should one steal a drug to prevent one's spouse from dying?). Elliot performed well on all these tests, also. However, he is reported as commenting at one point, with a smile, after analysing the possible outcomes in some tricky hypothetical situation in the laboratory, "and after all this I still wouldn't know what to do!" Eventually Elliot himself identified what was wrong with him: he described his total lack of emotional response saying, according to Damasio, that: "topics that had once evoked a strong emotion no longer caused any reaction, positive or negative" (Damasio, *ibid.*, p 45). Other patients with similar lesions have been found to behave in the same way as Elliot when subjected to these tests. The implication seems to be that effective choice-making involves an assessment of the feelings attached to the available alternatives, and without being able to experience the emotion, the 'motivational affect' – if one lacks the ability to care – the choice that is made is arbitrary. Although the person can predict the consequences of the actions they might choose, they seem to be

156

unable to assess how these consequences would *feel*, so they are unable to make a soundly based decision.

The implication of this is important: although cognition plays an important role in the choice of alternative actions and the analysis of the likely outcomes, with cognition alone, without the emotional responses associated with our 'values', our dispositions to experience certain types of feelings, a soundly based decision, a decision that is consistent with the preservation of the person's long-term welfare, cannot be taken. The information relating to the feelings likely to be experienced relating to the options for action that are available is necessary in order that sound decisions are taken, and there has to be some mechanism through which this information affects our actions: mental causation must operate.

As well as supporting the proposition that 'motivational affect' is important for the taking of deliberative decisions, and the idea that there is a structure in the brain which is necessary for such decisions to be taken, this evidence suggests that the experience of 'motivational affect' itself is associated with a structure in the brain, thus providing evidence in support of the proposition that consciousness arises in the context of certain material structures.

5.3 The role of consciousness in evolution

Effective decision-taking is crucial to survival, so if the ability to experience feelings improves decision-taking one would expect that it would be selected for in evolution; one would expect that creatures with the ability to take multi-variate decisions in the manner described in decision theory, to perform practical reasoning, would be more likely to survive than those without that ability. It could be that this ability to take multi-variate decisions effectively is unique to humans, or to mammals, or to vertebrates; on the other hand, it also could be that some of the more ancient creatures from whom we are descended evolutionarily also had this ability. Further, if we have inherited this ability from the ancient creatures from whom we are descended evolutionarily it seems likely that some of the other creatures alive today that are descended from the same ancient creatures as us, and so are related to us in evolutionary terms, would also have these brain structures. If so, one might expect that these creatures alive today would then experience feelings similar to some of those that we experience, enabling them also to take this type of decision (people are sometimes reluctant to accept that other species of creatures may experience some of the feelings that we experience, but it clearly is a possibility). In this section I describe some of the evidence now available that supports the proposition that other creatures alive today have brain regions *homologous* to our basal ganglia, that is, brain regions that have the same interconnections, use the same neurotransmitters and appear to play the same role in the creatures' survival as our basal ganglia play in ours.

For many years it has been well-established that different parts of the brain perform different functions. It has also been accepted that many creatures have brain regions that are homologous to ours implying that they have shared evolutionary ancestry with us (see Ghysen, 2003, for example). But, until quite recently it was thought that the cerebral cortex, where logical thinking and planning take place in humans, was unique to vertebrates. Also, although we have known for some time that all vertebrates have similar structures in their hindbrain which ensure that autonomic processes (continuous, automatic processes such as breathing, heart-beat, digestion *etc.*) continue to function effectively without the need for conscious control, it was thought that these brain parts, also, might be unique to vertebrates. Now it seems that in fact many other creatures may have brain structures that play the role our cerebral cortex plays. For example, Tomer *et al.* (2010) have found evidence suggesting that brain structures in marine ragworms (annelids), known as 'mushroom bodies', may be homologous to the vertebrates' pallium (the most highly developed part of the vertebrates forebrain), and this is generally interpreted as meaning that there must have been a common ancestor to both vertebrates and annelids that had this feature in its brain structure, with the implication that the origins of the cerebral cortex date back to the Precambrian era (more than 500 million years ago). And it has now been established that the vertebrates' hindbrain structures are very similar, both anatomically and functionally, to a part of the brain in the arthropod (animals with external skeletons, such as insects) which is called the 'sub-oesophageal ganglion' (see Ghysen, *ibid.*, p 559). So, it now seems likely that vertebrates, and therefore mammals, have an evolutionary ancestor in common with arthropods. This evolutionary ancestor has been named 'Urbilateria' (see de Robertis and Sasai, 1996), and is thought to have been extant about 600 million years ago, suggesting that some form of consciousness has been around for that length of time.

When it comes to the basal ganglia, it has been accepted for the last couple of decades that structures homologous to our basal ganglia are found in all jawed vertebrates (Medina *et al.*, 1995). But more recently, structures in arthropods, known as the 'central complex', have been found to play the same role as the vertebrate's basal ganglia (Strausfeld and Hirth, 2013). So, the presumption now must be that the basal ganglia, also, derive from the so-called Urbilateria. And if we are right in thinking that the basal ganglia are the brain structures that compare the intensity of 'motivational affect' associated with alternative options when choices are being made, this suggests that some form of feelings, and therefore consciousness, must exist in all the creatures, including insects, crabs and such-like, that are thought to have derived from the Urbilateria through evolution. It seems probable, therefore, that many of the emotions we experience, such as fear, anger, various 'needs', a desire to approach or seek, and so on, are also experienced in some form or another by the other animals that have these same brain structures. But, of course, there is no way of knowing what these might feel like for the creature concerned.

This is a proposition that has been espoused by Panksepp. He has proposed that our affective feelings derive from areas of the brain that we have inherited through the process of evolution, and that we should therefore assume that other animals that have evolutionary ancestors in common with us would experience feelings like the ones we experience; see for example his review article (2011) and his book (2012). So, a question arises as to whether there is any evidence that supports the proposition that the 'motivational affect' element of the feelings we experience as humans have developed in evolutionary terms from those of other animals (Panksepp, 2005).

This question was first put to the test in the middle of the last century. Stimulation of parts of the brain, either with electricity (applied to implanted electrodes) or using drugs, was found to cause animals to behave in a way very like the way in which humans behave in the same circumstances, and when humans behave in that way we know, because of what others tell us and because of what we, ourselves, have experienced, that it is the result of certain pleasurable or painful feelings being induced. Delgado *et al.*, as long ago as 1954, reported that a "fear-like reaction" could be elicited in cats by electrical stimulation of various brain regions; and noted that this reaction "had all the drive properties of a true emotion …" (p 592). Olds and Milner, also in 1954, showed that rats would press a lever that activated electrical stimulation of various regions in their brains, presumed to give them pleasure, in preference to eating or drinking; some eventually dying of exhaustion. There have been a great many experiments since then that are supportive of the proposition that other animals feel emotions like ours when similar brain regions are stimulated. For example, recent experiments suggest that a dog's caudate nucleus is activated when it perceives something pleasurable (Berns, 2015). This certainly

159

suggests that emotions play a key role in the selection of action, and therefore in survival, for other creatures besides us.

6 Implications for the ontology of consciousness

Finally, if feelings are *necessary* for the taking of effective multi-variate decisions, in that such decisions cannot be taken effectively in the absence of feelings (as spelt out above and in our third fundamental proposition in Chapter 2, Section 4.3, and as appears to be the case given the experiences of Phineas Gage and Eliot), then mental states *must* be causally effective. Further, since feelings are not reducible to the properties of matter studied in physics (physics is concerned only with such things as can be communicated perfectly from one person to another using language, and this is not the case with feelings), there must be something else besides that which is studied in physics. So then, if we rule out dual substances, there has to be another property of matter besides those that are studied in the science of physics and that property of matter has to be causally effective, in that it has to be capable of influencing actions; that is to say, it has to be capable of causing changes in the properties of matter that are studied in physics.

Put another way, if the role of consciousness is to enable decision-taking and we have seen in this chapter that there is considerable evidence in support of that proposition, feelings must be able to influence actions, so feelings and therefore consciousness must be causally effective.

7

Mental causation

1 Introduction

This chapter presents the case for mental causation, and therefore for causally effective property dualism, and notes some possible mechanisms by which it could come about. The chapter starts with a summary discussion of the main reason why it seems likely that mental states are causally effective (Section 2). In Section 3 we note the implications of causally effective property dualism for the causal completeness of physics. Section 4 then summarises the justification for the approach that I call 'causally effective property dualism'. In Section 5 I describe all the (perhaps somewhat fanciful) processes that I can imagine by which mental causation might operate in practice. The conclusion is in Section 6.

2 Are mental states causally effective?

The case for effective mental causation arises when one considers a choice between two or more courses of action with very different consequences (see also Chapter 2, Section 4.3 and Chapter 6). For example, what type of mechanism would *you* put in place, if you were designing the universe, to enable a choice to be made between two possible courses of actions that some creature might implement, one of which looks likely to result in something very

161

beneficial to its survival or to the survival of its species, but which also carries with it a substantial risk of physical damage or death, while the other gives rise to the certainty of some very minor increase in comfort?

If the species is going to survive it is of the utmost importance that the system you put in place enables a choice such as this to be made appropriately, on balance. Somehow, the system you design must be able to note the available options in a choice situation and identify the likely consequences of each. Then it must be able to transform the characteristics of these bundles of consequences into something that allows a direct comparison to be made of the influence the outcome of the choice will have on the welfare of the creature itself and of its species. Further, it would obviously be helpful if the mechanism you put in place for the making of such choices can somehow take account of all the information that could be available, including such things as the past experience of the creature making the choice, other creatures' past experience, technology, climate change, and so on. It will therefore be important for the creature to have access to some type of memory. Whatever mechanism you choose, if it does not end up picking the options that are the most beneficial/least detrimental to the survival of the chooser and/or its species, or options that are sufficiently close to being so, the species will not thrive and so is unlikely to survive and therefore unlikely to exist on this earth (see Chapter 6 for a fuller discussion of this issue).

The way such choices *are* made, for us and for other creatures, it would seem, is through the existence of and the experience of 'feelings'; so in this book I take it that the bundle of consequences that is chosen is that which initiates the greatest motivational affect in the chooser. But the ability to experience feelings such as motivational affect requires consciousness, and therefore mental states.[83] Importantly for our purposes here, if making choices such as these is the role of consciousness, it must be the case that mental states can influence physical (non-mental) events (see also Chapter 6).

The obvious question that arises then is: could there be another way of achieving the outcome that the ability to experience feelings makes possible? Could there be another mechanism, not involving feelings and therefore consciousness, which would enable a choice between two bundles of

---

[83] A recent study of the behaviour of bumblebees (Perry, 2016) suggests that their emotions play a role in their decision-making. The study found that in certain situations bumblebees exhibit what the investigators call "emotion-like" behaviour and that this behaviour disappears when the bees are treated with a dopamine antagonist.

162

characteristics that are not directly comparable (are incommensurable) and ensure, insofar as it is possible, that the choice made would enhance the likelihood of survival of the chooser and/or of its species, and that in circumstances in which unexpected, even unprecedented, events can occur? And if this is possible, could this other mechanism be as effective and efficient as the one we have identified here which, one might say, has been designed by nature (by evolution)? It may be that a process akin to the one described above could be programmed into the physics of some creature's brain or into a robot (silicon-based?) along with the necessary one-dimensional valuation function. If there were another way this type of choice could be made it may be that that *is* the way it is made, and if that were the case, consciousness could be epiphenomenal after all.

Whereas we cannot totally rule out this possibility, either using logic or given current knowledge of the laws of nature, by far the most likely outcome must surely be that it will be found to be nomologically impossible.

In this book, I take it that the 'role' of conscious mental states is to facilitate survival by enabling decisions of this sort to be taken effectively (see Chapter 2, Section 4.3 and Chapter 6).

3 Physics would not be complete but science could be

If it is the case that mental states are instantiations of a property of matter that is not reducible to physics, so materialism (physicalism in the broad sense) holds, and if everything is determined by causal processes, so science is complete (see Chapter 2, Section 2.4), there must be a causal process that is, at least in part if not wholly, outside physics; this would be so whether or not mental states were able to cause events relating to physics to take place. For there would be a property of matter, 'mind', that would be outside physics, and there must be a nomological process that requires that that property exists (see Chapter 2, Section 2.3) so there must be a nomological process that has a 'physical' (pertaining to physics) and/or a 'material' (pertaining to matter) cause, and an effect that is outside physics. Although it still could be that *causal* completeness of physics holds: "all physical effects are fully caused by purely *physical* prior histories", it might not, then, be the case that all the effects that are fully caused by purely physical past histories are physical, which would be required if the more general form of completeness were to hold.

The fact that mind, or at the very least aspects of mind, are outside physics does not give rise to any problems with our assumption that materialism (physicalism in the broad sense) might hold, but it does raise a question as to why one might wish to take mental states to be epiphenomenal, why they should not be taken to be causally effective, affecting some of the things that are suitable for study in physics. Why rule out that possibility when we are content to allow (as in supervenience physicalism) the possibility that there are effects of physical processes that are outside physics?

There is nothing incoherent about the proposition that a physical event (an event of the sort with which the science of physics is concerned) amongst the neurons can be caused by a mental state (an instantiation of a property of matter not suitable for study in the science of physics) as the result of some causal process of which we are currently unaware, but this would run counter to the assumption that physics is causally complete. With this type of causal process amongst the neurons operating the science of physics as currently construed, even as it would be if it were 'finished', could not be considered 'complete' in this broader sense.

With our proposal, causally effective property dualism, there is a type of mental state, a 'motivational' mental state, that can cause some physical (pertaining to the science of physics) event to be instantiated amongst the neurons as the result of a causal process which is such that the cause is not included in the science of physics; 'science' would therefore include other causal processes in addition to those incorporated into the physical sciences, and science would be complete.

4 Justification for 'causally effective property dualism'

In this section, I summarise the essential steps in the reasoning that has led me to the judgment that causally effective property dualism could be the correct explanation of the phenomenon of consciousness, and that it should therefore be taken seriously.

My starting point is the question of whether, if we take it that mind is a property of matter, it could be that mental states, instantiations of mind, are reducible to the properties of matter that are studied in the physical sciences. But to answer that question it is necessary to identify what must be the case about a property of matter if it is to be suitable for study in the physical sciences and therefore 'physics', and I could find nothing definitive on this in the literature (but see Chapter 2, Section 2.1). The definition of 'physics' that I use in this book (see Chapter 2, Section 2.1) follows from the requirement that in order for the results of an experiment in the physical sciences to be accepted by the scientific community it must be reproducible by others: it must be possible to communicate in language all the details of the manner in which an experiment is performed, along with its findings, so that somebody else, perhaps on the other side of the world, can reproduce that experiment and check that their findings are the same as those of the originator. It is therefore necessary that all the facts relating to a property of matter that is suitable for study in the physical sciences are 'public' facts, facts that are *equally available to everyone*, and so can be perfectly communicated between people in language.

It follows from this definition of the science of physics that if a mental state, such as a feeling of hunger, for example, were reducible to the properties of matter studied in the physical sciences, that is, if there were nomological relations that enabled all the facts pertaining to that feeling of hunger to be *identified* with facts that are suitable for study in the science of physics, it would be possible to describe, in the vocabulary of words used to communicate facts in the science of physics, *exactly* what it is like to experience that feeling of hunger. We would then be able to tell another person what it is like to experience such a feeling using the vocabulary of the facts and the laws that are part of the science of physics, and a person listening, and understanding the words used, would then *know* what it is like to experience that feeling without having ever experienced it themselves. But we know, from introspection, that we are unable to communicate in words exactly what it is like to experience a feeling (a feeling such as hunger, or seeing red, or tasting truffles, see Chapter 2, Section 4.2 and Chapter 3, Section 5). The approach known as "reductive physicalism" (see Chapter 4), therefore, does not describe reality as we experience it. We must look at the implications of consciousness being a property of matter that is *different* from those studied in the science of physics (as in Figure 1, and see Chapter 5) if we think that mind may be a property of matter and we want to understand the nature of consciousness.

The next question, then, is whether this property of matter, mind, instantiations of which are known as mental states, can be causally effective "in its own right", as can the other properties of matter (those suitable for study in the physical sciences). For if mind is a property of matter it could be the case that whenever a mental state arises some characteristic state pertains amongst the matter involved (the arrangement and type of the atoms involved *etc.*; presumably the matter involved is the neurons and such-like in the brain). If that were so, some set of physical properties that is also associated with that particular state of the matter would also arise whenever the mental state arose, so it would be impossible to have the mental state without also having the relevant physical state and *vice versa*; it would be the case that you couldn't have one without the other. And how could we then, ever, discover which of the mental and the physical is "doing the causing" when a person takes a decision and implements it (see, for example, Chapter 4, Section 7 and Chapter 5, Section 7)? If you speak to a neuroscientist or a physicist, or even a philosopher, about mental causation, and agree to take it that the mental is a property of matter and that you can't have the mental state without some associated, physical (non-mental) state and *vice versa*, he/she is likely to immediately assert that: "it is the physical state, not the mental state, that does the causing". But is it?

I claim in this book, see Chapter 2, Section 4.3, that we know, from introspection, that when we choose to go for a walk instead of going to the library, or decide to climb Everest instead of remaining safe at home, we choose the action we do because of the way we *feel* about the situations that we think may arise as the future unfolds given the various options available regarding our actions. I claim that we know, from introspection, that *feelings* (*e.g.*, Watson's 'valuation system', see footnote in Chapter 2 Section 4.3) are necessary for practical reasoning, and therefore, since consciousness is necessary for experiencing feelings, we know that it is the person's ability to experience mental states that enables the identification of the action which he/she *feels* is most desirable, all things considered. Somehow, the way the person feels about the expected outcomes of the available actions must affect the choice he/she makes, and implements, regarding which action to perform; the mental state must be able to influence the physics of the action. This assertion gains support from the observation that if the part of the brain thought to be involved in assessing the relative desirability of the available actions (the basal ganglia) is damaged in an accident, or following surgical intervention, there appears to be no effect on the person's cognitive function, but the decisions the person takes thereafter appear random, rather than reflecting the values a normal person would put on the consequences of the alternative actions available (see Chapter 6, Section 5.2)

It seems that feelings are necessary for effective decision-taking. Consciousness, with the ability that it bestows to experience feelings about alternative bundles of expected outcomes and to compare them, appears to be the "gadget" that evolution has found that enables decisions of this type to be

166

taken effectively; and because of this, consciousness is a great asset for enhancing the likelihood of survival.[84] It is worth noting at this point that the form of the law of nature that describes practical reasoning, spelt out in Chapter 2, Section 4.3, is quite different from the form typically taken by the laws of macro-physics, see Chapter 2, Section 2.2, and maybe this adds an element of plausibility to the *ab initio* judgment that it is necessary that there exist something different from the properties of matter studied in physics, something along the lines of a mental state, if it is going to be possible for decisions of this sort to be taken.

At present, we can only make guesses regarding the mechanism by which the taking of a decision might affect the neurons so that the appropriate action is initiated (see Section 5 of this chapter), but if the above justification is accepted, it surely must be the case that it does.

I conclude that, since feelings are necessary for practical reasoning, it must be the mental state associated with some configuration of matter that is responsible for the action chosen, not the state of the physical (non-mental) properties regarding that configuration of matter; it seems that the 'role' of consciousness is to facilitate survival by enabling effective and efficient decision-taking (see Chapter 6). And finally, with mental states causally effective we do, of course, have free will of a type, and there is therefore a sense in which a 'person' can be said to be morally responsible for the effects of his/her actions (see Chapter 8).

5 How mental causation might operate

5.1 Introduction

It is generally accepted amongst philosophers that there is a problem with accommodating mental causation in our understanding of the universe. Lynne Rudder Baker (1993, p 77) voices the concerns of many modern philosophers when she asks: "How can mental events, in virtue of having mental properties, make a difference to behaviour?" After spelling out the metaphysical assumptions that lead to this question arising, she then remarks: "we must either

---

[84] Even neuroscientists and physicists have been known to balk at the proposition that the type of process studied in the physical sciences can perform something that amounts to a form of cost-benefit analysis.

give up (part of) the metaphysical background picture or give up almost all explanations that have ever been offered for anything".

In the same vein, Crane notes at the beginning of his 1995 paper 'The mental causation debate' that abandoning the dual substance approach in favour of some type of physicalism does not solve the problem regarding mental causation. If we continue to take it that physics is complete in the sense that all physical effects are fully caused by purely *physical* (non-mental) prior histories, and we reject dual causation ("over-determination", see Chapter 5, Section 7), then, inevitably, there is no causal role for mental states to fulfil. The one substance, property dualism type of approach raises, once again, the issues relating to mental causation that Leibniz (1695) was concerned about (see Section A1.4) unless we abandon the assumption that physics is 'complete' in this sense.

5.2 *Hypothetical mechanisms for mental causation*

Giving up part of the metaphysical background that Baker and others, assume to prevail is precisely what I am suggesting in this book that we should do. If the role of consciousness is to facilitate the taking of complex decisions, as I suggest here (Chapter 2, Section 4.3), it *must* be the case that feelings have an influence on the outcome of the decision-making process; it must be the case that mental events, *in virtue of having mental properties*, affect behaviour and therefore actions. In this section, I note some of the possible practical implications of postulating that there must be effective mental causation *per se*. This section therefore carries a health warning: much of the material in it, if not all of it, will turn out to be the stuff of fantasy.

Familiar force fields

In physics, nowadays, 'causes' are generally taken to operate at a distance through a force. These forces are carried by one type of fundamental particle, called a boson, and they enable a different type of fundamental particle, a fermion (the 'cause', say), to affect the behaviour of another fermion (the 'effect') some distance away. According to the present understanding in physics, the Standard Model, there are four fundamental forces: electromagnetism, the weak nuclear force, the strong nuclear force and gravity (which operates on the large scale).

Arguably the most obvious possible source of consciousness, then, would be if the mode of operation of one of these fundamental forces, perhaps the weak nuclear force is associated with a process that takes the form of a maximising relation instead of the "if A then B given C" format generally taken by the laws of physics at the macro level (see Section 4.3 of Chapter 2 and Chapter 5, Section 9.4). Perhaps there is some interaction of particles (including an electron?) that involves the weak boson and uses a maximising or minimising process. This process could then be what we are calling 'proto-consciousness'. On the macro-level, consciousness would then use this 'proto-consciousness' phenomenon to transmit the effect of the mental state associated with the taking of a decision to the action neurons which implement the decision.

Such a process would entail 'motivational affect', the *feeling* that accompanies the taking of a decision (which we take in this book to be an instantiation of the property of matter we call 'mind'), directly influencing the physical (non-mental) behaviour of some fundamental particle, such as an electron, or directly instigating a chemical reaction. The explanation of effective mental causation would then lie simply in the fact that the taking of a decision, following the stimulation of the 'motivational affect' associated with the different options available, results in the emission of some neurotransmitter at one point amongst the neurons rather than at another, or influences the path of an electron operating through this force already known to physics.

A 'decision force'

However, it could be the case that the mental causation process involves a different force, a localised 'field', which one might call a 'decision force', different from the forces familiar to physics today. It would be initiated by the type of mental state that is associated with the taking of a decision and would therefore be related to what the psychologists call 'motivational affect'.[85] It would then have to be able to influence some aspect of the activity amongst the neurons that initiates actions; perhaps it influences the speed or direction of travel of an electron in a neuron, or perhaps the outcome of a chemical process. If such a field were to exist, we would consider it to be one of the fundamental properties of matter.

---

[85] When I contacted Tom Kibble, an ex-colleague from long ago, just before his death ("one of the world's foremost theoretical physicists", *The Guardian*, 9 June 2016) explaining my proposal and asking his view: "on the question of whether there is room in physics, as you know it and understand it, for an extra force or property that is not currently thought to exist", he responded saying: "… there is always room for the introduction of a new force …".

However, although theoretical physicists quite often postulate new forces to explain astronomical phenomena not already explained in a satisfactory way by physics as it is currently formulated, or phenomena related to high energy physics, I am told that today's physicists are reasonably confident about the existence of no more than these four forces operating on the terrestrial level.

Quantum mechanics

A third possibility arises in the context of quantum mechanics. Quantum mechanics describes a system in terms of its "wave function"; from this wave function the probabilities of the results of measurements made on the system can be derived. According to the Copenhagen interpretation of quantum mechanics, physical systems do not have definite properties prior to some measurement being made; quantum mechanics merely indicates the probability that a measurement will produce some result (see von Neumann, 1932, translated 1955). The act of measurement, therefore, causes the set of probabilities described by the wave function to reduce to only one of the possible values ("wave function collapse"). Thus, the position (or momentum) of some particle only becomes "certain" when it is measured by "an observer". On the Copenhagen interpretation of quantum mechanics, therefore, one could argue that there is a role just waiting to be filled by consciousness; because there is a role for something that "performs a measurement", something that "is 'an observer'" (the Copenhagen interpretation is, of course, highly controversial).[86]

So now, suppose that a person is taking a decision about what to do next. He/she is considering all the options for action, weighing up what the consequences of each are likely to be, examining the perceived benefits, the disadvantages, the extent of the uncertainties and the type of risks to which they are subject, and trying to assess which action would be most desirable (see Chapter 2, Section 4.3). Put another way, he/she is comparing the probability distribution of 'value' associated with the different available actions in order to decide which of those probability distributions is the most desirable, to identify the action that should be chosen (as noted in Chapter 2, Section 4.3, various moments of the probability distribution are relevant to its desirability, not just its expected value). The state of the relevant bit of the brain (presumably part of the basal ganglia, see Chapter 6) when this is happening could presumably be represented by a wave function. When the person identifies and decides

---

[86] See London and Bauer (1939), von Neumann (1955), Wigner (1961), Shimony (1963), Jammer (1974), and Hodgson (1991).

upon the option that appears to be the most desirable, when he/she makes that measurement regarding the 'motivational affect' associated with each of the different options, the wave function collapses picking out the chosen action with 100 percent probability (see Penrose, 1989 and Morrison, 2016).

If this were the correct option then we wouldn't be suggesting that there may be something missing in physics as it is today, because it doesn't take account of mental causation, we would instead be saying that there is already known to be a role in physics for an observer, a mind; that the measurement of the intensity of the 'motivational affect' associated with each of the available options, by the person (or creature), triggers the wave function to activate one action rather than another. We would be saying that this is how mental causation operates.

Dark matter

Finally, and perhaps even more 'fantastical', suppose there were another type of matter, perhaps dark matter, that had no interaction with the electromagnetic field but could be influenced by and influence other physical entities through gravity and the weak and/or, but less likely, strong nuclear forces. If this other type of matter carried something one might call 'proto-consciousness', and if it existed here on earth, could it be that this provides the answer? Mind would then be a property, not of the type of matter that we are familiar with here on earth but of a different type of matter, but one that also occurs here. Mental causation might then take place through the influence of mental states on ordinary matter via the weak nuclear force.

Conclusion regarding mechanisms for mental causation

All these possibilities are highly speculative and may seem unacceptably implausible. But the evidence in support of the proposition that consciousness is a property of matter and that it is not reducible to the properties of matter studied in physics, along with the evidence that mental states can be causally effective is quite compelling. As Baker says: "we must either give up (part of) the [current] metaphysical background picture or give up almost all explanations that have ever been offered for anything" (1993, p 77, my insertion).

5.3 Potential for testing the hypothesis

Since it is important in science that hypotheses can be tested, we should note that the hypothesis that the taking of a decision can have a direct effect on an action neuron could, in principle, be explored experimentally. For example, this could be done by investigating whether there are circumstances in which one creature's decision could directly initiate an action by another creature through triggering a relevant change in the second creature's action neurons instead of in its own. This might be done by connecting, in some way, the decision neurons of the first creature (perhaps the relevant part of the first creature's basal ganglia, since that is where it is currently thought such decisions take place, see Chapter 6, Section 5.1) with the action neurons in the second creature's brain. If some type of stimulation of the external senses of the first creature, perhaps suggesting imminent danger of damage or pain, were found to induce an avoidance movement by the second creature, this would support the proposal that mental causation involved the particular types of matter associated with those organs; and such experimentation might reveal the order of magnitude of the distances involved.[87]

The way this might be done could be similar to the way in which Kandel and his colleagues (see Kandel, 2006) were able to confirm their hypotheses regarding the way in which the short-term memory in sea snails (Aplysia) operates. The scientists tested their hypotheses about the way in which a stimulus to the tail of the sea snail results in the sea snail's gill withdrawal reflex by applying the chemicals they believed act as neurotransmitters in the appropriate places relative to the sea snail's sensory neuron instead of applying the external stimulus. This confirmed their hypothesis that these neurotransmitters were sufficient to trigger the response.

David Lewis, in his influential 1988 paper 'What experience teaches', said: "… if something nonphysical sometimes makes a difference to the motions of physical particles, then physics as we know it is wrong. Not just silent, not just incomplete – wrong" (p 95, and see Chapter 5, Section 2.3). But if one of the above proposals regarding mental causation proved correct it would simply mean that physics as we know it today is incomplete, because something which is "not physical" (in the pertaining to the science of physics sense) would have been shown to be able to make a small difference to the motions of some particles in the brain (and therefore, potentially, an enormous difference to the future path of the world). In all other circumstances, that is in any place other than inside the brains of certain types of creatures, the operation of the physical sciences would be likely to be totally unaffected. Further, *science*, which would

---

[87] A simple experiment that could be viewed as being in this type of class is reported in Pais-Vieira *et al.*, 2013.

include laws of nature relating to mental states as well as those that relate to physics, could be complete. There is nothing in physics as we know it today that suggests that no further developments of this sort can take place; indeed, theoretical physicists regularly postulate new phenomena to explain physical observations that do not fit easily into the current understanding; and decision-taking is certainly a case in point.

6 Conclusion on causally effective property dualism

In many ways, the assumption that mental states are instantiations of a property of matter that can be causally effective and that they are not reducible to the properties of matter studied in the science of physics is an appealing hypothesis. It constitutes a coherent description of the ontology of mind, and it explains *why* mind can be thought of as existing in the context of the material in the brain, so it suggests that the perception that there is an explanatory gap, the so-called 'hard problem', is misplaced. It also deals with both the knowledge argument (because it implies that phenomenal facts do exist) and the conceivability argument (because the conceivability argument only implies that physicalism cannot be true as a matter of logic, it says nothing about the possibility that physicalism could be true because consciousness is a property of matter, that it is true because of laws of nature, not logic).

The hypothesis seems to tick all the boxes except one. If mental causation is effective *per se*, then one type of causal process, a creature deciding to perform an action, has a mental (rather than a physical) cause, so physics is not causally complete. A causally incomplete physics has long been considered by many philosophers to be an unacceptable notion. But the approach is consistent with the proposition that science is complete, in the sense that all the causes and all the effects of all the laws of nature could be included within it. The implication is simply that there may be another property of matter, different from those that are studied in physics, and there may be other causal processes besides those of which we are currently aware; science may be wider in its scope than the physics that some had thought might explain everything.

What we are doing is postulating the existence of an additional property of matter, not presently considered by physicists, that can interact with the properties of matter already incorporated into physics, so that we can explain a phenomenon that we know exists and that is not explained by physics. Perhaps we should think again about the causal completeness of physics.

173

8

The free will problem

1 Introduction

My purpose in this chapter is to examine the question of whether our assumption of causally effective property dualism combined with some form of universal causation (deterministic or probabilistic) is consistent with an acceptable form of free will: that is, whether 'compatibilism' could hold.

However, the issues involved in the free will problem seem to be an order of magnitude more subtle than is the case for most of the other issues I address in this book. I start, therefore, for the avoidance of confusion, by spelling out precisely what I mean by each of the three key terms used in the analysis: 'determinism', 'free will' and 'moral responsibility'. We then turn to van Inwagen's Consequence Argument, which appears to carry the implication that 'compatibilism', the proposition that both determinism and free will can hold, is incoherent.

However finally, after a brief but important digression on the possible meanings associated with the personal pronoun (and the term 'person' and proper names) we establish that compatibilism, of a sort, is possible.

2 The meaning of 'determinism'

2.1 Determinism

According to the *Stanford Encyclopaedia of Philosophy*, the meaning of the term 'determinism' is given by: "The *world* is *governed by* (or is *under the sway of*) determinism if and only if, given a specified *way things are at a time t*, the way things go *thereafter* is *fixed* as a matter of *natural law*" (Hoefer, 2016).

It follows that if strict determinism were a true description of the universe, then every event that occurred would be related by a causal process to some collection of things that could be labelled its (immediate) 'causes' given the situation that pertained. Further, if determinism held the set of these causal processes would be 'complete', in the sense that *every* event, mental as well as physical, would have a cause of this kind; science would be complete. In the most obvious, simple, case there would be a law of nature that decreed that if event A were to be instantiated in circumstances C, then event B would follow with 100 percent certainty.[88] It would then follow that, with perfect knowledge of some situation in the past along with perfect knowledge of all the causal processes every future event could be predicted (and every event that had happened in the past could be known). It could therefore be said that determinism thus defined implies something that one might call 'predetermination': the proposition that everything that happens has been 'determined' in the above sense from the beginning of time, by the Big Bang.

But this definition of determinism rules out the possibility of probabilistic causal processes being included in a situation that is termed 'deterministic'. And if probabilistic causal processes are ruled out of 'determinism', by definition, then given the presumed fact that some of the laws of nature *are* probabilistic (*cf.*, the decay of a radium nucleus, and/or events that are explained by quantum mechanics and/or events that follow the decisions of creatures if those turn out to be probabilistically determined), determinism thus defined seems to be of little interest. We need to coin a term for the situation that allows probabilistic causal processes as well as the 100 percent certain causal processes of 'determinism'. In this book, I make use of the term 'universal causation' and

---

[88] Generally, any effect has several possible immediate causal factors, various subsets of which are necessary for its occurrence, and any causal event is likely to have more than one effect. Also, as we shall see, the causes of any event in fact go backwards in time, in a forking and combining set of chains, until finally arriving at the Big Bang.

this should be interpreted as including probabilistic causal processes as well as those causal processes that fix an outcome with 100 percent certainty.

There are, in fact, two alternatives to the theme of strict determinism, and both are generally known to philosophers as 'indeterminism' because in both cases outcomes are unpredictable, or random. But the term 'random' has two distinct meanings: it can be a technical term indicating that something is subject to a well-defined probability distribution; alternatively, it can indicate total unpredictability, that is, the lack of any identifiable cause.[89] This means that there are two forms of 'indeterminism'.[90] The two forms of indeterminism have very different implications for free will so it is important to distinguish them.

2.2 *Stochastic causal processes*

First, consider the type of indeterminism that involves the possibility that whereas there are causal processes relating to every event, some or all these processes are probabilistic in the sense of incorporating a well-defined probability distribution, so that if event A were to occur in circumstances C, a law of nature might decree that event B would follow with some predetermined probability, perhaps with event D being instantiated in the situations in which B is not. Every event would still have a cause, and therefore could be said to be "determined by a causal process", but it would not be the case that, given knowledge of the causal processes and the situation at some point in time, every event could be predicted. 'Predetermination' would not hold. However, events could, in principle, be predicted with an appropriate probability given perfect knowledge of what has gone before along with perfect knowledge of the causal processes.

This is the form of (so-called) indeterminism that I am including in the term 'universal causation', and I take it that it carries the implication that causal processes *may* be probabilistic. I reserve the term 'indeterminism' for the case in which an event has no identifiable cause (spelt out in the next section).

---

[89] See Eagle, 2016 for a discussion of these terms.

[90] Philosophers often ignore the possibility of the second, lack of any identifiable cause, type of unpredictability and consider only the possibility of an event being determined by a process that incorporates a probability distribution; see for example Robert Kane's 2007 paper; in which a probabilistically determined situation is referred to as being 'undetermined', or see Fischer (2007).

There is nothing incoherent about this more general, probabilistic, interpretation of the causal processes; indeed, I think we can be confident that there can be probability in a causal process: on a macro scale it seems plausible because of the stochastic way the nuclei of radio-active elements, such as radium, decay; on a micro scale it seems inescapable, because of the experimental support for quantum mechanics. However, it should come as no surprise that for many of the most familiar laws of nature, which relate to large-scale physics, such as Boyle's law and the laws of motion, the probabilistic element is either extremely small or non-existent; a large stochastic element attaching to such a law would make it much more difficult for us to discover it. It does not follow, of course, that the causal processes of psychology or economics, if such exist, would have minuscular probabilistic elements associated with them (see Chapter 5, Section 7.3), and nor do the causal processes that arise in modern medicine and weather forecasting have small probabilistic elements; predicting in those disciplines is more akin to gambling.

This form of indeterminism, which is an aspect of what we are calling 'universal causation', has the same implications for free will as does determinism: in neither case can the operation of someone's will change the substance of a causal process, including the probability distributions implicit within it. If, because of the causal processes, a person in circumstances C has a probability p of choosing action B and a probability $(1 - p)$ of choosing action D then their behaviour will be consistent with that fact, and observations would find that to be the case. If universal causation holds, the probability that a person will choose one action rather than another would be determined by a causal process, given the circumstances and given that person's values (their disposition to experience certain types of feelings in certain circumstances); but this does not mean that the person's freedom to make choices is fundamentally different in some way from that which would pertain in the absence of the probabilities. A person cannot influence the probabilities implicit in the causal processes.[91]

---

[91] Robert Kane justifies the existence of his self-forming acts (SFAs) on the basis that there can be "tension and uncertainty in our minds" (2007, p 26). He suggests that, when you take a decision in such circumstances, "(t)he indeterministic noise would have been an obstacle that you overcame by your effort" (p 27). On my view, Kane's SFAs could be about second order volition (Frankfurt, 1971), but cannot be about a person's will having an influence over the probability of an outcome in a law of nature because causal processes such as these, *by definition*, are not "up to us" (see van Inwagen, 1983, p 16).

It has been suggested (see Fischer, 2007, pp 44-46) that if it was discovered that the laws of nature had 100 percent probabilities associated with them rather than 99.9 percent (say), that might be a finding of key importance to people's views about the existence of freedom and moral responsibility. But the understanding of probabilistic causal processes spelt out in this section suggests that it would make no difference whatsoever.

2.3 A lack of causal processes

Now suppose that universal causation (either the deterministic or the probabilistic variety) operates for causal processes relating to most of the events that take place in the world, but that it does not operate for certain events relating to mental states; an assumption reminiscent of Davidson's anomalous monism. [92] The causal processes would then leave some mental events unexplained: there would not even be a probability distribution underlying the occurrence of these mental states, there would be *no* explanation; science would not be complete (see Chapter 2, Section 2.4). If this were so, and if it was also the case that mental states can be causally effective, so an agent's mental state involving a decision regarding action (an intentional mental state) could directly cause a physical event (the agent's action) to take place, there would be no identifiable prior cause of the mental state that gave rise to the action – the person would be "a prime mover unmoved" (see Chisholm 1964, para. 11: "In doing what we do, we cause certain events to happen, and nothing – or no-one – causes us to cause those events to happen")[93]. Key aspects of mental states would then be outside science. A circumstance relating to the ontology of mind in which this situation might arise would be if consciousness (and therefore mental states) were a property of another substance, different from matter; that is if the 'dual substance' approach to the nature of mind were to pertain (this is discussed in Appendix 1).

Importantly, this case (called 'indeterminism' in this book, with some events 'undetermined') can have differing implications for our views regarding free will depending on the point in the causal chain at which the indeterminism arises. The implications for free will depend on whether the undetermined event takes place at the time the decision is being arrived at, simply influencing individual

---

[92] Of course, it could be that determinism also does not always operate for the events that are not related to mental states, but this seems less probable and anyway would add nothing to our story.
[93] Pereboom calls this an 'undetermined agent-cause' (2007, see p 85).

actions, or whether it affects the person's values – their dispositions to experience certain types of feelings in certain circumstances.

First, suppose that the individual actions initiated by a person are sometimes 'uncaused' (no causal process, not even a probabilistic one). In this case one might interpret such choices as being outside the control of the 'person', and hold that the person who initiated the action could not, therefore, be held to be *morally* responsible for it (see later). This is the 'luck objection' to libertarianism, described in Mele (2006), and Pereboom (2007, p 102), which draws on the writings of Hume (1739/40, Book II, Part III, Sections 1-2). So, in this case, indeterminism of this second kind could be interpreted as implying that in these instances a person cannot be viewed as being morally responsible for his/her actions.

The more interesting situation, however, is that in which the person *is* viewed as being morally responsible for his/her actions, because the actions are determined by the person's values and it is the values themselves that have an element that is uncaused. This raises a question as to what it is that determines a person's values. I take it here that people arrive in this world with initial dispositions to experience certain types of feelings in certain sorts of circumstances, and that these feelings affect their choices. The values, the disposition to experience feelings, that a person has at any later point in time develop from these initial dispositions given the person's experiences during his/her life. The question that then arises is: "what determines these initial dispositions?" There are two possibilities. A person's initial dispositions could be determined by the causal processes, possibly with some stochastic element, in a manner consistent with the one-substance, universal causation approach to science described in Chapter 2, Section 2.2. If this is the case, the person's genes are likely to be at least partially responsible for the nature of their initial dispositions, although there would be probabilistic and environmental elements involved also. Alternatively, however, a person's initial dispositions may not be determined by a causal process, they may simply pop up, uncaused, in the foetus when the 'person' is *in utero*. An alternative to this would be if the person's values were subject to uncaused influences at some later point in their life. If either of these were so, there would be no cause that we can comprehend that determines the nature of the person's values. In this case the person's values would *not* be wholly determined by some prior happenings through a causal process, probabilistic or not, they would arise, at least in part, in a manner beyond our comprehension.

If a person's values were not wholly determined by causal processes albeit with a probabilistic element – if, instead, they were at least partially determined by something beyond our understanding, one might then feel able to argue that the person could be called a "prime mover unmoved" in the sense of Chisholm (1964, see above). In this case universal causation would not hold. This is therefore an example of the case known to philosophers as 'libertarianism'.

An uncaused element to the values a person has seems to be the only way in which libertarianism can arise, since as shown above, if we introduce an uncaused element into the way decisions are taken we find that the person cannot be held to be morally responsible for their actions.

2.4 Conclusion on determinism

The purpose of this chapter is to discover whether compatibilism is possible, given our causally effective property dualism approach to mind. It is clear from the above that universal causation, of either the deterministic or the probabilistic kind, would be consistent with the one substance approach to the ontology of mind, and therefore with property dualism. Libertarianism, with a person's initial values arriving 'uncaused', in a manner beyond our comprehension, carries with it the implication that science is not complete. Such a situation could therefore arise in a dual substance approach to the ontology of mind but not in our causally effective property dualism approach.

3 The meaning of 'free will'

In Chapter 6, Section 3 we addressed the meaning of the term the 'will', and looked at practical reasoning and the role of a person's values in determining the choices he/she makes. Here, after summarising the working of practical reasoning and looking in more depth at the role of the person's values, we examine what the adjective 'free' might mean in the context of the will.

3.1 The operation of the will

As we have seen in Chapter 6, the term 'the will', in philosophy, picks out an aspect of the mind. It describes the aspect of the mind that enables practical reasoning to be used so that a specific type of choice can take place: choice of action in the case of complex, multi-criteria situations. This aspect of the mind is one of the fundamental attributes of a person – without a will a person would not be able to operate in the manner we take to be normal for people; he/she could survive only as the result of automatic reflexes pre-programmed before birth and the responses that might become programmed into the system as a result of events in the person's life.[94] Along with making these choices, the person must have the ability to implement the choice he/she has made regarding what to do next, and therefore it is implicit in the proposition that a person has a will, and can perform practical reasoning, that the information relating to the person's feelings, his/her preferences relating to the options available, can affect his/her actions, and therefore that there are mental states that can be causally effective.

In Chapter 6, Section 3.2, we saw that there are three separate functions associated with practical reasoning. First, the person must collect a whole lot of facts from his/her long-term memory (see Appendix 2, Section 2.4) and form a view about what the likely outcomes of each possible action would be along with a rough estimate of how probable these outcomes are; these facts and probabilities, embodying what the person believes to be case about the world, could be called his/her 'beliefs' and they are based on the person's experience in the past and on what he/she has learned from others. Next, the person must identify how he/she feels about these likely outcomes in the light of his/her values including any perceptions regarding duties. Finally, the person's feelings about the bundle of expected outcomes of the actions, given the beliefs, must be compared, one against another, to identify the action deemed likely, on balance, to bring about the most desirable, or at least an acceptable, outcome. The person's conclusion would then be something like, repeating Watson's words: "the thing for me to do in these circumstances, all things considered, is *d*" (1975, p 346, see footnote 34 on p 36 for the full quote). The person will initiate the chosen action at the appropriate time (demonstrating the implicitly assumed effectiveness of mental causation).[95]

---

[94] As noted in Chapter 3, Section 4.2, the fact that Libet *et al.* (1982) have shown that some simple timing decisions can be taken on automatic pilot does not mean that *all* decisions are taken in this manner.

[95] In his 2007 paper, Fischer considers the case in which reductive physicalism holds and practical reasoning takes place but the action identified as best is, in fact, initiated by factors beyond the control of the person concerned rather than by the person. In this case the proposition that the use of the will in performing practical reasoning is effective in determining action would, rather obviously, be nothing more than an innocuous fantasy; mental states would be epiphenomenal.

There is then a question as to what aspect it is of a person that makes that person choose one action rather than another; what is it that makes a person's actions characteristic of that person.

3.2 The role of a person's values

Clearly, the component of the will that is important in determining the characteristic choices of some person is not their ability to make a comparison of the 'motivational affect' associated with different options. If the ability to make such comparisons were swapped between two people, leaving each person's values and beliefs unchanged so the 'motivational affect' associated with each of the options remained the same, there would no significant change in the choices the person made. It would be much the same as if one person's heart or kidney were swapped with another's.[96] It is therefore the person's values and their beliefs that are the factors determining the characteristic choices a person makes: what the person *believes* will be the likely consequences of their chosen action, and the way the person *feels* about those various possible consequences.

The feelings to which our values give rise, which influence the judgment of a person who is choosing between alternative actions, come in a great range of shapes and sizes. They concern our subjective experiences and involve consciousness of sensory perceptions, feelings, thoughts and emotions. On a trivial level, I may dislike vinegar while you may love it, perhaps because my taste buds are different from yours, or perhaps because the connections in my brain operate in a different way from yours so the 'what it feels like' experience for each of us is different, or perhaps because of different experiences we have had in the past. Similarly, some key aspect of the feelings to which our value systems give rise may differ: you may tend to give the effect of your actions on other people a greater weight than I, discounting them on average, relative to the effects on yourself, perhaps by only 10 percent compared to my 50 percent, say; or I might tend to leave effects that are likely to occur only in the far distant future out of the reckoning, while perhaps you generally take them into account, applying some appropriate internal time discounting rate. Our past histories may differ, so I may care deeply about the welfare of person X while this person

---

[96] See Bernard Williams (1970), where he postulates the switching of two people's brains.

is of no special importance to you. Some people base their actions on what they deem to be their 'duty' on appropriate occasions while others, perhaps, do not. Some of these important aspects of people's values may have their foundations in the genes they inherited, or they may have some source beyond our comprehension (see Section 2.3 in this chapter); but in both these cases the person's values are likely to have been heavily influenced by the person's experience, by all that has happened to the person during his/her life. Clearly, all these things can be crucial in determining which action is chosen in some situation.

The possession of a will therefore enables a person to make a certain type of choice, the type of choice that requires practical reasoning because the alternative options include several different types of outcome (such as sensory pleasure, risk of pain or effects on other people the chooser may care about) which are not directly comparable one with another. The feelings associated with the likely outcomes therefore may need to be evaluated thoughtfully and deliberated upon carefully if it is going to be possible to make a sound decision regarding which option appears, at the time the decision is taken, and to the person concerned, to be the one likely to lead to the best outcome.[97] Without a will, a person (if one could call a thing without a will a 'person') would be unable to take a decision.

3.3 When is the will free?

With this background, we can address the question of what we mean by the term 'free will'. If a person has a 'will' he/she can perform the various functions we have identified that enable first the choice and then the initiation of a preferred action, and of course we would not consider the will to be free if either of these functions was constrained.[98] So I now identify the circumstances in which we might wish to say that a person was *not* free in his/her choice and/or ability to initiate an action.

Most obviously, the person does not have free will if he/she is unable, for some external reason, to perform the action chosen as the one to be preferred.

---

[97] It may seem tempting to identify some part of the will with the 'self' or to suggest that it is within the will that something that one might call the 'agent' component of a person resides (see Velleman, 1992, for example), but we have no need to do this in this book.

[98] See Borges' short story 'The Garden of Forking Paths' (Borges,1941), much cited in the recent literature on free will, and see Kane (2007, p 6) and Fischer (2007, p 46).

A person can be in a situation in which his/her action selection function is able to operate freely but he/she is physically constrained from acting on a choice, as when a person's finger is forced upon the trigger of a gun to shoot another 'against their will' (as in Chisholm, 1964) or when a person is constrained unable to move when he/she wishes to help someone in distress. Hobbes (1651) saw this as the only constraint on what he called "free will", saying:

> "from the use of the words free will, no liberty can be inferred of the will, desire, or inclination, but the liberty of the man; which consisteth in this, that he finds no stop in doing what he has the will, desire, or inclination to do."

But nowadays we consider that freedom to perform a chosen action is only one aspect of freedom of the will. There are also situations in which one might argue that a person's *choice* (the identification of that which he/she "has the will, desire, or inclination" to do) is not free, perhaps because of interference from other people, perhaps because events have distorted some aspect of the person's choice mechanism. This may be because his/her values have been interfered with in some way, by other people or by events. The person may be without values (a psychopath?); the cases referred to as 'Frankfurt cases' (Frankfurt, 1969), and Pereboom's set of four cases involving Professor Plum (Pereboom, 2007, pp 94-97) are also cases in point, as are hypnosis, drug-administration and addiction. Or it may be that the person's beliefs concerning facts and probabilities have been tampered with; as when someone is deliberately (or not deliberately) convinced by another of the validity of false information. Or, again, it may be that the ability to remember the relevant facts has gone (as in dementia), so the data relating to the facts and probabilities needed for the weighing of alternative options are simply not available to the chooser or that the ability to experience the feelings that relate to values have been damaged by some illness or accident (as in the case of Phineas Gage, see Damasio, 1994). In all these cases, we might claim that a person's will is not 'free' in the sense required.

But here we are concerned with the question of whether it is *ever* possible for a person to have something that could be called 'free will', so we can leave aside those interesting cases in which the will might be said to be constrained or distorted or disabled in some way, and therefore not free, and in the rest of this chapter I take it that in the absence of any of these afflictions a person's will can be treated as being 'free' – in the sense that the person is free to use practical reasoning to choose and initiate an appropriate action from some set of available alternative actions, *given* that his/her values and perception of the facts of the case have not been tampered with.

However, there is a question as to whether this is really the 'free will' that has so often been referred to by philosophers, that we associate with moral responsibility and which is sometimes described as being the situation in which: "the ultimate sources of our actions lie in us and not outside us in factors beyond our control" (Kane, 2007, p 5). So before looking at the so-called free will problem, we need to consider what it is that we mean when we refer to 'moral responsibility'.

4 The meaning of 'moral responsibility'

In this section I first address the question of the meaning of 'responsibility' when a person is deemed to have 'responsibility' for the occurrence of an event; then I examine the meaning of the term 'moral responsibility'.

4.1 Responsibility

Where we have a causal process, we have a cause and an effect. It is often said that the event that is viewed as being the cause was 'responsible' for the event that was the effect. The phrase "was the cause of" appears to be synonymous with "was responsible for" in this context. Thus, the church clock was responsible for waking my guest, and the hurricane was responsible for blowing down your house. But causal processes come in forking chains running backwards in time to the Big Bang, so whatever it was that caused some event to take place was itself caused by some prior event or set of events. 'Responsibility' can thus be tossed around from the church clock to the vicar to the church committee to the maker of the church clock, and so on, forking into many branches along the way.

Clearly, there is never just one event that is responsible for something happening; there is always a forking chain of causes; if universal causation holds the forking chain will go back to the beginning of time, to the Big Bang. The meaning of the terms 'responsible for' and 'caused' are deceptive in their implications in this regard.

4.2 *Moral responsibility*

Now consider the question of how a person comes to be 'morally' responsible for something that happens rather than just being responsible for it as, one might say, some link in a set of forking chains of causes is responsible.

Neither the clock nor the hurricane would be charged with moral responsibility, it is going to be a 'person' that plays that role. And, as we have seen above, it is the person's values and beliefs that determine the choice a person makes, so it is the person's values, given his/her beliefs, that are the aspect of a person that makes him or her *morally* responsible for their actions. And this is so regardless of what has made those values what they are. It is irrelevant whether we think that the person's values are wholly determined by all that has gone before along with the laws of nature, as would be the case if universal causation held (where the person's initial disposition to experience certain types of feelings is determined by the laws of nature, which may be probabilistic, along with what has gone before), or whether we think of their values as being in part 'uncaused' as with libertarianism (or indeterminism, where the initial disposition to experience certain types of feelings appeared out of the blue, with a cause beyond our understanding). It also suggests that these judgments regarding the moral behaviour of others might remain the same even if a person's values are due to deliberate human intervention. However, in such a case, if neuroscientists and others were to create a person with obnoxious values, there might be moral opprobrium *also* for those concerned with creating such a person; it is not necessarily the case that only one person is involved in initiating an action that gives rise to moral approval or disapproval in others (see Pereboom's Professor Plum cases, 2007, pp 94-97, for example).[99]

With this approach, in effect, when we pass moral judgment on a person's behaviour what we are doing is praising or blaming the person for the perceived quality of the values that underlie their actions; we are saying: "I like your values and so I have much respect for you", or: "I dislike your values and so I have little respect for you". Whether we are justified in punishing a person who

---

[99] Fischer (2007) argues that so long as a person deliberates over some choice using practical reasoning (in his terminology, the person is 'reasons-responsive') we could say that a person has moral responsibility for their actions even though his/her actions are determined by external factors, because mental states are epiphenomenal. The moral responsibility is allocated because the action performed is the one the person has chosen. This is somewhat akin to the approach of Leibniz, noted in Appendix 1, where God has arranged things so that the mental and the physical act in harmony without either body or soul disturbing the laws regarding the other.

performs actions that we deem to be based on values we find obnoxious or rewarding a person of whose actions we approve is another question, and one that is beyond the scope of this book; here we go no further than the attempt to understand the nature of moral responsibility.

But if we accept that it is the person's *values* that are the issue here it raises the question of whether, when we praise or blame a person in this way for the actions that he or she has taken, we are praising or blaming the person's values *per se*, or the person, or whether the concept of a person necessarily encompasses their values, so the two come to the same thing. What, exactly, do we mean when we use the word 'person'? Is it necessarily the case that the person's values are included when we refer to the concept of a 'person'? Would it make sense to refer to a 'person', or use a personal pronoun, in a situation in which the thing referred to might have no values? I address this question, which turns out to be of considerable importance to the clarity of our thinking on these issues, in Section 7 of this chapter. First, we must examine the Consequence Argument.

5 The Consequence Argument

Peter van Inwagen (1983) says, summarising succinctly an argument he has set down at greater length in his 1975 paper:

"If determinism is true, then our acts are the consequences of the laws of nature and events in the remote past. But it is not up to us what went on before we were born, and neither is it up to us what the laws of nature are. Therefore, the consequences of these things (including our present acts) are not up to us" (1983, p 16).

This thought is known as the Consequence Argument, and had previously been spelled out by Carl Ginet (1966), among others. So if universal causation, either the deterministic or the probabilistic version, holds, it appears to follow as a simple matter of logic that our own acts are not "up to us"; and from that it follows that the proposition that we have moral responsibility for what we do is ruled out, so compatibilism is impossible. If the Consequence Argument is correct, not only is everything determined by what has gone before along with the laws of nature, but also our practical reasoning and decision-taking are totally irrelevant to those causal processes:

187

future events are, quite simply, not "up to us". Many philosophers have found this argument persuasive (see Fischer, 2007 p 56, Kane, 2007 p 10, Pereboom, 2001, pp 33-37, and many others).

However, now suppose that one of the laws of nature referred to in the first two sentences of van Inwagen's Consequence Argument is about how a person takes a decision, and is based on the third of our fundamental propositions (see Chapter 2, Section 4.3 and Section 3.2 of this chapter). Such a law of nature might say, paraphrasing somewhat: "a person uses practical reasoning to decide what to do next and implements whatever action he or she decides should be the one chosen". If this law pertained, it seems that it would be the case that when we take a decision the consequences of that decision *are* "up to us": the consequences would be the direct result of a decision that is taken by us using practical reasoning and is then implemented by us. Given this law of nature, these decisions would be part of the causal processes that determine the effect which the events in the past and present have on what happens in the future. But where a decision has been taken in this manner it is a *person* who has determined what should happen in the future in this regard, a *person* who has affected the future course of the world, using his/her own values and beliefs to make a difference to what happens in the future. There is a sense, therefore, in which these things that we call 'persons' do, actually, influence the future course of the world in a manner that depends on their own values. In these circumstances, therefore, we *can* say, *correctly*, that the choice is "up to" the person and we *can* say that there is a sense in which a person is free to choose; for the outcome of the choice depends on the person's values (indeed, a person with different values might well choose a different option). We *can*, therefore, hold a person responsible for the consequences of his/her actions.

There is no reason in logic why such a law should not operate, and so no reason why it should not be one of the laws of nature referred to in van Inwagen's summary statement of the Consequence Argument (above). Therefore, there must be something wrong with van Inwagen's argument. Before proceeding, however, it may be helpful to summarise the situation we are now considering.

6 The fundamental 'facts'

The two fundamental 'facts' that we take as given when addressing this issue raised by the Consequence Argument are the following:

First, that universal causation holds, so every event is determined by causal processes along with events in the remote past.

Second, that a person takes decisions about his/her actions using practical reasoning, and the values and beliefs that determine the outcome of his/her decisions have, of course, been determined by causal processes and events in the remote past.

Our question is then:

Given these, does a person have free will, that is, can a person be held to be morally responsible for the consequences of his/her actions (so long as circumstances such as those noted in Section 3.3 of this chapter do not pertain)?

In the next section, we see that if a person is to be held to be morally responsible for the consequences of his/her actions, a constraint must be imposed on the meaning that can be attributed to the word 'person' (and to any personal pronouns or proper names that are used in its place). We also find that, given that this meaning is attributed to the term 'person', there is a question as to whether what is then implied for the meaning of the term 'free will' is acceptable.

7 The concept of a 'person'

We start by considering Chisholm's famous example of the man who was forced by another man to shoot someone (Chisholm, 1964, p 4). Chisholm says:

"… if what we say he did was really something that was brought about by a second man, one who forced his hand upon the trigger, say, or who, by means of hypnosis, compelled him to perform the act, then since the act was caused by the *second* man it was nothing that was within the power of the *first* man to prevent. And precisely the same thing is true, I think, if instead of referring to a second man who compelled the first one, we speak instead of the *desires* and *beliefs* which the first man happens to have had. For if what we say he did was really something that was brought about by his own beliefs and desires, if these beliefs and desires in the particular situation in which he happened to have found himself caused him to do just what it was that we say he did do, then, since *they* caused it, *he* was unable to do anything other than just what it was that he did do. It makes no difference whether the cause of the deed was internal or external; if the cause was some state or event for which the man himself was not responsible, then he was not responsible for what we have been mistakenly been calling his act" (his italics).

In the first case, Chisholm's man was not responsible for shooting the person because he was forced to do it by the second man. In the second case, in just the same way according to Chisholm, the man was not responsible for what he did because he was forced to do it by his own beliefs and desires.

If universal causation holds, the man's beliefs and desires are not "up to him". And it is the man's beliefs and desires that caused his action. So, is the man responsible for his action, or is he not? That depends on whether the man's beliefs and desires are part of what the word 'man' (and the personal pronouns 'his' and 'he') connote, or whether they are not. If they *are*, the man is responsible for his actions because it is his beliefs and desires, which are part of *him*, that caused the action to occur. In this case, therefore, the consequences of things that are not up to us can be "up to us", so the conclusion of the Consequence Argument does not hold. If those pronouns do not connote the man's beliefs and desires, and in Chisholm's case they do not, for Chisholm defines "the man himself" as a thing without beliefs and desires, the man is not responsible for his actions.

Thus the "he" in the final clause of the Chisholm quote, which picks out the first man, has been explicitly stripped of the man's values (of his "beliefs and desires"). Chisholm has explicitly excluded the "they", the man's "beliefs and desires", from being implied by the "he". So whatever might be associated with the pronoun "he", as used on this occasion, there is certainly nothing there that could possibly be responsible for taking the decision to initiate an act. Chisholm's conclusion that something he calls "the man himself" was not responsible rests on his implicit assumption that a person's values are *not* an integral part of what he means when he uses the words "the man himself".

We can now see that van Inwagen's Consequence Argument would be valid only if the person's values (which, if universal causation holds, are the result of the laws of nature and what went on before we were born) are *not* connoted by the word 'us' in its final sentence since, given his/her beliefs (determined by previous experience *etc.*), a person's 'values' are the aspect of the person that is responsible for the decision that he/she takes concerning what to do next. The attributes of a person which are connoted by the word 'us' in van Inwagen's Consequence Argument therefore cannot include the person's values, if it is to hold. But if that is the case, the word 'us' in that context picks out a thing that is incapable of taking decisions in any manner other than randomly because it has no values.[100] So the Consequence Argument is then not of any interest.

The significance of this question about what is or is not associated with the concept of a person is nicely illustrated by Galen Strawson's impossibility theorem (1993, p 5). This states that: "We cannot be truly or ultimately morally responsible for our actions ...." Strawson justifies this result by pointing out that "Nothing can be *causa sui* – nothing can be the cause of itself", and then saying: "In order to be truly morally responsible for one's actions one would have to be *causa sui*, at least in certain crucial mental respects." If we accept this requirement for a person to be "truly morally responsible" for his/her actions, then Strawson is, of course, correct. But my values are the part of *me* that determines my actions. So, if I accept that the values that I happen to hold, whatever the reason for my holding them, are part of what I refer to as *me* (they are connoted by that pronoun) then it follows that *I* am morally responsible for my actions. I do not, then, have to be responsible for *causing* my values to be the way they are in order to be morally responsible for my actions, as Strawson suggests; all I have to do is accept that my values are an integral part of what I refer to as *me*; so that, although it is my values that determine what I do, it is *me* that is morally responsible for what I do: *I* am morally responsible for my actions so long as that personal pronoun connotes my values.

This question of whether a person's values are or are not viewed as being an integral part of the concept of a person, and therefore connoted by a personal pronoun, is also the key to understanding the significance of van Inwagen's Consequence Argument. As we have seen, he summarises this saying (1983, p 16):

---

[100] There seems to be an implicit assumption in the meaning that we generally attribute to the word 'person', namely that one could remove *all* the person's attributes and yet something fundamental about the person, some essence of the person, will remain. Perhaps we are hardwired to view a person in this way, perhaps it is the result of the culture that surrounds us. The analysis presented here suggests that such an implicit assumption is inappropriate; in order that a 'person' can be morally responsible for his/her actions the thing that is that 'person' *must* have values.

"If determinism is true, then our acts are the consequences of the laws of nature and events in the remote past. But it is not up to us what went on before we were born; and neither is it up to us what the laws of nature are. Therefore, the consequences of these things (including our present acts) are not up to us".

But of course, if that final "us" connoted the person's values, albeit that they have been determined by what went on before we were born and what the laws of nature are, then so long as the person used practical reasoning to decide what to do next, the conclusion of the Consequence Argument, in the final sentence, would be wrong. The consequences of our own acts could then be said to be "up to" the thing we call 'us'.

Given that it is 'our' values that determine our acts, for it not to be the case that 'we' are responsible for these acts requires that that final 'us' in van Inwagen's argument *excludes* the person's values (which in van Inwagen's case are, indeed, explicitly determined by "the laws of nature and events in the remote past"). So, although what he says can be viewed as being true if the word 'us' has no connotations, it would then be of no relevance whatsoever to the free will problem because, as we have seen, if the personal pronoun has no connotations, the thing that is picked out by the personal pronoun is unable to make considered choices and cannot be considered to be responsible for the person's actions.

Another way of making a statement along the lines of that of van Inwagen, in his Consequence Argument, but incorporating the use of a pronoun that connotes the person's beliefs and values, would be to say:

If determinism is true, then what went on before we were born along with the laws of nature determine our values. And since our values are the part of us that determines our acts, it can be said that if determinism is true our acts *are* up to us.

So long as determinism is true, and we define a 'person' as something that has a will, and therefore has values, the 'person' will be able to use practical reasoning when taking certain sorts of decision; so, the 'person' is able to choose freely and the consequences of the person's acts can then be said to be "up to" the person.[101]

8 The free will problem

8.1 The apparent paradox at the heart of the free will problem

We have seen that the decisions people make using practical reasoning are part of the unfolding of the predetermined (perhaps probabilistically) path of the universe. And the person doing the choosing, taking the decision, will experience that familiar feeling of having the power, which freedom of the will engenders, to use his/her values to influence the future course of the world. However, if universal causation (deterministic or probabilistic) holds, that decision is the result of the laws of nature combined with things that happened before that person was born

It is this that leads to the seeming paradox at the heart of the free will problem. Given effective mental causation, we are correct to think that we can influence the future path of the world with our decisions. But the decisions that we take about what to do next are determined by our values and, if universal causation holds, these in turn have been determined by the natural laws and what has gone before, so the future path of the world is, in fact, predetermined (perhaps probabilistically). Therefore, both of the statements:

"the future path of the world is predetermined (maybe probabilistically)"

and

"we influence the future path of the world with our decisions"

can be correct at the same time so long as the personal pronouns 'we' and 'our' are understood to connote a person's values and beliefs. As we have seen (Section 4.1 of this chapter), there is not just *one* cause of an event; responsibility

---

[101] Arthur Schopenhauer neatly summarised the fundamental aspects of this situation when he wrote: "You can do what you will, but in any given moment of your life you can *will* only one definite thing and absolutely nothing other than that one thing" (1841, see p 24; the precise wording depends on the translation).

for events comes in chains (with 'moral' responsibility only being involved when the cause of an event is informed by a person's values) and many important developments in the world have been, are being, and will be caused by people's choices regarding what to do next.

8.2 Can the will be said to be free?

We therefore find that, if we sign up to universal causation (deterministic or probabilistic), although a person can have this thing we call 'free will' in the sense of having freedom to choose, it must be the case that the values that he/she has, that determine the outcome of any choice, have been determined by laws of nature. A question then arises as to whether the word 'free' is appropriate in such circumstances.

If you think of the 'person' as a thing with no characteristics that is constrained by values foisted upon him/her by laws of nature (as in Chisholm, 1964), then that 'person' is clearly not free at all. But if you combine the person's values, along with the person's beliefs and their ability to compare the 'motivational affect' associated with different available options, into something called the 'will', and think of that will as being an essential element of the *person*, then this thing that is called a 'person' can operate freely, given whatever constraints operate in the external world, taking the decisions regarding actions that he/she deems appropriate. The set of options is *truly* available and the 'person', which is a thing with a will, is *truly* free to choose from amongst them. This is apparent from the fact that another person, with different values, might well choose a different option. In this case the 'person', the thing of which the will is an important part, *is* free to choose.

The key issue in deciding whether it can be said that a person has free will, therefore, is what exactly you mean by the word 'person', or the proper name or the pronoun that from time to time replaces that word. If the word 'person' connotes the will, and therefore it connotes the values and the element of a creature that can activate a 'maximisation' style law of nature (see Section 4.3 of Chapter 2), then the thing picked out by that word *can* be said to have 'free will', and *can* be held to be morally responsible for his/her (its?) actions. But if the word 'person' picks out some entity that has associated with it *no* qualities that have been determined by the laws of nature, so it does *not* connote the will, then the thing picked out *cannot* be said to have 'free will' (indeed, it doesn't have a 'will'), and *cannot* be held to be morally responsible for his/her/its actions.

194

Another approach to these issues would be to define a 'person' as "that which is able to determine what to do next in a complex choice situation". Then, since the key factor in determining what to do next is the set of values that operate, the key defining characteristic of a 'person' would be these values, that is, it would be the person's "disposition to experience certain types of feelings in certain circumstances" that was key to what to do next.

8.3 Do we have 'ultimate moral responsibility' for our actions?

Responsibility comes in chains, as we have seen. One thing causes another which in turn causes another and perhaps combines with other happenings to cause yet another. The ultimate responsibility for the hurricane that blew your house down goes back in time to the Big Bang, to the beginning of time.

Moral responsibility however, as defined in Section 4.2 of this chapter, rests with persons. This means that one *could* allocate 'ultimate' moral responsibility to the last person whose decision was necessary for the event in question to take place. For example, Vasili Arkhipov, second-in-command of the Soviet Submarine B-59, who refused his Captain's order to launch nuclear torpedoes against US warships at the height of the Cuban Missile Crisis, could be deemed to be 'ultimately' morally responsible for saving the world as we know it. However, Henry VIII, who decreed that Anne Boleyn should be publicly executed in 1536, must surely pick up some moral responsibility for that event (the executioner presumably had committed himself in advance and felt he had no choice) albeit that there is the possibility that his personality changed somewhat after his head was hit in a jousting session, which may modify our feelings of opprobrium. And where Pereboom's Professor Plum cases (*op. cit.*) are concerned, one could argue that some moral responsibility needs to be transferred, at least partially if not wholly, from the fictional Professor Plum to those who were said to have created the moral monstrosity that he was designed to be.

We therefore conclude that a person could be deemed to be 'ultimately morally responsible' for some event that he or she has intentionally caused, even though the ultimate *causal* responsibility for the event, the ultimate responsibility for its occurrence, must inevitably be with the Big Bang if universal causation is to hold.

8.4 *Conclusion on the free will issue*

Our conclusion on the free will issue is that, given that universal causation operates (deterministic or probabilistic) and so long as the term 'person' carries the implication that the referent has a 'will', and therefore by definition has values, a person has freedom of choice (unless one of the situations described in Section 3.3 of this chapter pertains); and this freedom of choice is what is picked out by the term 'free will' if universal causation holds. For some, this meaning for the term 'free will' may not be enough: it may not be acceptable.

However, *de facto*, in ordinary conversation, we hold that a person who has freedom of choice can be held to be what we call 'morally responsible', at least partially and often wholly 'morally responsible', for the consequences of the actions that he/she chooses to perform.

9 Causally effective property dualism and compatibilism

The purpose of this chapter has been to discover whether, if universal causation (deterministic or probabilistic) holds, something that could be called free will is consistent with the causally effective property dualism approach to mind under examination in this book.

Suppose that it were to turn out that science is complete so there is 'universal causation' (either deterministic or probabilistic), that people have feelings so there must another property of matter besides those that are studied in physics, and that mental states can be causally effective. With universal causation holding, people's values would be determined by the laws of nature given all that has gone before. There is then a question as to whether anything that could be called free will can operate in such circumstances; is something that we might call 'compatibilism' possible?

Since the key feature that determines the outcome chosen in any choice situation is the person's values, it follows that so long as these are viewed as being an essential part of what we refer to when we use the word 'person', or use a pronoun or a proper name, the person referred to can choose freely within the constraints of the external situation; and therefore, there is a sense in which a 'person' so defined *does* have something that one might call 'free will'. Given that practical reasoning is used for taking certain types of decision, it would be the person's values, and therefore the 'person', that takes the decisions which lead to the unfolding of the future course of the world.

Compatibilism (free will combined with universal causation) is therefore a viable position in the case of causally effective property dualism. It can rightly be said that 'we' have freedom to choose, and therefore we have free will, subject only to the requirement that our values are viewed as being part of 'us'. And the fact that, typically, we hold a person morally responsible for the consequences of their actions suggests that, typically, we *do* take the term 'person', and the personal pronouns and proper names, to connote the person's values.

Importantly, however, it is also true that if compatibilism holds, and substance dualism does not so consciousness is a property of matter, causally effective property dualism must be the case. This is because compatibilism holds that a person can be held responsible for the decisions he or she takes, so then it must be the case that a person has values. But it is the person's values determine the decision he or she takes in any choice situation; therefore, the mental states relating to the experience of the feelings that embody the values must be causally effective.

9

Conclusion

We have been considering the possibility that mind is a property of matter. There are then just two alternatives. Reductive physicalism could hold, with everything reducing to the science of physics, or non-reductive physicalism could be the case, with mental states not reducible to physics. We have also been looking at the implications of assuming that mental states can be causally effective, in that they can have a direct effect on physical (non-mental) phenomena.

So first consider the case in which reductive physicalism is the correct explanation. In this case it is taken that everything to do with minds and mental states is reducible to the properties of matter that are studied in the physical sciences. This means that nomological relations must exist that ensure that all the facts pertaining to mental states can be *identified with* facts of the type that are studied in the physical sciences; therefore, all these facts that pertain to mental states *are* of the type that can be studied in the science of physics. If this were so there would be no problem with understanding how mental states could have a causal influence on entities studied in physics; this would take place through the usual laws of nature that operate in the science of physics.

But it is a fundamental tenet of the science of physics that all experiments can be reproduced by other people, and this means that all the facts studied in physics must be perfectly communicable between people linguistically. So if we accept that we know *ab initio* (from introspection) that we cannot communicate to another person exactly what our feelings are like (that it is impossible to communicate linguistically exactly what it is like to experience something like tasting truffles to someone who has never had that experience), reductive physicalism can be ruled out as a possibility.

Then, if we are committed to the proposition that mind is a property of matter, we are left with no alternative other than the second option, non-reductive physicalism; the proposition that there must be another property of matter besides those currently studied by physicists.

But if consciousness is a property of matter that is different from those studied in physics, there are two interesting questions that need to be addressed:

First, how does this property arise? Could 'micro-psychism' be the case, with proto-consciousness one of the properties associated with fundamental particles or with quantum mechanics, so it has been around since soon after the Big Bang? Other possibilities in the philosophy literature include emergence and pan-psychism. But micro-psychism seems the more plausible answer, since all the other properties of matter arise in connection with the fundamental particles. So proto-consciousness could be associated with, for example, the bosons that mediate the weak interaction, or perhaps with the collapse of the wave function – who knows what proto-consciousness might look like in a laboratory? Mental states would then have developed in the brains of complex creatures during evolution, in such a way as to promote the likelihood of survival of the individual and the species. The fact that it is impossible to deduce from the physics of a brain state what it would be like to experience the corresponding mental state, however complete one's knowledge of it might be, would then be just what one would expect.

Second, if we want to maintain the proposition that mental states can be causally effective, what is the mechanism through which a mental state of decision-taking can affect the physical (non-mental) properties of matter? Could one of the usual forces studied in physics be involved (*nb.*, a "maximisation" process seems to be required by decision theory)? Or is there some other force that only operates in brains, with physicists and neuroscientists currently unaware of its existence? Could quantum effects be involved? Or could it be some other mechanism?

If the above simple argument that reductive physicalism is untenable is accepted, and if physicists and neuroscientists take the view that mind may be related to matter, they might wish to take account of the existence of mind when developing theories relating to the fundamental components of matter.

Appendix 1

Substance dualism

1 History of substance dualism

A natural starting point for thinking about the relation between mind and matter seems to be to consider the possibility that the two are separate in some way, as in Figure 5 below. Thus, to the extent that ancient philosophers identified the existence of consciousness, or of mental states, as something that required an explanation they tended to postulate that substance dualism must be the case, that is, they thought that there was probably some special substance, something different from ordinary "matter" (extensive stuff), which, in some sense, *is* consciousness or is something that one might call "spirit".

The ancient Indian philosophers, for example, following Samkhya, the oldest school of Indian philosophy (probably around the 6th Century BC), assumed there was a form of spiritual energy, or a 'being', which they called Purusha; they thought this must have pervaded the entire universe for all time (see Bernard, 1947). Thus, the name Purusha was originally a mythical being, but it came to mean "person," "self," "spirit," or "consciousness", or "the eternal, authentic being". Purusha could be set opposite Prakriti in Indian philosophy, where Prakriti is the basic matter constituting the universe; an early version of two substances approach.

There is still a school of thought, known as Vedānta that signs up to the proposition that consciousness is the fundamental 'substance' from which everything derives. Modern Vedāntic philosophers maintain that, whereas in the far-distant past philosophers had no problem in accepting the existence of consciousness in the same way as they accepted the existence of the physical world, since the advent of Newtonian mechanics Western scientists and philosophers have accepted the materialistic conception of reality (excepting, of course, Berkeley, 1710, who developed a theory named "immaterialism" which denies the existence of matter and maintains that objects like trees and stones only exist in the minds of those who perceive them).[102] The Vedāntic view has taken the opposite stance, it assumes that the origin of everything, either material or immaterial, is "sentient". It sees sentient life as primitive and "reproductive of itself"; life comes from life (see Shanta, 2015). Consciousness, which it sees as being fundamental, then must "manifest itself" in everything that has either a sentient or an insentient nature. So, in contrast to the idea of the evolution of bodies, as proposed by Darwin and his followers, Vedānta signs up to the proposition that the evolution of consciousness is the principle underlying the development of the world.

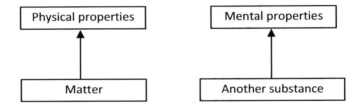

Figure 5 Substance dualism
In substance dualism, mental properties arise in the context of a different substance from that of 'matter', which gives rise to the properties studied in physics. This option is viewed as giving rise to problems relating to mental causation – how can a property of one substance have effects on a property of another substance?

Interestingly, starting from the materialist point of view, Western philosophers have postulated the bundle theory approach to the nature of a "substance" (see Chapter 2, Section 2.4); this assumes that there is just a bundle

---

[102] According to Harari (2011, p 60) it is thought that animistic beliefs were common amongst ancient foragers, who may have assumed that "every animal, every plant and every natural phenomenon has awareness and feelings, and can communicate directly with humans".

of properties with no substratum. If consciousness is taken to be one of the properties in the "bundle", as mass or electric charge might be, this could transform materialism into an approach somewhat akin to this ancient Indian view, effectively a form of pan- or micro-psychism, in which consciousness would be a property that has existed since the beginning of time, just as is postulated in Western philosophy for the properties studied in the physical sciences.

Spinoza, a Dutch philosopher, proposed a similar approach to this Indian concept in 1677. His proposal takes matter and mind to be two of a possibly infinite set of attributes of something all-pervasive that one might call God or Nature.

The closest the ancient Greeks came to a concept of consciousness seems to have been encapsulated in the word 'nous', a key term in the philosophies of Plato and Aristotle (see, for example, Perelmuter 2010). In Plato's later dialogues 'nous' refers to the highest activity of the human soul. A special type of value is attributed to things relating to nous as opposed to things that are perceptible or corporeal. Like the ancient Indian philosophers, the Greeks also saw 'nous' as pervading all things and believed that it had existed from the beginning of time.

The existence of two substances (Ryle's "ghost in the machine", 1949) is probably still where most people start when pondering the nature of consciousness.

2 The existence of mind

Descartes, right at the start of the Age of Enlightenment, began to consider the nature of mind, because he felt it was relevant to his study of science. Over the years he had become aware that there were several things that he was taking for granted without giving their validity any serious consideration, so he decided to sit down and give the whole matter of the fundamentals of 'science' and 'being' some serious thought. In the first of his *Meditations* (1641) he describes how he began by asking himself whether there was anything that he knew for certain. For example, could he be certain that he was sitting by the fire, and that the things he could perceive with his senses as he sat there actually existed? Was it possible that all the things he could perceive were a figment of his imagination, or a dream? He decided that there was no way in which he could be certain that these things were there. He thought, as surely many others must have done

203

before and since, that it could be the case that a demon was deceiving him and that everything, including his perceptions relating to his body and the messages he was receiving from his senses, might be nothing more than illusions. He could see no way of ascertaining whether this was or was not the case.

But then, if there is nothing that he could be certain exists, surely it ought to be the case that he, himself, also might not exist. Could he be certain that he existed? The answer to that question was indubitably yes, that he could – and that was because it was he that had realised that all these things his senses received messages about might not exist; it was he that had the idea that he might have been deceived by some demon, or some strange situation. Clearly, he could think, and that meant that it had to be the case that he existed. This, he concluded, is true beyond all doubt: whenever a person is aware of thinking, it must be the case that he/she exists.

A variant on this thought of Descartes' constitutes our first fundamental proposition (see Chapter 2, Section 4.1): the one thing that we know to be true beyond all doubt is the fact that if we can think, if we experience something that could be called a 'mental state', we know that mental states exist.

3 An argument for substance dualism

Descartes continued his project and reached another important conclusion, one of lasting significance although it is now thought that his reasoning was at fault. He decided that although he was inclined to believe that there was a space-occupying, extended body to which he was clearly very closely conjoined, he himself, by which he meant his mind because that is what he viewed 'himself' as being, was a thinking and non-extended thing, distinct from his body. It must therefore be the case, he concluded, that his mind could exist without his body. Mind cannot therefore exist only in the context of matter. There must be another 'substance'; in Descartes' view this must be a substance which can, as a matter of logic, exist on its own.

Descartes' justification for his view that mind relates to a substance different from that which is studied in physics is translated as follows (see his *Meditations VI*, paragraph 9):

"And, firstly, because I know that all which I clearly and distinctly conceive can be produced by God exactly as I conceive it, it is sufficient that I am able clearly and distinctly to conceive one thing apart from another, in order to be certain that the one is different from the other, seeing they may at least be made to exist separately, by the omnipotence of God; and it matters not by what power this separation is made, in order to be compelled to judge them different; and, therefore, merely because I know with certitude that I exist, and because, in the meantime, I do not observe that aught necessarily belongs to my nature or essence beyond my being a thinking thing, I rightly conclude that my essence consists only in my being a thinking thing [or a substance whose whole essence or nature is merely thinking]. And although I may, or rather, as I will shortly say, although I certainly do possess a body with which I am very closely conjoined; nevertheless, because, on the one hand, I have a clear and distinct idea of myself, in as far as I am only a thinking and unextended thing, and as, on the other hand, I possess a distinct idea of body, in as far as it is only an extended and unthinking thing, it is certain that I, [that is, my mind, by which I am what I am], is entirely and truly distinct from my body, and may exist without it." (Inserts by Lafleur, the translator).

This can be written in a structure somewhat similar to that of the summary of the conceivability argument (in Chapter 3, Section 6.2), thus:

- I know that all that which I clearly and distinctly conceive can be produced by God exactly as I conceive it *(if something is conceivable it is possible)*

- I know with certitude that I exist, and ... that my essence consists *only* in my being a thinking ... and unextended thing; while my body, with which I am very closely conjoined ... is only an extended and unthinking thing *(zombies are conceivable)*

- It is certain that I [am] ... entirely and truly distinct from my body, and may exist without it *(physicalism is false)*

The problem with this, of course, is that although the proposition that Descartes' 'thinking thing' cannot exist without his body does not run counter to logic, so can be conceived in the sense that it is not internally inconsistent, there could be a law of nature which has the implication that the situation he is considering is impossible. If that were accepted as being the case, the proposal that he could exist without his body would be *nomologically* inconceivable and the second point would then not follow from the first point, it would *not* be possible that his mind could exist without his body.

4 Mental causation with substance dualism

A problem that arises with substance dualism concerns the possibility of events relating to one substance influencing events relating to the other substance. If mind has no physical features such as spatial location, mass, volume, electric charge and so on, as is taken to be the case in substance dualism, then how can it interact with matter? This issue did not escape thinkers in Descartes' time. The Princess Elizabeth of Bohemia famously exchanged a correspondence with Descartes about his writings. In her first letter, dated 6 May 1643 (see Bennett, 2009), she set down her question thus:

> "Given that the soul of a human being is only a *thinking* substance, how can it affect the bodily spirits, in order to bring about voluntary actions?"

and continued:

> "The question arises because it seems that how a thing moves depends solely on (i) how much it is pushed, (ii) the manner in which it is pushed, or (iii) the surface-texture and shape of the thing that pushes it. … The first two of those require *contact* between the two things, and the third requires that the causally active thing be extended. Your notion of the soul entirely excludes extension, and it appears to me that an immaterial thing can't possibly *touch* anything else"

Similar arguments are still being made. Kim (2005) argues that: "… our idea of causation requires that the causally connected items be situated in a space-like framework" (p 84) and uses that when making the case that the proposition that events in one substance can influence events in another substance must be incoherent

Indeed, two problems commonly cited that arise regarding mental causation in the case of dual substances are: the problem of spatial contiguity and the problem of energy conservation. But neither of these seems fatal. Although spatial contiguity is generally a feature of causation in physics one could argue that there is no reason to assume that mental causation, a notion external to the physical sciences, will follow the conventions of physics (indeed, "quantum entanglement" appears to be an exception to this proposition). As for energy conservation, common-sense does not rule out the proposition that while energy conservation holds for all processes not involving mental causation, cases of mental causation could give rise to increases in the total energy in the universe, unless offset by sinks elsewhere (see Chapter 3, Section 4.3; although fundamental physics might rule out such a proposition). The idea that mental causation operates along with dual substances is known in the literature as 'interactionism', but it is not widely advocated.

Interestingly, Leibniz addressed this issue in his 1695 essay *A New System of the Nature and Communication of Substances*. He accepted that events relating to mind and body appear to develop in total harmony with each other, as if there were some causal process between the two, and he took the view that this situation arose because of pre-programming by God.

"God ... created each soul ... in such a way that everything in it arises from its own depths ... with no causal input from anything else ... and yet with a perfect *conformity* to things outside it. ...

"The organised mass in which ... the soul lies ... is ready, just when the soul desires it, to act *of itself* according to the laws of the bodily mechanism ... the motions that correspond to the passions and perceptions of the soul.

"All this happens without either body or soul disturbing the laws of the other; it is a mutual relationship, arranged *in advance* in each substance in the universe" (para. 14, translation by Bennett, 2004).

The idea that God has set the system up so that mental states always seem appropriate to the material state that is instantiated seems singularly unappealing nowadays as an explanation of the appearance that mental causation exists.

5 Conclusion on substance dualism

It seems that many Western philosophers now reject the dual substance view. This may be largely because they think that everything related to the material world can be 'explained' by things to do with physics, that is, they believe in the completeness of physics (see Chapter 3, Sections 3 and 4), and that leaves no causal role for a second substance.

But substance dualism is not obviously false. It cannot be rejected as the result of any of the fundamental principles set out in Section 4 of Chapter 2, although it certainly seems an unlikely explanation of the existence of consciousness in this materialistic age given our increasing understanding of the mental roles associated with different structures in the brain (see Chapter 5, Section 3). Whereas the problems with mental causation may make dual substances seem implausible, there are problems relating to mental causation associated with all the other potential explanations for the existence of consciousness. I don't discuss the dual substance approach in any depth in this book, but we do encounter it in Chapter 8, in the context of the questions relating to free will.

Appendix 2

Structure of the mind

1 Consciousness and memory

'Memory' is defined in the 2016 version of the *Stanford Encyclopaedia of Philosophy* by the statement:

> "'Memory' labels a diverse set of cognitive capacities by which we retain information and reconstruct past experiences, usually for present purposes" (Sutton, 2016).

Psychologists have found that we have a range of memory stores, which vary in their properties and functions. As we shall see, these memory stores bear a close relation to the different types of thing of which we can be conscious.[103] Mapping these memory stores and their interactions, along with various other features, therefore suggests that a mind has a certain structure. In this appendix I sketch the basic form this structure may take.

Consciousness has been linked with memory in academic writing for well over a century. Richet said, in 1886: "Sans mémoire pas de sensation consciente" (1886, p 570). William James, writing in 1890, quotes Richet on the possibility of a direct connection between phenomenal consciousness,

---

[103] Suggesting that if memories are stored in some part of the material of the brain, consciousness could be a property of that bit of material.

which he calls "conscious sensation", and memory (see James, 1890, Chapter XVI, footnotes 2 & 6). He says Richet stresses the fact that a sensation needs to persist for a short time to enable phenomenal consciousness to occur:

" ... for a conscious sensation ... to occur, there must be a present of a certain duration, of a few seconds at least"; and: "to suffer for only a hundredth of a second is not to suffer at all; and for my part I would readily agree to undergo a pain, however acute and intense it might be, provided it should last only a hundredth of a second, and leave after it neither reverberation nor recall"(Richet, 1884, p 32).

Francis Crick, in 1994, in his book *The Astonishing Hypothesis* (p 14-15), notes that: "as long as one hundred years ago" an idea that was "already current" was that "consciousness involves some form of memory, probably a very short-term one". More recently, Ray Jackendoff writes of "awareness" as being "supported by the contents of short-term memory" (1987, p 280). Cowan (1997, p 77) says he sees: "Short-term memory taken as a whole, including both sensory and nonsensory aspects ..." as representing "the subject's present mind".

Psychologists, neuroscientists and philosophers have all speculated about the whereabouts in the brain of some neural correlate of consciousness and the possible nature of the mechanisms involved. Is it localised or dispersed? Could there be a specialised type of neuron or a specific neuronal mechanism underlying it (such as, for example, oscillatory or synchronized discharges, see Rees *et al.*, 2002, p 266)? Is a satisfactory answer to such questions possible (Noë and Thomson, 2004)? There are several suggestions for the neural correlates of consciousness in the literature, but strangely, none of them relates to short-term memory stores.[104]

---

[104] Crick, in his 1993 book *The Astonishing Hypothesis*, suggests (p 251) that the neural activity associated with consciousness might be largely in the lower cortical layer (layers 5 and 6), which he says: "expresses the local (transient) results of 'computations' taking place mainly in other cortical layers". Baars, in his 1989 book *A Cognitive Theory of Consciousness*, presents a possible structure of brain activity which he suggests may be relevant, calling it Global Workspace Theory. This proposes that there is a 'module', in a person's brain and that the information that is selected for inclusion in this module at any point in time is what the person will be "conscious of", or "attending to". The key aspect of Dennett's "explanation" of consciousness, in his 1991 book, is that it is a property that arises whenever a certain type of physical structure obtains. Dennett

Another relevant concept, of which people have been aware for many years, is 'attention'. It seems that we are presented with a situation in which there are many things that are immediately available to consciousness and we select from these what to focus on, what to pay attention to, at any point in time. William James (1890) famously refers to attention as "... the taking possession by the mind, in clear and vivid form, of one out of what seem several simultaneously possible objects or trains of thought" (Chapter XI, p 403). Sir Francis Galton (1883) describes it in the following way: "... the ideas that lie at any moment within my full consciousness seem to attract of their own accord the most appropriate out of a number of other ideas which are lying close at hand, but imperfectly within the range of my consciousness" (p 203).

Baars (1997) has suggested that attention is akin to the spotlight that picks out some activity on a theatre stage leaving the rest of what is on the stage in the dark. In his words:

"In the working theatre, focal consciousness acts as a 'bright spot' on the stage, directed there by the selective 'spotlight' of attention. The bright spot is further surrounded by a 'fringe' of vital but vaguely conscious events .... The entire stage of the theatre corresponds to 'working memory', the immediate memory system in which we talk to ourselves, visualize places and people, and plan actions" (p 292).

If this is the case, and introspection certainly suggests that it may be, the sensory memory stores must include what the psychologists call a "buffer" containing phenomenal information that is available to consciousness but is not attracting attention.

---

suggests that the structure in question must be a "virtual machine", and that the key feature it must have is what he calls a "Joycean" nature. This Joycean property refers to the "stream of consciousness" type of monologue used by James Joyce in his novels. In conjunction with Hameroff (see Hameroff and Penrose, 1996) Penrose has suggested that the microtubules within neurons might provide the brain with the hardware needed for quantum effects relating to consciousness to take place. These suggestions regarding quantum mechanics have been criticised by Tegmark (2000); they argue that the time scale of neuron firing, and of excitations in microtubules, is out by more than one order of magnitude from what it would need to be for Penrose's theory to be plausible.

2 A structure for the mind[105]

2.1 Introduction

In this section I sketch a structure for the mind (see Figure 6, below) in terms of a "central executive", that is postulated by psychologists to facilitate and coordinate cognitive activities, along with the different types of memory store identified by psychologists and the type of consciousness to which each of these is related.

2.2 The central executive

Probably the least well understood of the functions presented in Figure 6 is the one that psychologists call "the central executive". This is envisaged by psychologists to be a system that "facilitates a range of cognitive activities, such as reasoning, learning and comprehension" (Baddeley, 2003, p 829). But it must also provide interfaces between information received by the senses (perception), information available from the long-term memory and the initiation of speech and action (Baddeley and Hitch, 1974). Indeed, Baddeley remarks that: "In some ways the central executive functions more like an attentional system than a memory store" (1997, p 85).

Baddeley has identified several functions that this 'central executive' needs to fulfil (Baddeley, 2003, p 835). One is to take the decision about what, out of the multitude of information that turns up in the sensory and working memories, should be stored in the long-term memory. Then, although all the information in the sensory memories is viewed as being available to consciousness, what one is conscious of at any moment in time is determined by 'attention'. In Baddeley's view another role of the central executive is to decide which features of the visual scene before one, the sounds one can hear, the sights one can see and the complicated range of emotions one feels at any moment, should receive this conscious attention (see for example Baddeley, 1996, p 8). A third task that needs to be done is the selection of appropriate items from the long-term memory stores for availability to the working memory, given what is going on. If the central executive is to play the key role Baddeley envisages for it in cognitive activities, then it must be able call on

---

[105] The material in this section has been published in Rowlatt, 'Consciousness and Memory', 2009.

information from both internal and external senses, both in immediate form and in 'visualised' form (drawn from the long-term memory). It needs to be able to call on proprioceptive information (so that it can initiate action and speech) and on emotional information (so that it can assess whether some course of action is likely to increase or decrease welfare) – interestingly, Alan Baddeley says: "… it is useful to conceptualize action as ultimately steered by emotion" (2003, p 837), a statement that is consistent with the approach to decision-taking described in Chapter 2, Section 4.3.

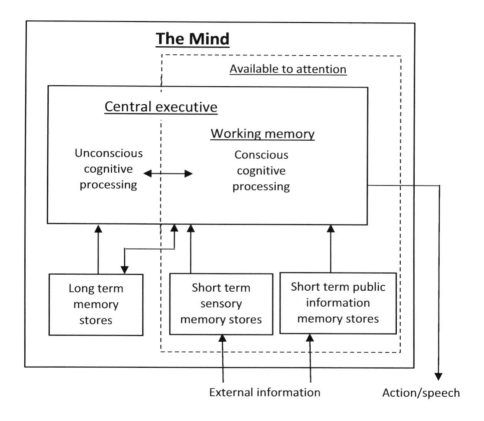

Figure 6: A structure for the mind

The figure shows a stylised arrangement of some of the relations between consciousness, attention, and the memory stores postulated by psychologists and referred to in the text.

But of course, the processes involved in thinking extend far beyond these limited, but necessary, functions. Effective logical thought requires that a person can both identify logical relationships between the items that are focused upon, and use logical processes to draw conclusions from a collection of related items; and effective creative thought must have another set of requirements involving aesthetic judgment.

2.3 Short-term memory stores

The memory stores that we are concerned with in this section are the short-term memory stores where information is typically held, available to consciousness, for a period of less than a second, but once gone it cannot be recalled from this source.

It seems that we humans probably possess three different versions of short-term memory stores of this type. I make a clear distinction in this book between things that can and things that cannot be communicated perfectly using language (Chapter 2, Section 2.1). Given this distinction, which is not always stressed by psychologists, it seems likely that we have short-term sensory memory stores which contain phenomenal information corresponding to our senses, and short-term memory stores that contain public information. All sensory experiences continue for a short period after the original stimulus has gone, being experienced precisely as if the stimulus were still operating.[106] There must therefore be short-term memory stores related to all sensory experiences; these will be memory stores that contain phenomenal information, and they must store the information in phenomenal form, the 'what it feels like' aspects of that sensory experience. This persistence of sensory perception has been confirmed a great many times and its characteristics have been studied in some depth for both visual and auditory experiences; it is not so easy to experiment with this phenomenon for other senses. Psychologists call memory

---

[106] The visual form of sensory memory store is called the 'iconic memory store', the auditory form is called the 'echoic memory store', and the olfactory form the 'odor memory store'. The duration of sensations in the iconic and echoic memory stores has been studied in considerable depth in recent decades and it seems to be well-established that information remains in them for a minimum of a few hundred milliseconds. This was demonstrated originally by Segner in 1740. He attached a red-hot coal to a cartwheel and rotated the cartwheel at a speed just fast enough for the light to form a complete circle to the eye in order to estimate the duration for which a signal remained in the iconic memory store. Later, more complex, experiments have confirmed that duration (see Neath and Surprenant, 2003 and others).

stores of this type the "short-term sensory memory stores" (I abbreviate this to 'sensory memory stores').

It is difficult to see how we could be aware of pain or itching, emotions, or proprioception if there were no sensory memory store associated with these, too. As William Burnham (1889, p 575) said: "Each sense … of the body may be said to have its memory …", but not surprisingly, no-one seems to have attempted the investigation of the likelihood of similar types of memory store for the internal senses.

As well as these sensory memory stores, there must be a short-term memory store that can contain public facts, the type of fact that can be expressed in words. Information of the type that can be expressed in words, and may be needed for cognitive or creative purposes, is likely to turn up from three sources:

- it may be recalled from the long-term semantic memory store (see later); this will consist of public facts long known, such as "grass is green", personal factual memories such as "I had trout for lunch yesterday" or facts that have been learned from others, such as the likely causes of the French revolution;

- it may arise from recent experiences that have been processed and stored in the form of facts that can be communicated in words to others, for example, the information on a road-sign recently passed;

- it may be the result of cognitive processing, such as "it seems likely that it will rain soon".

This memory store would be likely to have a different material structure from that pertaining to the sensory memory stores. Where information of this sort is available to consciousness it is said by psychologists to be in the 'buffers' of the conscious part of "the central executive".

In addition, there must be another sort of short-term memory store, known as the working memory. This is the name psychologists use for the short-term memory store where both public information and phenomenal information are used in thinking, cognitive analysis, decision-taking and such-like. It can therefore hold the beginning of a train of thought, or a sentence, or the early parts of the imagining of some incident, while the person's thoughts are moving on towards the end. It therefore seems likely that it is this memory store that uses the information to arrive at decisions concerning speech and actions. The 'working memory store' is a term much used by psychologists, but with varying nuances of meaning depending on the author (see Baddeley and Hitch, 1974; the names used for the various memory stores differ considerably according to the author involved, so care is needed). Again, the capacity of the working memory store, the part of the central executive that is in the spotlight of consciousness, and the duration for which information remains within it, has been much researched.[107]

It would not be possible to create something in one's imagination, or follow a line of reasoning, or take a decision and implement it if one were unable to remember the early parts of some train of thought. As explained in Chapter 2, Section 3.2, Block (2001) has referred to consciousness of something along these lines as 'reflexive consciousness'. If this is to be treated as a separate concept from phenomenal consciousness and access consciousness, there is a question as to the memory store in which the information about these trains of thought is stored. Many psychologists take the view that this is a task that is performed by the working memory and that this is part of what they call "the central executive".

The short-term sensory memory stores are associated with feelings, that is, with phenomenal consciousness; the short-term public information memory store is associated with awareness of things, thoughts, that can be expressed linguistically; the working memory is generally associated with more complex thoughts of which some elements can be expressed perfectly linguistically but it must also be able to contain feelings if this is where the conscious parts of practical reasoning is performed and where creative thinking takes place, as seems to be the psychologists' intention.

---

[107] The capacity of the working memory store that is in the focus of attention is surprisingly limited. Psychologists have found that it can hold only about seven items of information (plus or minus two) at any point in time (in an experimental setting these may be numerals, "chunked" numerals – 4-digit dates, for example – or short syllables). To hold information in this memory store for any length of time you need to repeat it verbally, either aloud or silently; this is illustrated by the effort needed to remember the directions someone gives you to find a location, or the difficulty of remembering a telephone number as you cross the room. Without such reinforcement, an item of information will remain in this memory store for less than a minute at most (see the classic paper by Miller, 1956). It is not yet clear whether the information in this memory store is replaced by new information or whether it simply decays over time.

2.4 Long-term memory stores

There are other types of memory store besides these short-term memory stores (see Atkinson and Shiffrin, 1968, for a sketch of a possible system of human memory stores). Short-term memories that are converted into long-term memories are thought to end up stored in what the psychologists call the 'declarative memory store'. Memories in this store may remain for a lifetime, although retrieval can be an issue. They are 'available to' consciousness in that they can, in principle, be recalled into the working memory store if needed. This long-term memory store is therefore fundamentally different in nature from the short-term memory stores described above: it is a 'recall' type of store.

It has been suggested that the declarative memory has two main subdivisions: the 'episodic memory store', which holds events involving a person's memories of external and internal sensory experiences and the temporal relations between them, that is, phenomenal facts (this is also known as the 'autobiographical memory'), and the 'semantic memory store' which stores knowledge about the meanings of words and the relations between them, that is, public facts (that Paris is in France, for example, or that driving a car too fast could result in a fine). This classification, due to Tulving (1972), is still not universally accepted.

There is another type of long-term memory store where motor skills are stored. This has been called the 'procedural' memory store by psychologists and is dubbed an 'implicit' memory store because its contents cannot be brought into consciousness.

This memory store is well illustrated by the patient known as HM, whose case it was that led to the realisation that this memory store must be distinct from the declarative memory store (Scoville and Milner, 1957). HM had crippling epilepsy. Following the removal of his hippocampus and the inner surface of his temporal lobes he lost the ability to transfer information from his working memory store into his long-term (declarative) memory store: he could no longer remember what had happened an hour ago. However, he was still able to learn a new skill and maintain that knowledge over the long-term (Milner *et al.*, 1998). Hence there must be a second kind of long-term memory store, independent of the hippocampus, where learning associated with skills is located. Neuroscientific investigation suggests that the cerebellum may be involved. Psychologists take the view that this (so-called) procedural memory store contains knowledge of the "knowing how" variety (but as we have seen in Chapter 2, Section 3.3, there are other ways in which the words "knowing how" can be used, and in some of these cases one *is* aware of 'how' one is doing something).

The three types of long-term memory store described above, that have been identified by psychologists and neuroscientists, therefore correspond to three of the types of 'knowing' described in Chapter 2, Section 3.3 which have been identified by philosophers: "knowing that" something is the case, "knowing what it is like" to experience something, and "knowing how" to do something.

Appendix 3

Glossary

In this appendix I have gathered, for easy reference, some of the notes relating to the meanings attributed to some of the key words used in this book. These notes should not be viewed as constituting definitions that are generally accepted amongst philosophers; many of these terms are not generally given any formal definition in philosophical works.

Causally complete (*as in "physics is causally complete"*)
The science of physics would be 'causally complete' if: "all physical effects are fully caused by purely physical prior histories", where "physical" is taken to mean non-mental (see Chapter 2, Section 2.4).

Complete (*as in "science is complete"*)
Science would be 'complete' if all the causes and all the effects of every event along with all the causal processes were included within it (see Chapter 2, Section 2.4).

Concept

The word 'concept' has many different meanings. In this book the term 'concept' arises when some specific bundle of entities (or a single entity), stored in the long-term memory, turns up in the working memory on a regular basis because it is relevant to some material or abstract, real or imaginary object (see Margolis and Laurence, 2014, for a discussion of this, and other, meanings of 'concept'). In such a case it is convenient, for communication purposes, to attach a verbal label to the bundle (or single entity); we call the bundles of entities that have been allocated labels in this way 'concepts' (see footnote 63 on p 94).

Conscious

We consider a thing to have conscious mental states if we take the view that it has the property of there being something it is like to *be* that thing – something it is like *for* the thing (see Chapter 2, Section 3.1).

Consciousness

To suggest that a creature "is conscious" or may be "conscious of" something seems to be a meaningful suggestion. Because that is so, we have coined a noun, 'consciousness', but it is unclear to what, exactly, it refers (see Chapter 2, Section 3.1).

Contingent

There are two circumstances in which the truth or falsity of a statement is generally considered to be 'contingent', meaning that it is not necessarily true (or not necessarily false). First, this can be the case when we don't know whether the statement is true or false until we've made some observations, but once we have made those observations we do know, once and for all, that it is or that it is not true; I call this type of contingency the "needs investigation" type. Alternatively, a statement can be considered contingent if the statement is true in some circumstances but not true in others; I call this one the "happenstance" type (see footnote 15 on p 17).

Dual substances

'Dual substances' is the name given to the theory of the ontology of mind that has mind a property of a substance different from matter (see Chapter 1. Section 1 and Appendix 1).

Fact

The word 'fact' is generally defined as: "a thing that is known or proved to be true". In philosophy, as Mellor (1995, p 8) makes clear, 'facts' are taken to be: "actual states of affairs, corresponding to true statements". If we accept this meaning for the word 'fact', the implication is that when I say to my friend: "you've got the facts wrong" that statement is incoherent. I take it in this book that all we can be sure about regarding a 'statement of fact' is that it is a proposition the truth of which is conceivable; that is, the proposition is not incoherent, it does not express a contradiction (see Chapter 2, Section 2.3).

Identity

The word 'identity' has two meanings; it can mean that two words have the same referent (numerical identity), or it can mean two things appear to us to be so similar that we cannot tell them apart (qualitative identity). The grammar of saying that two things are 'identical' when the situation is that there are two words for one thing seems can result in some confusion (see footnote 17 on p 19).

Materialism

The term 'materialism' generally applies to the metaphysical or ontological proposition that there is only one substance. Materialism is therefore a form of monism and it requires that the substance referred to, which we call 'matter', has certain properties that distinguish it from the form of monism known as 'idealism', in which reality is viewed as being fundamentally mental. 'Materialism', with this definition, allows for the possibility of property dualism, the situation in which mind, albeit a property of matter, is different in some fundamental way from the properties of matter that are studied in physics. In recent years the term 'materialism' has often been used to describe the proposition that everything is of the sort that is suitable to be studied in physics (see Chapter 2, Section 2.5).

Matter

The way in which the word 'matter' (*cf.*, "there is only one 'substance' and we call it 'matter'") is used in philosophy of mind encapsulates a view of the universe that is now somewhat out of date: that view can be characterised as viewing matter as consisting of particles shaped much like billiard balls or marbles in that they occupy space and have mass (along with other properties). We now know that some so-called particles, photons, have no mass and so cannot really be said to be "made of matter" in the old-fashioned understanding of that term, and we also know that energy is as fundamental to our understanding of the universe as mass and that the two can convert, one into the other. In general conversation, the word 'matter' is often implicitly taken to imply "non-experiential"; in this case, 'matter' would lack consciousness because of its definition (see Chapter 2, Section 2.4).

Mental state

I take a mental state to be something of which a person/creature could be aware, if they were attending to it, but at any point in time may not be (see Chapter 1, Section 1 and Chapter 2, Section 3.1).

Mind

The term 'mind' could simply be a convenient way of referring to the range of our possible mental states. Or it could pick out a property of matter that instantiates (gives rise to) mental states, as in the title of this book (see Chapter 1, Section 1).

Necessarily true

Some true propositions are true as a matter of logic ("no bachelor is married" is a case in point), others come into the class referred to as 'laws of nature' or 'natural laws' in which case the truths they convey are deemed to be 'nomologically necessary'. Some of these truths that are deemed to be nomologically true are necessarily true in our world, *e.g.* those that relate something to its composition; some could be found to be false given future observations, most obviously, those that take the form "all x's are y's" (see Chapter 2, Section 2.3).

Non-reductive physicalism

Non-reductive physicalism takes mind to be a property of matter that cannot be reduced to the properties of matter that are studied in the physical sciences (see Chapter 1, Section 1).

Phenomenal facts

'Phenomenal fact' is the term we use for facts regarding what something *feels* like (see Chapter 2, Section 3.2).

Physicalism

In the philosophical literature 'physicalism' is nowadays generally taken to relate explicitly to the science of physics, implying that every aspect of everything that exists is of the type that can be incorporated into the science of physics, and that the cause of every event could be explained by the science of physics if physics were a finished science. In the main, I retain that meaning in this book; a notable exception is the case of "non-reductive physicalism" (see Chapter 2, Section 2.5).

Physical

The term 'physical' has two distinct meanings in common parlance: it sometimes means "pertaining to objects such as the body, as opposed to the mind" and on other occasions it means "pertaining to matter" (see for example *http://www.dictionary.com/browse/physical*). In modern philosophy, however, the term 'physical' almost invariably has the meaning: "pertaining to that which is studied in the physical sciences" which I take to be the sciences that reduce to physics, such as chemistry and neuroscience, as well as physics itself (see Chapter 2, Section 2.5).

Physics (the science of)

The science of 'physics' comprises the results of our investigation of the properties of matter that are such that all the facts relating to them are public facts, facts that are equally available to everyone and that can therefore be communicated perfectly between people using language (see Chapter 2, Section 2.1).

Public facts

I call a fact a 'public fact' if it is equally accessible to everyone (the weight of a stone in certain specified conditions, for example), so that it can be referred to in words with no ambiguity ("this stone weighs 5 kilograms" combined with the definition known as the International Prototype Kilogram or IPK). 'Public facts' can therefore be examined and noted by any number of people on an *equal* basis (see Chapter 2, Section 2.1).

Reducible
A phenomenon is 'reducible' to the properties of matter studied in the science of physics if there are causal (nomological) relations that carry the implication that all the facts pertaining to that phenomenon can be identified with facts that are suitable for study in the science of physics ('public facts'). Any statement involving the 'is' of composition is a case in point, *e.g.*, "water is H_2O", "temperature is the motion of molecules" (see footnote 2 on p 2).

Reductive physicalism
'Reductive physicalism' assumes that mental states are ontologically reducible to the properties of matter studied in the science of physics (see Chapter 1, Section 1).

Science
'Science' is the name given to the systematic study, through observation, experiment and analysis, of the structure and the behaviour of everything in the universe (see Chapter 2, Section 2.1).

Substance
The word 'substance', as used in this book, takes the meaning 'substratum'; it picks out that which instantiates or gives rise to properties (see Chapter 2, Section 2.4).

Valuation system
Watson says (1975, p 346): "The valuation system of an agent is that set of considerations which, when combined with his factual beliefs (and probability estimates), yields judgements of the form: the thing for me to do in these circumstances, all things considered, is a" (see Chapter 2, Section 4.3).

References

Armstrong, David (1968), *A Materialist Theory of Mind*, London: Routledge.

Armstrong, David (1989), *Universals: An Opinionated Introduction*, Westview Press.

Arndt, M., O. Nairz, J. Voss-Andreae, C. Keller, G. van der Zouw, and A. Zeilinger (1999), 'Wave-particle duality of C60', *Nature*, **401**, pp 680-682.

Ashcroft, F. (2012), *The Spark of Life*, London: Penguin Books Ltd.

Atkinson, R. and R. Shiffrin (1968), 'Human memory: a proposed system and its control processes', in K. W. Spence and J. T. Spence (eds.), *The Psychology of Learning and Motivation* vol. 2, New York: Academic Press.

Baars, Bernard (1989), *A Cognitive Theory of Consciousness*, Cambridge: Cambridge University Press.

Baars, Bernard (1997), 'In the theatre of consciousness, Global Workspace Theory, a rigorous scientific theory of consciousness', *Journal of Consciousness Studies*, **4** (4), pp 292-309.

Baars, Bernard (2002), 'The conscious access hypothesis: origins and recent evidence', *Trends in Cognitive Sciences*, **6** (1), pp 47-52.

Baddeley, Alan (1996), 'Exploring the central executive', *The Quarterly Journal of Experimental Psychology*, **49A** (1), pp 5-28.

Baddeley, Alan (1997), *Human Memory: Theory and Practice*, Hove and New York: Psychology Press.

Baddeley, Alan (2003), 'Working memory: looking back and looking forward', *Nature Reviews: Neuroscience*, **4**, pp 829-839.

Baddeley, Alan and Graham Hitch (1974), 'Working memory', in G. A. Bower (ed.), *The Psychology of Learning and Motivation: Advances in Research and Theory*, 8, New York: Academic Press, pp 47-89.

Baker, Lynne Rudder (1993), 'Metaphysics and mental causation', in *Mental Causation*, John Heil and Alfred Mele (eds.), Oxford: Clarendon Press, pp 75-95.

Ball, Derek (2009), 'There are no phenomenal concepts', *Mind*, **118** (472), pp 935-962.

Beckermann, Ansgar (1992), 'Introduction – reductive and nonreductive physicalism', in Beckermann, A., H. Flohr and J. Kim (eds.), *Emergence or Reduction? - Essays on the Prospects of Nonreductive Physicalism*, Berlin/New York: Walter de Gruyter, pp 1-21.

Bennett, Jonathan (2004), 'A New System of the nature and communication of substances, and also of the union that exists between the soul and the body G. W. Leibniz', *http://www.earlymoderntexts.com/assets/pdfs/leibniz1695c.pdf*.

Bennett, Jonathan (2009), 'Correspondence between Descartes and Princess Elisabeth', *http://www.earlymoderntexts.com/assets/pdfs/descartes1643_1.pdf*.

Berkeley, George (1710), A treatise concerning the principles of human knowledge, *http://www.earlymoderntexts.com/assets/pdfs/berkeley1710.pdf*.

Bernard, C. (1865), *Lectures on the Phenomena Common to Animals and Plants*, trans. H. E. Hoff, R. Guillemin and L. Guillemin, 1974, Springfield (IL): Charles C Thomas.

Bernard, Theos (1947), *The Hindu Philosophy*, New York: The Philosophical Library, pp 69-72.

Berns, Gregory S., Andrew M. Brooks, Mark Spivak (2015), 'Scent of the familiar: An fMRI study of canine brain responses to familiar and unfamiliar human and dog odors', *Behavioural Processes,* **110**, pp 37-46.

Block, Ned (1978), 'Troubles with functionalism', in C. W. Savage (ed.), *Perception and Cognition: Minnesota Studies in the Philosophy of and Science IX*, pp 261-325, University of Minnesota Press.

Block, Ned (1995), 'On a confusion about a function of consciousness', *Behavioral and Brain Sciences*, **18** (2), pp 227-287.

Block, Ned (2001), 'Paradox and cross-purposes in recent work on consciousness', *Cognition*, **79**, pp 197-219.

Block, Ned and Robert Stalnaker, (1999), 'Conceptual Analysis, Dualism, and the Explanatory Gap', *The Philosophical Review*, **108**, pp 1-46.

Borges, Jorge Luis (1941), *The Garden of Forking Path*s, London: Penguin Books.

Boya, Luis J. (2003), 'The thermal radiation formula of Planck (1900)', *Rev. Real Academia de Ciencias; Zaragoza*, **58**, pp 91–114.

Broad, C. D. (1925), *Mind and its Place in Nature*, London: Routledge and Kegan Paul Ltd.

Burge, Tyler (1993), 'Mind-body causation and explanatory practice', in John Heil and Alfred Mele (eds.), *Mental Causation*, Oxford: Clarendon Press, pp 97-120.

Burnham, William H. (1889), 'Memory, historically and experimentally considered', *The American Journal of Psychology*, **2** (4), pp 568-622.

Carnap, Rudolph (1932), ‚Die physikalische Sprache als Universalsprache der Wissenschaft‘, *Erkenntnis*, II; English translation *The Unity of Science*, London: Kegan Paul, 1934,

Carruthers, P. (2000), *Phenomenal Consciousness: A Naturalistic Theory*, Cambridge: Cambridge University Press.

Cartwright, Nancy (1983), *How the Laws of Physics Lie*, Oxford University Press.

Chalmers, David J. (1995), 'Facing up to the problem of consciousness', *Journal of Consciousness Studies,* **2**, pp 200-219.

Chalmers, David J. (1996), *The Conscious Mind*, Oxford: Oxford University Press.

Chalmers, David J. (2002), 'Consciousness and its place in nature', in Stephen P. Stich and Ted A. Warfield (eds.), *Blackwell Guide to the Philosophy of Mind*, Blackwell, pp 102-142.

Chalmers, David J. (2007), 'Phenomenal concepts and the explanatory gap', in Torin Alter and Sven Walter (eds.), *Phenomenal Concepts and Phenomenal Knowledge*, New York: Oxford University Press, pp 167-194.

Chisholm, Roderick M. (1964), 'Human freedom and the self', The University of Kansas Lindley Lecture, in G. Watson (ed.), *Free Will*, Oxford: Oxford University Press, pp 26-37.

Churchland, Paul (1981), 'Eliminative materialism and propositional attitudes', *The Journal of Philosophy*, **78**, pp 67-90.

Claparède, É. (1911), 'Recognition et moite', *Archives de Psychologie Geneve*, **11**, pp 79-90.

Cowan, Nelson (1997), *Attention and Memory*, Oxford University Press: Oxford.

Crane, Tim (1995), 'The mental causation debate', *Proceedings of Aristotelian Society*, Supplementary Volume 69, pp 211-236.

Crane, Tim (2001), *Elements of Mind*, Oxford: Oxford University Press.

Crane, Tim and D. H. Mellor (1990), 'There is no question of physicalism', *Mind*, **99**, pp 185-206.

Crick, Francis (1994), *The Astonishing Hypothesis*, Simon & Schuster Ltd.

References

Damasio, Antonio R. (1994), *Descartes' Error*, New York: G. P. Putnam's Sons.

Davidson, Donald (1970), 'Mental events', in Lawrence Foster and J. W. Swanson (eds.), *Experience and Theory*, pp 207-222, Amherst, Mass., reprinted in Davidson, D., *Essays on Actions and Events*, 1980, Clarendon Press: Oxford.

Davidson, Donald (1993), 'Thinking causes', in John Heil and Alfred Mele (eds.), *Mental Causation*, Oxford University Press, pp 3-17.

Dehaene, Stanislas and Lionel Naccache (2001), 'Towards a cognitive neuroscience of consciousness: basic evidence and a workspace framework', *Cognition*, **79**, pp 1-37.

Delgado, J. M. R., W. W. Roberts and N. E. Miller (1954), 'Learning motivated by electrical stimulation of the brain', *American Journal of Physiology*, **179**, pp 587-593.

Delgado, M. R., V. A. Stenger and J. A. Fiez (2004), 'Motivation-dependent responses in the human caudate nucleus', *Cerebral Cortex*, **14**, pp 1022-1030.

Dennett, Daniel (1991), *Consciousness Explained*, Little, Brown & Company.

Descartes, René (1637), *Discourse on the Method*, trans. Laurence J. Lafleur 1960, New York: The Liberal Arts Press.

Descartes, René (1641), *Meditations on First Philosophy*, Paris: Michael Soly.

Dijkaterhuis, A., and L. F. Nordgren (2006), 'A theory of unconscious thought', *Perspectives on Psychological Science*, **1** (2), pp 95-109.

Eagle, Antony (2016), "Chance versus randomness", *The Stanford Encyclopedia of Philosophy*, Edward N. Zalta (*ed.*), <*http://plato.stanford.edu/archives/in2016/entries/chance-randomness/*>.

Eddington, A. (1928), *The Nature of the Physical World*, New York: Macmillan.

Feigl, H. (1958), 'The "mental" and the "physical"', in Herbert Feigl, Michael Scriven, and Grover Maxwell (eds.), *Minnesota Studies in the Philosophy of Science: Concepts, Theories, and the Mind-Body Problem, Volume II*, University of Minnesota Press.

Feyerabend, P. (1963), 'Materialism and the mind-body problem', *Review of Metaphysics*, **17**, pp 49-66.

Fischer, John Martin (2007), 'Compatibilism', in, John Martin Fischer, Robert Kane, Derk Pereboom and Manuel Vargas, *Four Views on Free Will*, Blackwell Publishing Ltd.

Flanagan, Owen and Thomas Polger (1995), 'Zombies and the function of consciousness', *Journal of Consciousness Studies*, **2**, pp 313–321.

Foot, Philippa (1967), 'The problem of abortion and the doctrine of the double effect', *Oxford Review*, **5**, pp 5-15.

Frankfurt, Harry G. (1969), 'Alternate possibilities and moral responsibility', *The Journal of Philosophy*, pp 829-39, and in Watson, G. (ed.), *Free Will*, 2003, Oxford: Oxford University Press pp 167-176.

Frankfurt, Harry G. (1971), 'Freedom of the will and the concept of a person', *The Journal of Philosophy*, pp 5-20, and in Watson, G. (ed.), *Free Will*, 2003, Oxford: Oxford University Press pp 322-336.

Frege, Gottlob (1892), 'On sense and reference', *Zeitschrift fur Philosophie und philosophische Kritk*, **100**, pp 25-50, (translated 1960).

Galton, Francis (1883), *Inquiries into Human Faculty and its Development, Part 4*, London: Dent.

Gardner, Thomas (2005), 'Supervenience physicalism: meeting the demands of determination and explanation', *Philosophical Papers*, **34**, pp 189-208.

Geach, Petyer and Max Black (1960), *Translations from the Philosophical Writings of Gottlob Frege*, New York; Oxford.

Ghysen, A. (2003). 'The origin and evolution of the nervous system', *International Journal of Development Biology*, **47**, pp 555-562.

Ginet, Carl (1966), 'Might we have no choice?', in Keith Lehrer (ed.), *Freedom and Determinism*, New York: Random House.

Godfrey-Smith, Peter (2017), *Other Minds: The Octopus and the Evolution of Intelligent Life*, London: Collins.

Gould, S. J., and R. C. Lewontin (1979), 'The spandrels of San Marco and the Panglossian paradigm: a critique of the adaptationist programme', *Proceedings of the Royal Society B*, **205**, pp 581-598.

Graham, George (2016), 'Behaviorism', *The Stanford Encyclopedia of Philosophy* (Spring 2017 Edition), Edward N. Zalta (ed.), URL = <https://plato.stanford.edu/archives/spr2017/entries/behaviorism/>.

Grau, Carles, Romuald Ginhoux, Alejandro Riera, Thanh Lam Nguyen, Hubert Chauvat, Michel Berg, Julià L. Amengual, Alvaro Pascual-Leone and Giulio Ruffini (2014), 'Conscious brain-to-brain communication in humans using non-invasive technologies', *Plos One,* **9** (8), pp 1-6.

Greene, J. (2001), 'An fMRI investigation of emotional engagement in moral judgment', *Science*, **293**, pp 2105-2108.

Hameroff, Stuart and Roger Penrose (1996), 'Orchestrated reduction of quantum coherence in brain microtubules: a model for consciousness', *Mathematics and Computers in Simulation*, **40**, pp 453-480.

Harari, Yuval Noah (2011), *Sapiens*, (first published in English, 2014), London: Vintage.

Harnad, Stevan (2000), 'Turing indistinguishability and the blind watchmaker', in Fetzer, J. and Mulhauser, G. (eds.), *Evolving Consciousness*, Amsterdam: John Benjamins.

Hempel, C. G. (1945), 'Studies in the logic of confirmation', *Mind*, **54** (213), pp 1–26.

Hempel, C. G. (1949), 'The logical analysis of psychology', in H. Feigl and W. Sellars (eds.) *Readings in Philosophical Analysis,* New York: Appleton-Century-Crofts.

Hesketh, Gavin (2016), *The Particle Zoo*, London: Quercus.

Hobbes, Thomas (1651), 'Of the liberty of subjects', Chapter XXI paragraph 2 in *Leviathan.*

Hodgson, David (1991), *The Mind Matters: Consciousness and Choice in a Quantum World*, Oxford: Oxford University Press.

Hoefer, Carl (2016),"Causal determinism", *The Stanford Encyclopedia of Philosophy,* Zalta (ed.), http://plato.stanford.edu/archives/spr2016/entries/determinism-causal.

Honderich, T. (1982), 'Donald Davidson's anomalous monism and the champion of mauve: The argument for anomalous monism', *Analysis*, **42** (1), pp 59-64.

Horgan, Terence (1984), 'Jackson on physical information and *qualia*', *Philosophical Quarterly*, **34**, pp 147-152.

Horgan, Terence (1993) 'From supervenience to superdupervenience: meeting the demands of a material world', *Mind*, **102**, pp 555-586.

Hume, David (1739/1740), *A Treatise of Human Nature*, ed. Ernest C. Mossner, reprinted Penguin Classics, 1985.

Humphrey, N. (2006), *Seeing Red*, The Belknap Press of Harvard University Press, London.

Humphrey, N. (2008), *The Mind Made Flesh*, Oxford: Oxford University Press.

Jackendoff, Ray (1987), *Consciousness and the Computational Mind*, MA: Bradford Books, MIT Press.

Jackson, Frank (1982), 'Epiphenomenal qualia', *Philosophical Quarterly*, **32**, (82), pp 127-136. Reprinted in W. G. Lycan and J. J. Prinz, (eds.), *Mind and Cognition: An Anthology*, third edition (2008), pp 657-663.

Jackson, Frank (1986), 'What Mary didn't know', *The Journal of Philosophy*, **83** (5), pp 291-295.

James, William (1890), *The Principles of Psychology*, New York: Henry Holt.

Jammer, Max (1974), *The Philosophy of Quantum Mechanics: The Interpretations of Quantum Mechanics in Historical Perspective*, New York: Wiley.

Johansson, Lars-Goran (2006) 'Natural necessity', *Uppsala Philosophical Studies*, **53**, 231-246.

Jönsson, C. (1961), 'Electron diffraction at multiple slits', *Zeitschrift der Physik*, **161**, pp 454-461; translated by Dietrich Brandt and Stanley Hirschi, 1974, *American Journal of Physics*, **42**, pp 4-11.

Kahneman, D. (2011), *Thinking Fast and Slow*, London, Penguin Group.

Kahneman, D. and A. Tversky (1979), 'Prospect theory: an analysis of decision under risk', *Econometrica*, **47**, pp 263–291.

Kandel, Eric R. (2006), *In Search of Memory*, W. W. Norton and Company Inc., New York.

Kane, Robert (2007), 'Libertarianism', in John Martin Fischer, Robert Kane, Derk Pereboom and Manuel Vargas, *Four Views on Free Will*, Blackwell Publishing Ltd.

Kim, Jaegwon (1984), 'Epiphenomenal and supervenient causation', *Midwest Studies in Philosophy*, **9**, pp 257-270, reprinted in David M. Rosenthal, *The Nature of Mind*, (1991), OUP: Oxford.

Kim, Jaegwon (2005), *Physicalism, or something near enough*, Princeton: Princeton University Press.

Kirk, Robert (1974), 'Zombies v. materialists', *Aristotelian Society Supplementary Volume*, **48**, pp 135-152.

Knutson, B., and S. M. Greer (2008), 'Anticipatory affect: neural correlates and consequences for choice', *Philosophical Transactions of the Royal Society B Biol, Sci.*, **363** (1511), pp 3771-3786.

Koch, Christof (2012), *Consciousness: Confessions of a Romantic Reductionist*, Cambridge MA: The MIT Press.

Kremers, Dorothee, Juliana López Marulanda, Martine Hausberger and Alban Lemasson, (2014), 'Behavioural evidence of magnetoreception in dolphins: detection of experimental magnetic fields', *Naturwissenschaften*, **101** (11), pp 907-911.

Kripke, Saul (1972), *Naming and Necessity*, Blackwell, 1981 (first published 1972).

Leibniz, Wilhelm Gottfried (1695), *A New System of the Nature and Communication of Substances, and also of the Union that Exists Between the Mind and the Body*, translated by Jonathan Bennett, 2004, www.earlymoderntexts.com.

Levine, Joseph (1983A), 'Conceivability identity and the explanatory gap', *Towards a Science of Consciousness*, **3**, pp 3-13.

Levine, Joseph (1983B), 'Materialism and qualia: the explanatory gap', *Pacific Philosophical Quarterly*, **64**, pp 354-361.

Levine, Joseph (1993), 'On leaving out what it's like', in Martin Davies and Glyn W. Humphreys (eds.), *Consciousness: Psychological and Philosophical Essays*, Blackwell.

Levine, Joseph (2001), *Purple Haze*, Oxford: Oxford University Press.

Levine, Joseph (2007), 'Phenomenal concepts and the materialist constraint', in Torin Alter and Sven Walter (eds.), *Phenomenal Concepts and Phenomenal Knowledge*, pp 145-166, New York: Oxford University Press.

Lewis, David (1966), 'An argument for the identity theory', *Journal of Philosophy*, **63**, pp 17-25.

Lewis, David (1986), *The Plurality of Worlds*. Oxford: Oxford University Press,

Lewis, David (1988), 'What experience teaches', *Proceedings of the Russellian Society*, Sydney, Australia: University of Sidney. Reprinted in *There's Something About Mary: Essays on Phenomenal Consciousness*, Peter Ludlow, Yujin Nagasawa and Daniel Stoljar (eds.), 2004, pp 77-103, MIT Press.

Libet, B., E. W. Wright Jr and C. A. Gleason (1982), 'Readiness-potentials preceding unrestricted 'spontaneous' vs. pre-planned voluntary acts', *Electroencephalography and clinical Neurophysiology*, **54**, pp 322-335.

Loar, Brian (1970), 'Phenomenal states', in J. Tomberlin (ed.), *Philosophical Perspectives*, vol. 4; repr. in a revised form in N. Block, O. Flanagan, and G. Guzeldere (eds.), *The Nature of Consciousness*, Cambridge, Mass.: MIT Press, 1997.

Locke, John (1690), *An Essay Concerning Human Understanding*, Oxford: Oxford University Press.

London, F. and E. Bauer (1939), 'The theory of observation in quantum mechanics', in J. A. Wheeler and W. H. Zurek, *Quantum Theory and Measurement*, (eds.), 1983, Princeton: Princeton University Press, pp 217-259.

Louie, K. and M. A. Wilson (2001), 'Temporally structured sleep replay of awake hippocampal ensemble activity during rapid eye movement sleep', *Neuron,* **29**, pp 145-156.

Luce, R. Duncan and Howard Raiffa (1957), *Games and decisions: introduction and critical survey*, New York: John Wiley and Sons, Inc.

Mace, C. A. (1948), 'Some implications of analytical behaviour: the presidential address', *Proceedings of the Aristotelian Society*, **49**, pp 1-16.

Margolis, Eric and Stephen Laurence (2014), "Concepts", *The Stanford Encyclopedia of Philosophy* (Spring 2014 Edition), Edward N. Zalta (ed.).

Markowitz, H. M. (1952), "Portfolio Selection", *The Journal of Finance,* **7** (1), pp 77-91.

Marsden, C. D. (1981), 'The mysterious motor function of the basal ganglia: the Robert Wartenberg Lecture', *Neurology.* 1982, **32** (5), pp 514-539.

Marsh, Henry (2014), *Do No Harm*, Weidenfeld and Nicholson, London.

McGinn, Colin (1982), *The Character of Mind*, Oxford University Press: Oxford.

McGinn, Colin (1989), 'Can we solve the mind-body problem?', *Mind*, **98** (391), pp 349-366.

McLaughlin, Brian P. (2010), 'Consciousness, type physicalism, and inference to the best explanation', *Philosophical Issues*, **20**, pp 266-304.

Medina, L. and A. Reiner (1995), 'Neurotransmitter organization and connectivity of the basal ganglia in vertebrates: implications for the evolution of basal ganglia', *Brain Behaviour and Evolution*, **46**, pp 235–258.

Melchert, Norman (1986), 'What's wrong with anomalous monism?', *The Journal of Philosophy*, pp 265-274.

Mele, Alfred R. (2006), *Free Will and Luck*, Oxford: Oxford University Press.

Mellor, David H. (1995), *The Facts of Causation*, London: Routledge.

Melnyk, Andrew (2003), 'Papineau on the intuition of distinctness', *http://lgxserver.uniba.it/lci/mind/forums/004_0003.htm*. SWIF Forum on Thinking about Consciousness.

Melnyk, Andrew (2008), 'Can physicalism be non-reductive?', *Philosophy Compass*, **3** (6), pp 1281-1296.

Miller, George A. (1956), 'The magical number seven, plus or minus two: some limits on our capacity for processing information', *Psychological Review*, **63** (2), pp 81-97.

Milner, Brenda, Larry R. Squire, and Eric R. Kandel (1998), 'Cognitive neuroscience and the study of memory, review', *Neuron*, **20**, pp 445-468.

Mink, Jonathan W. (1996), 'The basal ganglia: focused selection and inhibition of competing motor programs', *Progress in Neurobiology*, **50**, pp 381-425.

Morrison, C. S. (2016), *The Blind Mindmaker*, CreateSpace Independent Publishing Platform.

Morsella, Ezequial (2005), 'The function of phenomenal states: supramodular interaction theory', *Psychological Review*, **112** (4), pp 1000-1021.

Nagel, Thomas (1974), 'What is it like to be a bat?', *The Philosophical Review*, **88**, pp 435-50.

Neath, Ian and Aimée M. Surprenant (2003), *Human Memory,* Thomson: Wadsworth.

Nemirow, Laurence (1980), 'Mortal questions by Thomas Nagel', *The Philosophical Review*, **89**, pp 475-477.

Nichols, Shaun and Todd Grantham (2000), 'Adaptive complexity and phenomenal consciousness', *Philosophy of Science*, **67,** pp 648-670.

Noë, Alva and Evan Thomson (2004), 'Are there neural correlates of consciousness?', *Journal of Consciousness Studies*, **11**, pp 3-28.

Nordby, Knut (2007), 'What is this thing you call color: can a totally color-blind person know about color?', in Torin Alter and Sven Walter (eds.), *Phenomenal Concepts and Phenomenal Knowledge,* pp 77-86, New York: Oxford University Press.

O'Connor, Timothy (1995), 'Agent causation', in *Agents, Causes and Events: Essays on Indeterminism and Free Will*, (ed.) Timothy O'Connor, New York: Oxford University Press, pp 173-200.

O'Donohue, Richard and William Kitchener (1998), *Handbook of Behaviorism*, Academic Press.

Olds, J. and P. Milner (1954), 'Positive reinforcement produced by electrical stimulation of septal area and other regions of rat brain', *Journal of Comparative and Physiological Psychology*, **47** (6), pp 419-427.

Pais-Vieira, Miguel, Mikhail Lebedev, Carolina Kunicki, Jing Wang and Miguel A. L. Nicolelis (2013), 'A brain-to-brain interface for real-time sharing of sensorimotor information', Nature, *Scientific Reports* **3**, Article number: 1319.

Panksepp, J. (2005), 'Affective consciousness: core emotional feelings in animals and humans', *Consciousness and Cognition*, **14**, pp 30-80.

Panksepp, J. (2011), 'The basic emotional circuits of mammalian brains: do animals have affective lives?' *Neuroscience and Biobehavioural Reviews*, **35**, pp 1791-1804.

Panksepp, J. and S. Biven (2012), *The Archaeology of Mind*, New York: W. W. Norton & Company Inc.

Papez, J. W. (1937), 'A proposed mechanism of emotion', *Archives of Neurology and Psychiatry*, **38** (4), pp 725-743.

Papineau, David (1990), 'Why supervenience?', *Analysis*, **50**, pp 66-71.

Papineau, David (2002), *Thinking About Consciousness*, Oxford: Oxford University Press.

Papineau, David (2011), 'What exactly is the explanatory gap?', *Philosophia*, 39, pp 5-19.

Pascal, Blaise (1660), *Pensées*, translated by W. F. Trotter, Gutenberg.

Paulus, Martin, P. (2007), 'Decision-making dysfunctions in psychiatry – altered homeostatic processing?', *Science*, **318** (5850), pp 602-608.

Peacocke, Christopher (2007), 'Mental action and self-awareness (1)', in Brian P. McCloughlan and Jonathan Cohen, (eds.), *Contemporary Debates in Philosophy of Mind*, Blackwell Publishing, pp 358-376.

Penrose, Roger (1989), *The Emperor's New Mind*, Oxford: Oxford University Press.

Pereboom, Derk (2001), *Living Without Free Will*, Cambridge: Cambridge University Press.

Pereboom, Derk (2007), 'Hard incompatibilism', in John Martin Fischer, Robert Kane, Derk Pereboom and Manuel Vargas, *Four Views on Free Will*, Blackwell Publishing Ltd.

Perelmuter, Zeev (2010), 'Nous and two kinds of epistêmê in Aristotle's Posterior Analytics', *Phronesis*, **55** (3), pp 228-254.

Perry, Clint J., Luigi Baciadonna and Lars Chittka (2016), 'Unexpected rewards induce dopamine-dependent positive emotion-like state changes in bumblebees', *Science*, **353** (6307), pp 1529-1531.

Place, U. T. (1956), 'Is consciousness a brain process?', *British Journal of Psychology*, pp 44-50.

Planck, Max (1900), 'On an improvement of Wien's equation for the spectrum', *Verh. Dtsch. Phys. Ges. Berlin*, **2**, pp 202-204.

Potter, Beatrix (1902), *The Tale of Peter Rabbit,* Frederick Warne & co.

Prinz, Jesse J. (2007), 'All consciousness is perceptual', in Brian P McLaughlin and Jonathan Cohen (eds.), *Contemporary Debates in Philosophy of Mind*, Blackwell Publishing, pp 335-357.

Puccetti, Roland (1976), 'The great C-fibre myth: a critical note', *Philosophy of Science*, **44**, pp 303-305.

Putnam, Hilary (1963), 'Brains and behaviour', in Ronald J. Butler (ed.), *Analytical Philosophy: Second Series*, Blackwell.

Putnam, Hilary (1967), 'The nature of mental states', originally called 'Psychological predicates', in Capitan and Merill, Pittsburgh (eds.), *Art, Mind and Religion*, (reprinted with the revised title 'The nature of mental states' in *Readings in Philosophy and Psychology*, ed. Block, 1980, Methuen).

Quine, W. V. O. (1951), 'Two dogmas of empiricism', *The Philosophical Review*, 60, pp 20-43. Reprinted in Quine, W. V. O, *From a Logical Point of View* 1953, Harvard University Press.

Quine, W. V. O. (1960), *Word and Object*, Cambridge, Mass.: MIT Press.

Quine, W. V. O. (1985), 'States of mind', *The Journal of Philosophy*, **87**, pp 5-8.

Quine, W. V. O. (1987), *Quiddities*, Cambridge, Massachusetts: The Belknap Press.

Redgrave, P, T. J. Prescott and K. Gurney (1999), 'The basal ganglia: a vertebrate solution to the selection problem?', *Neuroscience*, **89** (4), pp 1009-1023.

Redgrave, P, T. J. Prescott, and K. Gurney (2001), 'A computational model of action selection in the basal ganglia', *Biological Cybernetics*, **84**, pp 411-423.

Redgrave, P, N. Vautrelle and J. N. J. Reynolds (2011), 'Functional properties of the basal ganglia's re-entrant loop architecture: selection and reinforcement', *Neuroscience*, **198**, pp 136-151.

Rees, Geraint, Gabriel Kreiman and Christof Koch (2002), 'Neural correlates of consciousness in humans', *Nature Reviews: Neuroscience*, **3**, pp 261-270.

Rey, G. (1983), "A reason for doubting the existence of consciousness", in R. Davidson, G. Schwartz and D. Shapiro (eds.), *Consciousness and Self-Regulation* Vol 3. New York: Plenum, pp 1-39.

Richet, Charles R. (1884), *L'Homme et L'Intelligence*.

References

Richet, Charles R. (1886), 'Les origines et les modalités de la memoire', *Revue Philosophique*, XXI, p 570.

De Robertis E. M. and Y. Sasai (1996), 'A common plan for dorsoventral patterning in Bilateria', *Nature*, **380**, pp 37-40.

Robinson, H. (2014), 'Substance', in E. N. Zalta (ed.,) *The Stanford Encyclopedia of Philosophy*, https://plato.stanford.edu/archives/spr2014/entries/substance/.

Rorty, Richard (1965), 'Mind-body identity, privacy, and categories, *The Review of Metaphysics*, **19** (1), pp 24-54.

Rosenthal, David M. (2008), 'Consciousness and its function', *Neuropsychologia* **46**, pp 829-840.

Rowlatt, Penelope A. (2009), 'Consciousness and memory', *Journal of Consciousness Studies*, **16** (5) pp 68-78.

Ryle, Gilbert (1949), *The Concept of Mind*, London: Hutchinson.

Sakitt, Barbara (1976), 'Iconic memory', *Psychological Review*, **83** (4), pp 257-276.

Schneider, Susan (2013), 'Non-reductive physicalism and the mind problem', *Nous*, **47** (1), pp 135-153.

Schopenhauer, Arthur (1841), *Essay on the Freedom of the Will*, New York: Dover Publications Inc. Originally *Uber die Freiheit des Menschlichen Willens*, 1841, Frankfurt am Main: Joh. Christ. Hermannsche Buckhandlung.

Scoville, William Beecher and Brenda Milner (1957), 'Loss of recent memory after bilateral hippocampal lesions', *Journal of Neuropsychiatry and Clinical Neurosciences*, **20**, pp 11-21.

Searle, John R. (1983), 'Why I am not a property dualist', reprinted in *Journal of Consciousness Studies*, 2002, **9** (12), pp 57-64.

Segner, Johann Andreas (1740), *Specimen Logicae Universaliter Demonstratae*, ed. Mirella Capozzi, Bologna: CLUEB, 1990.

Sellars, W. (1956), 'Empiricism and the philosophy of mind', in Feigl H. and Scriven M. (eds.), *The Foundations of Science and the Concepts of Psychology and Psychoanalysis: Minnesota Studies in the Philosophy of Science*, Vol. 1. Minneapolis: University of Minnesota Press, pp 253–329.

Shanta, Bhakti Niskama (2015), 'Life and consciousness – the Vedāntic view', http://www.tandfonline.com/doi/full/10.1080/19420889.2015.1085138, *Communicative & Integrative Biology*, (retrieved 10/8/2016).

Shimony, Abner (1963) 'Role of the observer in quantum theory', *American Journal of Physics*, **31** (10), pp 755-773.

Skinner, B. F. (1974), *About behaviourism*, New York: Knopf.

Slovic, P. (1987), 'Perception of risk', *Science,* **236**, pp 280-285.

Smart, J. J. C. (1959), 'Sensations and brain processes', *The Philosophical Review*, **68** (2), pp 141-156.

Smith, L. (1986), *Behaviorism and Logical Positivism: A Reassessment of Their Alliance*, Stanford, CA: Stanford University Press.

Snowdon, Paul (2003), 'Knowing how and knowing that: a distinction reconsidered', *Proceedings of the Aristotelian Society*, pp 1-29.

Soon C. S., M. Brass, H-J. Heinze, and J-D. Haynes (2008), 'Unconscious determinants of free decisions in the human brain', *Nature Neuroscience*, **11**, pp 543-545.

Spinoza, Benedictus de (1677), *The Ethics*, Penguin Classic.

Stanley, Jason and Timothy Williamson (2001), 'Knowing how', *Journal of Philosophy,* **98** (8), pp 411-444.

Strausfeld, Nicholas J. and Frank Hirth (2013), 'Deep homology of arthropod central complex and vertebrate basal ganglia', *Science*, **340** (6129), pp 157-161.

Strawson, Galen (1993), 'The impossibility of moral responsibility', *Philosophical Studies*, **75**, pp 5-24.

Strawson, Galen (1994), *Mental Reality*, London: The MIT Press.

Strawson, Galen (2006), 'Realistic monism: why physicalism entails panpsychism', *Journal of Consciousness Studies*, **13**, pp 3-31.

Strawson, Galen (2008), *Real Materialism*, Oxford: Oxford University Press.

Suppe, Frederick (2000), 'Definitions', in *A Companion to the Philosophy of Science*, *ed.* W. H. Newton-Smith, Maldon: Blackwell.

Sutton, John (Summer 2016 edition), 'Memory', *The Stanford Encyclopedia of Philosophy*, http://plato.stanford.edu/archives/sum2016/entries/memory/, *ed.* Edward N. Zalta.

Tegmark, Max (2000), 'Importance of quantum decoherence in brain processes', *Physical Review E,* **61**, pp 4194-4206.

Tomer, R., A. Denes, K. Tessmar-Raible, and D. Arendt (2010), 'Profiling by image registration reveals common origin of annelid mushroom bodies and vertebrate pallium', *Cell*, **142**, pp 800-809.

Tulving, Endel (1972), 'Episodic and semantic memory', in E Tulving and W Donaldson (eds.), *Organisation of Memory,* New York: Academic Press.

Thomson, Judith Jarvis (1976), 'Killing, letting die, and the trolley problem', *The Monist*, **59** (2), pp 204-217.

Tye, Michael (2009), *Consciousness Revisited: Materialism Without Phenomenal Concepts*, MIT: MIT Press (page references from 2011 printing).

Van Gulick, Robert (1985), 'Physicalism and the subjectivity of the mental', *Philosophical Topics*, **8** (3), pp 51-70.

Van Horn, John Darrel, Andrei Irimia, Carinna M. Torgerson, Micah C. Chambers, Ron Kikinis and Arthur W. Toga (2012), 'Mapping Connectivity Damage in the Case of Phineas Gage', *Plos One*, *http://dx.doi.org/10.1371/journal.pone.0037454*.

Van Inwagen, Peter (1975), 'The incompatibility of free will and determinism', *Philosophical Studies*, **27**, pp 185-199.

Van Inwagen, Peter (1983), *An Essay on Free Will*, Oxford: Oxford University Press.

Velleman, J. David (1992), 'What happens when someone acts?', *Mind*, **101** (403), pp 461-481.

Von Neumann, J. and O. Morgenstern (1947), *Theory of Games and Economic Behaviour*, 2nd edition, Princeton N. J.: Princeton University Press.

Von Neumann, J. (1955), *Mathematical Foundations of Quantum Mechanics*, translated from the German edition by Robert T. Beyer Princeton U.P.; Oxford U.P, 1955.

Watson, John B. (1913), 'Psychology as the behaviourist views it', *Psychological Review*, **20**, pp 158-177.

Watson, Gary (1975), 'Free agency', *Journal of Philosophy*, **72** (8) pp 205-220; reprinted in *Free Will*, *ed.* Gary Watson, 2003, Oxford: Oxford University Press pp 337-351.

Watson, Gary (2003), *Free Will*, Oxford: Oxford University Press.

Wigner, Eugene, O. (1961), 'Remarks on the mind-body question', in I. J. Good, (ed.), *The Scientist Speculates*, London: Heinemann.

Williams, Bernard (1970), 'The self and the future', *Philosophical Review*, **79** (2), pp 161-180.

References

Wilson, Jessica (2005), 'Supervenience-based formulations of physicalism', *Nous*, **39**, pp 426-459.

Wittgenstein, Ludwig (1922), *Tractatus Logico-Philosophicus,* London: Barcourt, Brace and Company.

Woollett, Katherine and Eleanor A. Maguire (2011), 'Acquiring "the knowledge" of London's layout drives structural brain changes', *Current Biology*, **21** (24), pp 2109–2114.

Yablo, Stephen (1992), 'Mental causation', *The Philosophical Review*, **101** (2), pp 245-280.

Yoo, Julie (2016), 'Mental causation', *(http://www.iep.utm.edu/mental-c)*, *The Internet Encyclopedia of Philosophy* (retrieved 25/9/2016).

Zajonc, R. B. (1980), 'Feeling and thinking: preferences need no inferences', *American Psychologist*, **35** (2), pp 151-175.

Index

A

B

C

D

E

27286155R00160

Printed in Poland
by Amazon Fulfillment
Poland Sp. z o.o., Wrocław